THE LANGUAGE OF PLANTS

the Language *of* Plants

A Guide to the Doctrine of Signatures

Julia Graves

Lindisfarne Books | 2012

2012

LINDISFARNE BOOKS

An imprint of SteinerBooks / Anthroposophic Press, Inc.

610 Main Street, Great Barrington, MA 01230

www.steinerbooks.org

Copyright © 2012 by Julia Graves

Book design: William Jens Jensen

Printed in China

LIBRARY OF CONGRESS CATALOGING-IN-PUBLICATION DATA

Graves, Julia.
The language of plants : a guide to the doctrine of signatures / Julia Graves.
    p. cm.
Includes bibliographical references and index.
ISBN 978-1-58420-098-7 — eBook ISBN 978-1-58420-103-8
1. Materia medica, Vegetable. 2. Medicinal plants. 3. Holistic medicine. I. Title.
RS164.G673 2011
615'.321—dc22

                                                                        2011008410

CONTENTS

ACKNOWLEDGEMENTS

My foremost acknowledgement must go to Wilhelm Pelikan, through whose books *The Healing Plant* (volumes 1 to 3) I was able to teach myself the doctrine of signature at age eighteen and learn to converse with nature. I would like to thank my friend and colleague Lise Wolff for asking me to teach a class on the doctrine of signature, which made me realize I had enough to say about this topic to fill a book; my friend and colleague Peter Schell for his help in finding the relevant literature in the Chinese pharmacopeia; Jacquelin Guiteau for ongoing help and encouragement; and Sandra Lory for allowing me to use many of her beautiful photos. My greatest thanks go to my dear friend and master teacher herbalist Matthew Wood, who inspired me on the path of herbalism in ways beyond description.

Dedicated to Mother Nature

for nurturing me with her breath

FOREWORD

"The intuitive mind is a sacred gift and the rational mind is a faithful servant.
We have created a society that honours the servant and has forgotten the gift."
—ALBERT EINSTEIN

The following book on the doctrine of signatures is the most thorough and systematic text written on the subject to date. It unites wisdom gleaned from plants through the ages, revealing that signatures are the universal underpinning of all traditional systems of plant healing. In doing so, *The Language of Plants* is a remarkable achievement. It goes far beyond the narrower culturally restrained term *doctrine of signatures,* enlarging it to become a script for plant knowledge that goes beyond culture.

There are two basic approaches to the doctrine of signatures. One is via skillful sensory perception, the other via intuition. The former has a long history, coming down to us via the works of Goethe and Steiner; the latter includes an approach that Native North American might call "dreamtime." These two may be causally related. If we train our sensory perception carefully, it will become a faithful servant (to paraphrase Einstein) to the holistic insight called intuition. The ability to glance at a jumble of facts or objects and recognize a meaningful pattern is called "intuition." The rational mind provides a cause-and-effect explanation, but intuition shows us "the big picture" behind it. This is also called "holistic thinking." The intuitive approach looks for the pattern that brings the pieces together into a meaningful whole. This book lays out a path on how the phenomena we perceive with our senses become the basis for this holistic perception. According to both Eastern and Western mystics, it is a well-trained mind relying on well-trained senses that leads to genuine intuition. It is possible to cultivate the intuition via sense perception, and that is what this book is about.

The English language, dedicated as it is to logic and materialism, has been purged of the terms and perspectives needed for intuitive education. Nonetheless, through many centuries, holistic thinkers have developed terms for naming and explaining their perceptions. One of the terms used by intuitive thinkers is *signature*. When one who thinks holistically looks at a collection of sensory perceptions, that person is seeking signatures that indicate the patterns behind the information or a characteristic that matches something else to which it is analogous. The signature is a "tag" or "sign" through which the meaning, or pattern, that unites the phenomena is expressed. The intuitive approach clearly sees a pattern in the signatures and thus becomes a "principle," or "doctrine."

The "doctrine of signatures" is largely a medical or medicinal doctrine. It teaches us to look for a sign in a plant that describes its medicinal properties. The short story is that the signature resembles an organ or pattern of health or disease. For instance, the bud of the peony looks like a cranium with suture lines running across its surface. Thus, it is used for the brain and head and is indeed a traditional remedy for epilepsy, minor fits in children, and brain injury. It is also a medicine for healthy delivery. A baby arrives head first, with the head squeezed in a process similar to incurring a concussion. The use of peony for epilepsy goes back to Galen during the second century CE. This type of thinking is politely called "analogical" thinking by rational science and dismissed as naive and superstitious. However, what is dismissed by conventional science-based culture was once a mainstream view and persists around the world.

I have used this method in my practice as an herbalist and found it to be of utmost importance and relevance to the practice of clinical herbalism today. It has led me to discover many new uses for herbs, to confirm traditional uses, and to explain the "energetics" of plants more clearly. *Energetics* is another word coined by intuitive and holistic thinkers. It refers to the energy pattern, or basic configuration, of energy in a plant, animal, or human being.

If rationalistic science has thrown this method of thinking away, then why should we revive it? There are several answers to this question. First, the lack of holistic understanding has resulted in the development of a lopsided environmental and social edifice that is not sustainable in its hostility toward nature and, ultimately, toward life. Science, as practiced today, is based on the destruction and exploitation of nature, reductionism (the microscopic rather than the macroscopic view), materialism rather than spirituality, and corporate greed in place of a sustainable social contract. Holistic thinking such as the doctrine of signatures can offer us a way out of this cul-de-sac.

Second, many non-Western cultures think intuitively, holistically, or analogically. If we seek a balanced and wide view of culture, others, ourselves, and ultimately truth, we should not value one cognitive method over another. I remember an Anishinabe Ojibwe elder asking, "How can we understand Nature if we do not even know how to think properly [about her]?" The Anishinabe term to describe the proper way of thinking, though difficult to translate, could be rendered as "intuitive" or "pre-cognitive."

Third, the holistic perspective has not been eliminated completely and is still sought out, learned, and practiced within Western culture, including in science, even if ignored.

Holistic thinking goes hand in hand with imagination, or "holistic seeing," so to speak. We need to be able to see with our mind's eye and to let our perceptions play with the sensory data to find underlying meaning. "I don't think like you do," said one of the old doctors. "I let my imagination play about the case." This book is an eye-opener, showing us with many examples how to *see* plants in their entirety, and thus to know their essence. By showing the path, it helps us to look more deeply and to behold the message of plants wherever they surround us.

The doctrine of signatures is based on the broader concept of "sympathetic magic." This principle holds that two different objects or life forms resonate with each other if they share the same intrinsic character or "essence." In the case of the doctrine of signatures, this means the outer characteristics. The person who thinks holistically is not insulted when told that signatures are an aspect of sympathetic magic, or that it is entirely unscientific. Sympathy is a universal principle of healing. For instance, you stay in a warm bed when you have a fever (heat cures heat) and use plants that make you sneeze and have a runny nose, such as onion and radish for pollen allergies (what makes you sneeze cures sneezing). The "magic" here indicates the astounding ease and speed with which a cure comes about when herbalism is practiced in this way. "Sympathetic medicine" means that the plant is "similar" to the sick person (either the disease or an organ or tissue state), and that it will have a therapeutic influence. Consequently, I have used peony root successfully for head injury, and some of my students have used it curatively or palliatively for convulsions.

I have written on these subjects in the past and considered writing a book about the doctrine myself. However, when Julia Graves told me of her intention to write this book, I knew the project was in good hands. She has the kind of training needed for this undertaking. She grew up in a household that practiced herbal medicine. Her mother, trained to work in botanical apothecaries, taught Julia the botanical identity and healing properties of medicinal herbs when she was barely old enough to walk. At the same time, her father was an orthopedic surgeon, and Julia received a medical education in Germany. However, sympathy (there's that word again) pushed her, in the magical way that sympathy does, toward holistic solutions. Among other areas, Julia studied anthroposophic medicine, which uses the doctrine of signatures, and the development of flower essences at the Findhorn community in Scotland. While most scientists and doctors were content to watch traditional medicine decline and disappear, Julia studied with healers in Zimbabwe and Haiti. She spent years meditating and learning Tibetan Buddhism in America, Europe, and India. In New York City, she trained under Dr. Rudolph Ballentine, one of the medical doctors who led the early move toward holistic medicine and the author of *Diet & Nutrition: A Holistic Approach* and *Radical Healing: Integrating the World's Great Therapeutic Traditions to Create a New Transformative Medicine.*

And finally, she is a friend. For years, Julia and I have exchanged therapeutic tips and useful signatures. There is something about holistic, intuitive communication that brings joy to those of us fortunate enough to have such experiences. Intuitive insight generates "aha" moments that lift the mind to a level of spiritual perception in which one knows the essence and the higher purpose of a creature. This gives the mind and the soul a feeling of joy and liberation from materialism, which rational science can never generate. In holistic thinking we recover a part of ourselves that is missing in everyday life. The fact that we lost that component is part of the disease of modern life, and we need to recover it to be healthy and whole.

Matthew Wood, MS (Herbal Medicine)
Registered Herbalist (American Herbalists Guild)
Martell, Wisconsin, 2011

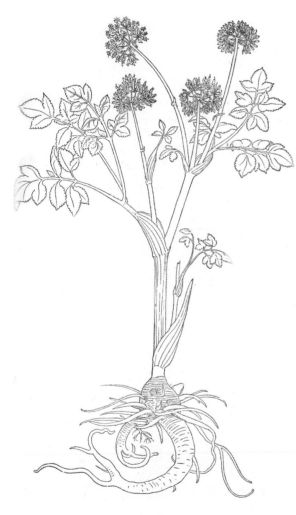

Angelica

O sweet spontaneous
earth how often have
the
doting

       fingers of
purient philosophers pinched
and
poked

thee
,has the naughty thumb
of science prodded
thy

    beauty   .how
oftn have religions taken
thee upon their scraggy knees
squeezing and

buffeting thee that thou mightest conceive
gods
        (but
true

to the incomparable
couch of death thy
rhythmic
lover

      thou answerest
them only with

           spring)

—E. E. CUMMINGS

PART ONE

THEORY

"I testify that it is true that those who wish to acquaint themselves deeply with Nature must turn her pages with their feet [by walking]. Her handwriting is learned from the letters. Nature, with her various vast landscapes, of which each is one of her books. Such is the Codex naturae *through the pages of which human beings must leaf."*

—Paracelsus

INTRODUCTION

The Doctrine of Signature, as ancient as humankind itself, is the art of knowing from the outer appearance of a plant or its environment what its medicinal properties are. That is, by way of reading its colors and shapes, to know what it will heal. In a way, it is the art of decoding the secrets of nature itself. I like to think of it as reading the Book of Nature. It is the idea that the same formative force that forms a skull with sutures in a human will form a peony bud that looks just the same. It is the Taoist "as in the macrocosm, so in the microcosm" and the hermetic "as above, so below." The ancient Indian seers saw man as a microcosm containing within him the kingdoms of the elements, minerals, vegetables and animals. Each culture has imbued this art with its own flavor, and each epoch added its own twist. Since this is an art of observation that cannot be quantified in a reductionist sense, it cannot be validated by natural science as is practiced today. I used to explain to my surprised friends that I was training in a way of reading plants so I could go anywhere on the planet and recognize the medicinal virtue of plants, even if I had never seen them before. Since then, I have indeed been able to practice on three continents and put my theory to the test. I agree with pharmacist Ben Harris that the doctrine of signature simply makes sense, and works, however quaint it may seem (Harris 1985, p. 4). While one might raise countless intellectual debates as to it's scientific worthiness, from the point of view of someone who wildcrafts and cultivates herbs, makes them into medicines, and uses those to actually heal people, those debates are irrelevant, because the practicing herbalist in the living tradition of nature knows her language.

When I set out to write this book, I hoped to be able to provide a complete guide to the doctrine of signatures, documenting the meaning of every characteristic a plant might have. While I had a whole outline of what I wanted to show in my mind, writing it all down and making it into the following book surprised even me with the scientific consistency of the doctrine of signatures. Up to the present, herbal literature has only provided either one signature for some herbs mentioned, and very rarely more than one per plant. The first herbal that gave one or more signatures for every herb mentioned is Ben Charles Harris's *Complete Herbal* from 1985. Before him, Willhelm Pelikan wrote his *Heilpflanzenkunde* in three volumes starting in 1958, discussing plants in the context of their plant families. However his Goethean approach is less directly useful to a practicing herbalist than the classical doctrine of signatures. In part inspired by Grohmann and Pelikan, Patricia Kaminski's *Flowers that Heal* (1998) tie the color of a flower together with its shape and the plant family. The present book is the first of its kind in the sense that it provides a key for understanding every color, shape, taste, and other characteristic of a plant. It empowers the attentive reader to understand the totality of signatures of any plant in the planet, and thus read its healing properties.

The doctrine of signature has been called a memory aid. This is a reductionist view that fails to understand that the doctrine of signature really is the way to see and read how the plant expresses its essential way of being. My friend, herbalist Gabrielle Simon, said with emphasis, "I just can't work with a plant if I don't know what it looks like!" This echoes what I have been saying for years. This is the sentiment of someone who knows how to read plants—if you do not know what it looks like, you are working like a blind painter. This is the holistic matrix of meaning in which all the countless medicinal effects take their place *and make sense*. The modern herbal tradition, which belies the doctrine of signature, can present to us only exhausting lists of chemical details about a plant, but fail to imbue them with sense and life, nor can they provide a vivid meaningful image of the plant as a whole. Last, the mere chemical analysis of medically active ingredients fails to both explain the effect the herb unfolds in the body, and predict which organ it will chiefly act on. This is the forte of the doctrine of signature.

One of the oldest medicinal systems, Traditional Chinese Medicine (TCM), had a working knowledge of signatures for most plants it used. Most has been lost from medicinal texts as it moved into the twentieth century, asking to be acknowledged by biomedicine. We see the same tendency in all other traditional herbal systems. While now at the brink of extinction, the doctrine of signature was standard in the Western tradition and traditional medical systems worldwide. Many different schools arose; for instance, the Middle Ages saw an interest in correlating plant *signatures* with the archetypal qualities of the *planets.* The Northern Native American, with their concept of "animal medicine," the archetypal healing powers of certain animals, developed the idea of the *animal signature,* correlating plants to animals. Ancient India developed Ayurveda as a medicinal system, teaching that consciousness exists in all forms of life. Their doctrine of signature is phrased in images of shifts in consciousness. Even in remote areas of Africa, I was able to confirm from conversations with shaman doctors that they were well aware of a correlation between the growth habitat and medicinal qualities of a plant, this being the *environmental* aspect of the *signature.*

For as long as I have worked with and taught the doctrine of signature, I have called it *the language of flowers,* or *the language of plants.* I thought that I was the only one using this term, until in the process of writing the present book, I discovered that several other contemporary herbalists use this term to talk about the topic of this book. Matthew Wood calls it *the green tongue.* While the term *doctrine of signatures* come down to us from the middle ages and bears a Christian touch (the meaning being stamped upon creation by God), in our present times as spirituality embraces Nature as a living, meaningful energetic phenomenon again and spans out to include all other planetary traditions, this creator God model seems too restricted, and thus, it seems, a new language has arisen. I see the term *language of plants* as larger than the doctrine of signatures, since it includes a spiritual model that holds within it the possibility that the meaning is determined in part or completely by the observer and the act of observation. By doing so, it reinstates the ultimate mystery to Nature herself, setting her free from human-created limitations and constructs of meaning.

Last though not least, this topic is part of *biology,* the science of life, and as such directly tied to observation of living nature. In today's culture, which worships molecular biology, the idea of not killing the object to be observed has been lost from the *science of life*. The mind-boggling lists of details on molecules, enzymes, coenzymes, and coenzyme cofactors have nothing in common with our direct experience of a flower. We should bear in mind that in the field of nature studies, the whole is greater than the sum of its parts, no matter how innumerably many we manage to isolate.

CHAPTER ONE

HISTORY

"*The history of herbal medicine is of course as old as man himself, and our present knowledge is the product of thousands of years of observation and trial and error by primitive peoples all over the world, and codification and experimentation by the great herbalists of the past 500 years. Modern medicine is but a miniscule part of man's attempt to overcome disease; for a million years before the hospital and the laboratory, man searched for green medicine in the plants that grew all around him. Thousands were remarkably effective, and after their uses were established many plants took their common names from the organ they benefited.*"
—BEN CHARLES HARRIS (*The Complete Herbal*, p. 3)

It is outside of the range of this book to discuss the history of the doctrine of signature in all world cultures. However, I will trace its history mainly within Western culture since those sources are most easily available to me.

NATURE WISDOM ENCODED IN FOLKLORE— PLANT WISDOM ENCODED IN PLANT NAMES

No overview of the history would be complete without referring to the wisdom of folklore—the history of the peoples, representing the most ancient part of plant wisdom. We have to imagine countless generations of shepherds, spending their entire lives in nature under the open skies—billions of lifetimes worth of observations of what the animals nibble, what makes them sick and what cures them, what they are drawn to graze on when sick, and of course themselves

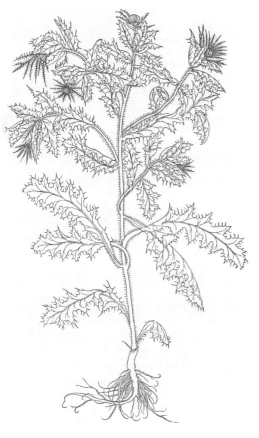

Blessed Thistle

chewing on grass, leaves, sticks, picking flowers, rubbing them between their fingers, sniffing, and throwing those things in the pot by the campfire for tea or food. It is arrogant to dismiss this wisdom that comes down to us as folklore as quaint and whimsical. The folkloric names of plants carry encoded in them the wisdom of this unbroken stream of oral transmission of native wisdom. We could say that it is the ancient form of "clinical anecdotes." Many of the European herb names have their medicinal use encoded in them, such as Rupturewort or Pilewort. This can be either by way of naming the organ healed by it, as in *Lungwort* or *Eyebright*, or by the disease it will cure, such as *Gravelroot* or *Heartsease*. The latter is even more specific; it tells us that it will ease the heart, when afflicted with uneasy thoughts. Dandelion is called *Pissenlit* in French, which means bed-wetting, a nickname it acquired owing to its diuretic properties.

The names transmit to us the wisdom of their spiritual uses and dimensions of healing, too, such as Angelica (*Angelica archangelica*), "Angelroot" or Archangel–Angel–Plant, invoking a very high spiritual reach. Blessed Thistle became named such after it was proven to ward off pestilence and poisons such as those of Scorpion and other bites—a blessing indeed. The Chinese call *Epimedium sagittatum* "Horny Goat Weed," so we can easily imagine how it came to be used as a prime herb to increase male virility; and *Ganoderma* "Mushroom of Immortality," one of their most prized herbs for rejuvenation. *Gu sui Bu* is a Chinese herb literally called "Mender of Shattered Bone." When the pioneers learned the use of *Eupatorium perforatum* from the Native Americans, they called it accordingly Boneset. Another Western herb is called Self-heal or Heal-all. We have to assume that there are good reasons for a large population living a life in touch with and dependent for their survival upon nature, to call a plant this way. These names were created by our ancestors to convey directly and unmistakably the essence of the plant. While the name of the plant is one dimension of plant wisdom in folklore, sayings are another—for instance, we say that something is mushrooming. This really refers to the speed with which mushrooms appear within hours on the forest floor once a rainfall is followed by warmth. Or we call someone a "shrinking violet." Violet flower essence has proven to be for shyness. Other kinds of sayings include advice, like the French: "Don't sleep under a walnut tree, or you might get a headache."

A lot of this folk wisdom is carried forth in the plant names in local or native languages. For example, there was a custom to fumigate crying and fussing babies that could not sleep at night with dried "Moon Flower" in rural Austria. This name is not official, and by now no one remembers which flower was once called Moon Flower—an appropriate name for a sleep-inducing plant. The same fast loss of wisdom occurs with the loss of native languages in Northern America. Many of the old Indian snakebite remedies have English folk names such as Rattlesnake Weed or Rattlesnake Root. In Cherokee, Self-heal is called *Snakehead* and used for rattlesnakebites, while Black-Eyed Susan is called *Deer Eye,* employed to cure Lyme disease (David Winston). As my Cherokee friend Cynthia Thomas pointed out, herbalists should therefore take a special interest in learning and preserving native languages. Native Americans also encoded the medicinal use in the name for the plant:

> Thus, the Chippewa, for instance, designated names of plants that usually were compound nouns; and these nouns, in turn, indicated the place where it grew, the appearance of the plant, its principal use or characteristic property. In addition, a suffix indicated which part of the plant was employed, such as the leaf, the root, or the flower. (And indeed that was how the candidate for the office of medicine man studied herb lore.)
>
> To the self-taught students of nature, the herbalists and healers of the American Indians, symbolism and sympathetic principles were inseparable from their diagnoses and remedies." (Harris 1985, p. 30)

For the creation myth of Bittersweet Vine, see under *rabbit medicine* in the chapter on *animal medicine.*

Another association that people close to nature have made is between a plant and an animal that might use it to cure itself—thus Celandine has also been called *Swallow Wort* after the swallows who pick some to rub on the eyes of their young to help them open them. This is different from plant names such as *Crane's Bill* or *Larkspur*, by which a plant is named after the animal part it resembles. These associations, in a way similar to *organ signatures*, will be covered more fully in the section on animal signatures.

Plant Wisdom Encoded in Myth

Ancient Indian culture used the Lotus as a spiritual allegory. This happens to be a fine example of the doctrine of signature, too: We are supposed to be in the world, but not of it, just as the Lotus grows from the mud, rising above the murky waters and opening it's splendid, untainted flower above the water toward the sky. This example makes more sense once you have seen Lotus grow wild in India and not in a pond at a botanical garden. Lotus flowers will bloom in filthy swamp lands an smelly, stagnant waters, often filled with the wastes of a nearby village and cattle, along with clouds of the most vicious mosquitoes hovering over it, not to mention the leeches. It is the scariest kind of murky water, and you'd do everything to avoid going into it. Similarly, on the spiritual journey, we are supposed to transcend ordinary life, beginning with the realization that it is as disgusting as the mud from which the lotus grows, while using that very muck as the nourishment for our growth to produce a magnificent spiritual bloom and to bear nutritious fruit. (See the section on *Reproductive Plant Parts* for more details on the lotus signature.)

The Lotus is "India's most sacred plant and symbol of spiritual unfoldment." It is sacred to Lakshmi, goddess of abundance and wisdom (Frawley and Lad 1986, p. 176f). This superimposition of a deity is another typical way of a culture giving its stamp of approval to a plant with high virtue. The more universally useful and healing a plant, the more likely it will be called sacred (such as *Yerba Santa,* "Sacred Herb"), and associated, dedicated or identified with a divinity that suits the theme of its healing powers. Lotus leaves, flowers, root and seeds have of old been used as a rejuvenating and strengthening herb that bestows mental clarity. Thus, its healing powers are embodied by Lakshmi, or else, it embodies Lakshmi's gifts. Lotus calming the heart and giving clarity of mind is of course what we need for spiritual unfoldment. The spiritual journey being long and arduous, rejuvenation is much needed. In India, Lotus seeds are said to bestow devotion and aspiration. We can see that there is much more to Lotus than a mere allegory of the spiritual journey—in fact, Lotus is the helper and guide. Lotus flower essence opens the head chakras and helps avoid falling for ego, thus sidestepping the pitfalls of the spiritual path. In the same way, various other Indian herbs are seen as the embodiment of the other countless divinities of the Hindu pantheon.

Ayurveda, an ancient Indian medicine, graces us with another version of plant wisdom being encoded in their names: Aloe species, for instance, are called *kumari*, which means young girl or virgin. They are called thus, because of the rejuvenating effect it has on both the feminine reproductive organs, as well as the energy of youth and renewal of the "female nature" (Frawley and Lad, 1986, p. 100). Going far beyond physiological effects, the plant's name is meant to express its psychological and spiritual effect. The closely related Lily, *shatavari*, an asparagus species root,

Lotus

translates as "she who possesses a thousand husbands." It is a tonic to the female reproductive organs, giving—as it is said—the woman the strength and capacity to enjoy a thousand husbands (ibid., p. 183). Calamus root is called *vacha*, which means "speaking," denoting the power of the word and intelligence or self-expression it gives rise to (ibid., p. 106).

Tibetan lore has it that one of the wives of the Tibetan king, a Chinese princess, was in possession of the elixir of life. When its thief who had drunk the elixir was beheaded, garlic sprang forth. No Tibetan will hear this story thinking that this is in reality how garlic was created, but understand that this points to garlic being an elixir for long life—which indeed it is. Not only has garlic been scientifically proven to have countless health benefits that prolong life, it is also classified as a rejuvenating herb in both Ayurveda and Tibetan medicine. In this way, folklore encodes herbal wisdom in allegories.

The Taoist philosophy of ancient China had the ways of nature at its core; seeing man as a microcosm inside the universe, the macrocosm. Both are composed of the five elements, which relate to the five major organs and so on. Taoist thought is akin to the hermetic "as above, so below." They prescribed exercise, food and medicines to realign the person with the cosmic force, and thus heal or stay healthy, or extend one's life. They saw Ginseng, a root in human form, as the prime tonic for people in general. The Ganoderma mushroom is called *Ling zhi,* "Herb of Spiritual Potency" or "Mushroom of Immortality" for its rejuvenating properties and refreshing action on the mind. It has been prized as one of the most potent yet side-effect–free herbal compounds for the last 4,000 years in Asian medicine. Traditional Chinese Medicine built its *materia medica* on careful observation of nature as a one of the pillars. One of the legends tell the story of a farmer who beat a snake with a hoe to death. A few days later, the snake reappeared, and the farmer beat it again until it bled. He watched the snake slither off to eat a certain herb. The next morning, its wounds were healed and it was slithering around again. This plant subsequently became one of the main ingredients of *yunnan bai yao,* an herbal preparation that stops internal and external bleeding (Blum, 1995, p. 32).

It was common in ancient Greece to encode the psychological use for a plant in their mystical lore. You might have noticed that about every myth involves a flower or plant, or someone or something being turned into a flower or tree (which henceforth exists). These creation stories of plants are a specific cultural way of encoding plant wisdom—for instance, the story goes that Anemone was a beautiful nymph beloved by Zephyr, the God of the West Wind. His wife, the goddess Flora, became jealous of her and transformed Anemone into the Windflower, *Pulsatilla.* The God of the West Wind dropped her. She has since been wooed by Boreas, the God of the North Wind, and she opens her blossom every spring at his bidding (McIntyre 1996, p. 67). The Wind or Pasque Flower is called *Anemone pulsatilla.* We see how the transformation in the myth is really a way of saying: what is as follows in the human realm (being in love and being forsaken) corresponds to the following plant in the vegetable realm. Another story, about another anemone, tells of when Aphrodite (Venus) fell in love with Adonis, and her jealous lover Ares (Mars) killed his competitor. From the tears Aphrodite shed over Adonis' death, anemone flowers sprang. What better flower to express this situation, since *Anemone pulsatilla* is the plant that is suited to gentle, loving females who weep easily and grieve, as well as to fear or the grief of abandonment? Murphy suggests that *Pulsatilla* being an eye remedy (as well as one of the best gynecological ones) points to the story of Venus shedding tears from her eyes (2000, p. 1425). I think that the grief is more to the point here, and in modern terms, *Pulsatilla* would be one of the prime remedies for codependence: being heart broken over the loss of one's partner and being forsaken. It is of interest here again that the goddess superimposed to the creation of this flower is Aphrodite, called Venus by the Romans, who of course embodies archetypal femininity. *Pulsatilla* is one out of the two chief "female" remedies in the huge homeopathic repertory of hundreds of remedies. The other one, *Sepia,* is not suitable to gentle nor grieving females… and we shall learn more about the association between Venus, the eyes and reproductive organs in the section on *Planetary Signatures.*

The cultural phenomenon of associating attributes of the deities and divinities of the day with a medicinal plant that represents similar values was also widespread in the Christian tradition—plants were named after the Christ, the Virgin or Mary, St. John and all kinds if other Saints. Harris gives a long list of them. Examples include Christ's Thorn, Madonna Lily (a synonym for Lily of the Valley in this case), St. Mary's Seal, St. John's Wort, and St. Barbara's Hedge mustard (Harris 1985, p. 40).

No account of folk wisdom and plants would be complete without mentioning Celtic plant lore. In Celtic tradition, plants and trees are often seen as the abode of the fairies, the elemental spirits. Celtic spirituality is based on an understanding that the four elements are alive and spiritual, or inspirited. The elementals were experienced as an expression of this animated, alive and breathing natural world. Thus, the Oak and Rowan are fairy trees, as to a lesser degree are Elder bushes. My herbalist friend Pat Holtz writes: "I met a crone from Ireland who told me as a child they were forbidden to eat Elderberries. She questioned this after seeing cows eat mouthfuls. Then her mum admitted Elder had a powerful plant spirit. If one was unsure what herbal remedy to use, lore had it that sitting under the Elder would tell you the correct one to choose. Her family used Elder as medicine but didn't want the children to get entangled with the Elder spirit or the fairies." The folk relationship with plant spirits and elementals is another whole chapter on plant folk wisdom. Elder has a folk history of being associated with transcendence into other realms in Celtic and Germanic fairy tales (also called *Hollerbusch* in German, which relates to the name *Frau Holle* in the fairy tale of the same name), even down to the Greeks who associated the Elder with Pan, the god of the power of nature himself. His flute, *sambucus,* made of the hollow branches of Elder, is called *Sambucus nigra,* or Black Elder. Wood worked out the spiritual herbal dimension of the use of Elder, connected to knowledge of the underworld, as well as astral traveling—or, in a more mundane way, as opening up the imagination (1997, p. 423ff).

The Native Americans do not have a pantheon of divinities. Their culture seeks and finds the sacred in nature, all around. Native Americans group substances according to their *medicine power,* the inherent healing qualities, or what they carry that can return a certain harmony to an imbalance with the cosmos. As such, White Pond Lily holds a similar medicine power as the water snake, also called the underwater panther (Wood 1997, p. 384). It is striking to see how much a Pond Lily root when scrubbed and defoliated looks like a snake, with the insertion marks for the leaves making an eerie scale-like pattern. The long creeping rootstock, shaped like the body of the reptile, seems to creep along in snake-like motion. Being filled with tiny air pockets, it swims on the surface of the waters once the rootlets are severed. It makes you shudder to step into the intertwining Pond Lily roots at the bottom of the lake and find your foot caught—sending a shock wave of all terrible things imaginable through the subconscious. This all put together makes the water snake remedy Pond Lily a most powerful medicine for all things related to the body's waters, the kidneys, as well as swampy wet tissue states, and psychologically subconscious issues.

And thus, in studying a medicinal plant we would be wise to study all of its lore, for this is the rich tapestry of nature wisdom handed down to us from our ancestors.

TRACING THE SIGNATURE THROUGH THE AGES

Little has been written on the development of the concept of the doctrine of signature, especially by today's herbalists. Some of it is embedded in Matthew Wood's *The Magical Staff.* Some cultures use the concept without having a name for it: Wood once asked a Native American herbalist whether he knew of the doctrine of signatures. His friend answered: "I was taught in that way, only we never called it thus."

The doctrine of signature as we know it today in the West probably was shaped more by the hermetic tradition and alchemy as practiced across all of Eurasia than other philosophical movements. Both sought not only to grasp the essence, *essentia,* of plants, but of all of creation—the elements, minerals, metals, planets, animal substances, humans, etc. To the ancients, the most important thing was to understand how things in the macrocosm, the universe, correspond to those in the microcosm, the individual person. "The individual human is a tiny microcosm, corresponding to and personifying the totality, the Divine, the Macrocosm" (Wood 1992, p. 18f). Wood traces the emergence of this idea back to the shamanistic roots of ancient Greece, then shaped into a philosophical system by **Plato** (428–348 BCE), expounding the existence of the archetypal *ideas* that were the blueprint behind everything. Records of the doctrine of signature predate that—the Egyptians saw the universe with its spherical layers of the heavens and the planetary pathways reflected in the layers of onion bulbs, thus pronouncing them sacred. Onion in all its forms is a shock remedy that restores our sense of belonging to the group, as well as being a harmonious member of the universe. Ancient Egyptian knowledge merged with classical Greek wisdom in Hellenistic Egypt, giving rise to the hermetic tradition in the third century C.E. The merging of the Greek god Hermes and the Egyptian god Thoth gave rise to a Hermes who at the same time represented the Greek god Hermes and the image of an old sage, called **Hermes Trismegistos**, "the thrice-great Hermes." The merging fused the knowledge of the ancient masters of the mysteries from both civilizations. It remains questionable whether Hermes Trismegistos was an actual individual, although he is depicted as such. Related to the image of the water bird (an ibis in the case of Egypt and animal symbol of Thoth), *geranos* in Greek, he symbolized the wisdom of old age (as in *gerontology*). Both entities were gods of writing and magic; Thoth furthermore of wisdom and science, and Hermes of communication, as well as other things. Both were thought to go between the human and divine realm, taking messages. The texts of this philosophy, the hermetic writings, date from about 150 to 250 CE. The hermetic teachings gained and lost popularity many times throughout history, and were reintroduced into European thought in about 1450 by Cosimo **Medici** (1389–1464), ruling merchant of Florence and patron of the arts and science who found those texts in Byzantium and had them translated in Florence. Hermeticism being about astrology, magic and alchemy, these writings have always been popular with the alchemists. It is in this way that Paracelsus and his contemporaries came to know of them. The *Emerald Tablet,* a short text, outlines the hermetic principles. It is interesting to look at the various translations of this one teaching that has been the foundation of the doctrine of signatures in the West for about two thousand years. The second point is as follows:

The Arabic translation reads, "It states: What is the above is from the below and the below is from the above. The work of wonder is from one."

Isaac Newton's translation renders it, "That which is below is like that which is above, and that which is above is like that which is below; to do the miracle of one only thing."

The translation from *Aurelium occultae philosophorum* by George Beato says, "Whatever is below is similar to that which is above. Through this the marvels of the work of one thing are procured and perfected."

The English translation of the Latin version goes, "That which is below is as that which is above, and that which is above is as that which is below, to perform miracles of the one thing."

The second part of the statement gives us an idea of what alchemist herbalist doctors such as Paracelsus meant when they spoke of magic in healing. The magic happens when medicine is practiced according to these laws, and with a profound understanding of them. Paracelsus was famed for his miracle cures that he was able to bring about based on these principles. The tenth point of the *Emerald Tablet* says, "The formation of the microcosm is in accordance with the formation of the macrocosm," just as the Taoists would have it.

Aristotle (384–322 BCE), the great Greek logician, worked with the principle of the law of correspondence, applying to hot, cold, dry, and damp their opposites. This system is strictly logical, and lacks the inspirational and artistic flavor of true doctrine of signature.

Paracelsus (1493–1541) was a highly trained physician, accomplished alchemist and magician. The effects of his work onto conventional and complementary medicine continue to this day. I was taught he was the father of modern medicine, chemistry and surgery when in medical school—so I was surprised to find that he was, in fact, also a highly trained alchemist and occultist. Living at the brink of modern times before the advent of rationalism, Paracelsus states that the two essentials of scientific investigation are experience and experiment (Wood 1992,

p. 9). We can see from this one statement how he could at once be the father of all science, where only what is validated by experiment can be true, *and* folk wisdom, entirely based on experience handed down through the ages. "He saw life force as an active, directing intelligence that maintained and repaired the organism in a dynamic fashion" (ibid., p. 15).

Paracelsus formulated three important principles of healing; *the doctrine of correspondence*, which lead him into the *doctrine of signature* and the *law of similars*. Since then, these three run like a thread through the history of natural healing. The doctrine of correspondence is the ancient understanding that an archetypal idea is expressed in many different forms in the phenomenal world, grouping metals, minerals, body parts, planets, animals, and so on as having corresponding essences. Thus, for instance, Venus, women, femininity, copper, Birch trees, kidneys, beans, and larch trees would all share a corresponding principle. This is also true of diseases and medicines, which according to Paracelsus must be matched in this way to achieve healing. Here are some of his examples:

> If you look at the root of Satyrion [*Satyrion trifolium*, an orchid nowadays called *orchis*], is it not shaped like the groin of a man? Nobody can contradict that. Because of that, magic has discovered it and pointed out that it can restore in men their lost virility and enjoyment. And then thistle; don't its spines prick like needles? By way of this sign the art of magic discovered that there is no better herb for inner stitching. "Victory Root" [Siegwurz, *Gladiolus paluster*] has a web around it like an armor; that also is a magical sign for the fact that it protects from weapons like an armor. And the root Syderica bears on each of its leaves the image of a snake and thus protects, according to magic, from all kinds of poisonings. The root of Plantain is under special solar influence; one can see that from its flowers that are always inclined toward the Sun, as if showing gratitude. Because of this, it is most effective when the Sun shines, while the Sun is in the sky. As soon as he sets, its powers wean.[1]

Orchid

---

1   In Jakobi, 1991, p. 171f; modern plant identification according to Fuchs, 1543, chapter 270 and Fitter

What does Paracelsus mean by magic? It is the magic of correspondence that Paracelsus graces with this term. To him, a correspondence or similarity based on linear logic is not magical—such as using the right eye of an animal to heal the right eye of a human, a prevalent idea in ancient medicine. However, healing the liver of a human with the leaf of a plant, Liverwort, that looks like a liver is magic to him, and more powerful in healing. It is in keeping with "as above, so below," and as the *Emerald Tablet* expounds, that is the basis for miracles, like magic. Natural magic means that it naturally arises, that through signs and archetypes and correspondences healing springs forth. Magic also means that it is not based on a cause–effect relationship, but one that can be intuited only, without physical explanations. The explanation is the law of similar—that similar things have similar origins. The Arabic translation of the third tenet of the *Emerald Tablet* states, "And all things sprang forth from this essence through a single projection. How marvelous is its work!" Paracelsus often refers to this, insisting the physician must see how the outer and inner are in truth one. This hermetic idea is the earliest reference I found to the notion that the mind plays a part in what we perceive, how we perceive it, as well as what we can effect in the world.

When reading Paracelsus' works, we can feel the incredible enthusiasm for this truth flowing from each line. The doctrine of signature is the practical application of the doctrine of correspondence. "The idea is that the shape, color, appearance, environmental niche, taste, smell, etc., of a plant or medicinal agent will display the tell-tale signs, marks, or configurations indicating how that agent may be used in medicine. This is called *signatum,* or signature" (Wood 1992, p. 19f). When I explained this idea once to an amazed friend, he said: "So you are saying that like this, you can know the underlying rules of the universe!" This is it. Paracelsus was adamant that there is a sensible structure to outer phenomena, and that by learning to read these signs like a sign language, we can understand them. Based on this, we can influence or manipulate outer phenomena according to those rules. "The virtue is signed in the form, figure, corpus and substance," writes Paracelsus. He went on to formulate the law of similars, *similia similibus curantur,* or like cures like. This became *the* basis for homeopathy several centuries later. Paracelsus' contribution is not that he created the law of similars, but that he gave it a clearer

---

et al., 1974, p. 276. I was not able to identify *Syderica.*

status within the edifice of his teachings than his ancient forbearers (ibid.). He popularized the term *doctrine of signature*.

There is a fourth and fifth principle of healing, the *law of contraries* and the *law of action and reaction*. While the law of contraries was not approved by Paracelsus, it is still valid in the context of reading the doctrine of signature. See more below in the section on *definitions*.

The Italian **Giambattista Della Porta** (1535–1615), nicknamed "the professor of secrets," was another genius living at the dawn of modern times. Professor of occult and natural philosophy, astrology, alchemy, what we would consider science and many other things, his writings include *Natural Magick* (1558), a compilation of works on physiognomy, and *Phytognomonica*, a work in which he includes exotic plant species, discovers the spores of ferns, discusses the doctrine of signature and much more. Chapter 6 of the first book of *Natural Magick* is called "From where Form Comes," in which he attributes it to cosmic influences that, in the end, go back to God. In chapter 11, "That the Likeness of Things Shows Their Secret Virtue," he gives examples of the doctrine of signatures. It also shows how this principle was applied to all of nature, not just plants, as he explains it for various gems. The following chapter is called "How to Compound and Lay Things Together, by Their Likeness."

The Christian mystic German Jakob **Böhme** (1575–1624), a disciple of Paracelsus, had mystic visions in which he understood all of creation as being marked with a sign, or signature, by God for humans to understand His intention for their creation. Although sometimes presented as such, Böhme is not the father of this ancient idea nor the term "doctrine of signatures," and the works of Paracelsus, his teacher, abound with the idea that God marked His creation with signs for us to decipher. The doctrine of signatures originates within the alchemical tradition, which has its roots in the pre-Christian Egyptian and Greek cultures. Since Paracelsus was both a devout Christian and advanced alchemist, his scriptures read at once like those of a saint and a pagan.

"Astrology was for Paracelsus primarily a language of pattern. He was not interested in erecting charts and forecasting, but he used astrology as a language expressing archetypal relationships" (Wood, 1992, p. 24). Using astrology as a system of grouping phenomena including organs, diseases, mental states, plants and healing substances is as old as all great world civilizations. After Paracelsus, the famous physician, botanist, herbalist and astrologer Nicholas **Culpeper**

(1616–1654) was trying to work out the planetary correspondence for each herb, thus working with what I call the *planetary signature*. Like Paracelsus, he did charts for people and their disease, determining for instance whether it was caused by witchcraft or not. Since there are also body parts and diseases corresponding to the planets and signs of the zodiac, this is again a therapeutic model of matching corresponding phenomena—in this case, pairing the disease with the opposing planetary influence. His major works are *The English Physitian* (1652) and *The Complete Herbal* (1653); he takes the doctrine of signature as a given. It is noteworthy that Culpeper studied medicine in Cambridge, being one of the highly educated people of his times. Like Paracelsus and many of those referred to below, they were not quacks, but rather cutting edge experts of their time who grew disenchanted with the prevailing view and went back to the roots, basing their medical practice on clinical experience. Both Paracelsus and Culpeper refused to write their texts in Latin, preferring the language of the common people, and spent their entire lives providing free medical services to the poor.

Culpeper's contemporary, botanist and herbalist William **Coles** (1626–1662), authored *The Art of Simpling* and *Adam in Eden*. In these works, he gives numerous examples of the doctrine of signature. For instance, he offers an detailed description of the analogy in shape between a walnut and the human head, concluding that they are therefore good for curing head ailments (see Part Three, "Plant Portraits" for more details). His source of signatures is the German professor of medicine and alchemy and a disciple of Paracelsus, Oswald **Kroll** (1560–1608), a hermetic philosopher whom Coles calls the "exquisite discoverer of Signatures." Also called Oswaldus Crollius, Kroll authored the *Book of Signatures,* from which Coles draws. Unfortunately, Coles's examples of signature are not always clear, as he might just say that the herb "heals this disease by way of signature" without specifying which color or shape he refers to. From all that I have been able to glean from the above ancient authors, the examples of signatures given are the same over and over again. This leaves me with the impression that they were handed down from antiquity, and studied by each following generation. Thus, Coles could assume that his readers, the well educated, would know what he is referring to.

We saw how Paracelsus connected the law of similars to the doctrine of signature. Although **Hahnemann** (1755–1843), the father of homeopathy, denied having taken this idea from

Paracelsus, there is no doubt to those who studied the history of medicine that he did. The biggest difference between their two approaches is that Paracelsus based his understanding of the law of similars on the doctrine of signature (plants looking like organs or the disease they cure), while Hahnemann based it on the symptomology picture derived from states of intoxication with poisonous plants. This is called drug or homeopathic provings. Rather than the plant being similar to the disease, it is the ill effect of the overdose of the toxic remedy that is similar to the sickness. We could call this the *intoxication signature*. Hahnemann took a path away from matching the plant to the organ, unlike some of his peers who "relied upon their intuitive understanding of the workings of the organism"—his intoxication-picture-matching being too intellectual (Wood 1992, p. 62). It is not surprising to find that whenever a philosophy wishes to portray itself as rational only, the ancient holistic and intuitive methods fall into discredit. Still, we find an ongoing fertile exchange between the discovery of similars and doctrines of signature within homeopathy, possibly thanks to the not-so-dogmatic wing of the homeopaths, as well as the eclectic doctors who gleaned a big part of their plant wisdom along with knowledge of the signatures from the Native Americans.

To this day, the doctrine of signature is weaving in and out of the homeopathic *materia medicas,* mentioned whenever illustrating a keynote symptom worthwhile remembering. Examples are for instance the observation that poison ivy is much more poisonous in the night hours and in damp, shady places. "The plant's signature will not fail to connect the cardinal aggravations of Rhus-t. [*Rhus toxicodendron,* Poison Ivy] at night and from damp with the increased virulence of the plant at night and in damp atmosphere" (Murphy's *Homeopathic Remedy Guide,* 2000, p. 1481). Hence, it is a prime remedy for rheumatism brought on or worsened by dampness and after the night's rest. I also noticed that in cases of Poison Ivy poisoning, the itch is worse at night. St. John's Wort, *Hypericum perforatum,* looks as if perforated, because of the presence of tiny oil glands. The sap is reddish, and when made into a medicinal oil, tincture or tea, will color them red. "These [oil glands] which are most conspicuous in Hyper. [*Hypericum perforatum,* St. John's Wort], have evidently given the signature which has led to the chief use of the plant in medicine" (ibid., p. 852). St. John's Wort is one of the most valuable wound remedies, particularly for puncture wounds or narrow, deep wounds or burns—for being perforated. For those, it is a veritable specific. The homeopathic provings also brought out some of the mental qualities found in the plant's signature—Yellow Jasmin, *Gelsemium semprevirens,* is a climber (a plant that holds on to another for support), and it is a valuable remedy for people who are anxious, dread falling and feel that they need to hold onto someone else for support. This is seen as an indication for a woman in labor needing this remedy in the homeopathic hospitals. The stools are "yellow like the flower" (ibid., p. 730f).

Homeopathic proving brought proof for the principle that "like cures like" and "it can heal what it can cause." For Hahnemann, the law of similars meant only "it can heal what it can cause." It means that if touching Poison Ivy can cause the most horribly weepy and itchy eczema, then Poison Ivy in the right dose and preparation can cure just such eczema. I would like to call this the *doctrine of similes* or *homeopathic signature.* This has added another dimension to the understanding of the doctrine of signature—that if the plant can cause a certain kind of dreadful pain, that it will heal to just such dreadful pain. However, this is only one part of the law of similars, leaving out the fact that "it can cure what it looks similar to." This means, for instance, that Stone Root (*Collinsonia* for the homeopaths) emerges from the ground by sending up livid purple hoops that later become the straight stems. These hoops look exactly like nascent hemorrhoids, and Stone Root is one of the chief remedies for venous congestion in hemorrhoids. It cures what it looks like, what it looks similar to. The homeopathic definition of like cures like is reduced to the intoxication symptoms only.

During the time of the pioneers in America, Thompson and the **Eclectic doctors** learned about the healing plants from the Native Americans, who included how they read the signatures. Hence, they often called themselves "Indian" or "root" doctors. John Milton **Scudder** (1829–1894) pioneered the symptom lists organized into coherent patterns that capture the practitioner's imagination. He was the first to propose not only that herbal medicine, the patient and the disease should be understood as a dynamic process, but also that practitioners themselves are alive, and it is their trained dynamic life force apprehending the patient that gives rise to a correct diagnosis (Wood 1992, p. 107ff.). This is the first notion we find that what we observe does not only depend on what is out there, but on the mind and senses apprehending. While this has hit home in physics since Heisenberg's *uncertainty principle* and is known in psychological and medical testing (requiring double-blind studies to undercut), it still has to make its way into mainstream science and herbal practice.

The great German poet and natural scientist Johann Wolfgang von **Goethe** (1749–1832) developed his approach to natural science with an emphasis on the study of morphology. His scientific works include studies on the weather, colors, geology and mineralogy, osteology and botany. He was keenly interested in the metamorphosis of shapes between botanical species, and within one species, relating these to inherent qualities. He envisioned the existence of the *Urpflanze*, the archetypal, or primal, plant, a generic ancestor to all of higher plant life, less specialized hence transformable into all the other plant families. During his famous journey through Italy and Sicily, Goethe intuited his theory of the metamorphosis of plants, inspired by watching the slow change in plant forms as he journeyed south. He published his *Versuch die Metamorphose der Pflanze zu erkennen* (*Metamorphosis of Plants*) in 1790. In this work, he explains how the petals and fruits of a plant are a metamorphosis of the basic archetypal leaf. He formulated that the archetypal plant shape is the leaf: "from top to bottom a plant is all leaf, united so inseparably with the future bud that one cannot be imagined without the other" (*Italian Journey*, vol. 6). He saw the first two untrue leaves, the subsequent evolving true leaves, the sepals and petals all as an evolutionary metamorphosis of the same blueprint. Goethe was a great advocate of precise observation of nature with the naked senses, deeply mistrusting the use of devices such as microscopes. He did not embrace the mechanistic worldview that many started to share during his era.

Goethean natural science was further developed by the philosopher and founder of Anthroposophy, Rudolf **Steiner** (1861–1925). Having served as the editor to Goethe's scientific writings for the Kürschner edition of Goethe's collected works, Steiner was thoroughly familiar with the material. He called Goethe's scientific approach phenomenological rather than one based on theory or a thought model. In his *Goethe's Worldview*, Steiner clarifies how the Goethean approach calls for the need of one's intuition becoming well developed like a sense organ. Steiner himself thought about plants and nature in terms of *formative forces*, the underlying internal and external energies and their interplay that shapes the plants, themselves at the same time equal to and expressing certain qualities. Steiner spent countless hours in nature as a boy, and was trained by a folk herbalist. Being deeply familiar with the alchemical tradition, he taught that a plant is threefold, analogous to the three primary substances of the alchemists, as proposed by Paracelsus, mercury, sulfur and salt, and the threefold human being (metabolic sphere, rhythmical sphere of heart and lungs, nerve pole with the brain). In his teachings of anthroposophic medicine, he relates this as the threefold nature of the human being, an idea that goes back to the hermetic tradition, and proposes that the matching of the plant medicine and the disease should be made according to those correspondences. He explains, "What we call the beauty of nature is really an imitation of disease processes. Inside of a human being it is a disease process, outside wonderfully beautiful nature. But one has to understand the connection and know how from the wide range of natural processes we can bring disease into man, and thus thereby relieve the metaphysical bodies of humans of the disease processes" (Pelikan 1980, p. 10). Steiner saw the human being as endowed with three layers of metaphysical bodies, called ether body, astral body and "I"-being. Like cures like; if we can find and use a plant that imitates the disease process, it will heal the specific disease. Steiner outlines the process of gaining insight into the essential nature of plants in four steps, starting with sense perception, followed by imagination and inspiration, and crowned by intuition.

Steiner inspired works such as **Grohmann**'s book, *The Plant* (in 2 volumes), a wonderful overview of the interplay of forces in nature and the plant, also giving insights into the vegetation of all climate zones—the first work on what I would call spiritual botany. Gohmann analyzes the formative forces acting on the plant, as well as their cosmological implications, but does not consider the plants' healing virtues nor the doctrine of signature as such. The second volume discusses all major botanical families. Steiner also inspired the first systematic work on the doctrine of signature that I am aware of: Wilhelm **Pelikan**'s (1893–1981) monumental work *Healing Plants* (the German title exactly translated is *Herbology, Heilpflanzenkunde*), published over the time span from 1958 to 1975 in three volumes, of which unfortunately only the first has been translated into English. The strength of this *magnum opus* is his coverage of all botanical families, presenting the major healing plants in the context of formative forces within their own clan, and their individual deviation from the general blueprint of this plant family. A chemist and pharmacist, Pelikan also added invaluable insight into how the doctrine of signature, that is morphological phenomena, are reflected in, and correspond to, the plant's chemistry. I like to call this the *biochemical signature.* It is an echo, or a reflection, of the morphological aspect—"as above, so below." Pelikan describes the three volumes as being of ascending order in spiritual depth of understanding. The first volume focuses on the threefold nature of humankind and plant. The second volume has the etheric formative forces at its core. In the third and final volume, Pelikan presents the elemental beings behind those formative forces. Invaluable though this work is, its accessibility is unfortunately limited severely by the fact that it is written in anthroposophic terminology, which makes it hard to digest for most readers. The art of Goethean plant study and analysis of a plant from the point of view of interplay of formative forces is alive today in the work of biodynamic farming, a movement pioneered by Rudolf Steiner. I find, however, that the mere analysis of the formative forces acting on the plant without a reading of the signature (that is, a match to the human body or other correspondences) makes their work a lot less interesting and alive than the application of the doctrine of signature as practiced, for example, in traditional societies and by Matthew Wood and his students. One is left with endless detailed descriptions of morphological phenomena, while the essence or personality of the herb thus slips away.

Pharmacist Ben Charles **Harris** published his *Complete Herbal* in 1985, a modern herbal giving one or more signatures for each of the plants listed. Being a practicing herbalist, an art he learned from his grandfather and from Native American sources, he states, "Instead of the tedious memorization of the various uses of a plant, the doctrine of signature offers in many (though not all) cases a reliable system of connecting the herb with its remedial use through symbolic association" (Harris 1985, p. 37). He calls the doctrine of signature "probably the earliest system of applied therapeutics in the history of medicine" (ibid., p. 38). *The Complete Herbal* has a useful introductory part on the doctrine of signature, and offers original signatures for a great range of herbs, especially those native to Northern America. His *Herbal* is the most complete book on the doctrine of signature to this date. Unfortunately, he does not specify his Native American sources for the most part.

The contemporary influential Minnesotan herbalist and historian Matthew **Wood** uses poetic examples of the doctrine of signature in the discussion of almost every plant he writes about, adding many fine new examples to the traditional ones. Today's foremost thinker in Western herbalism, he has authored six works on herbalism to date. Wood's contribution to herbalism is his tireless effort to bring together the pieces of the Western herbal traditions from its ancient Greek roots via the alchemists and eclectic doctors to the present day, integrating folk herbalism and traditional medical systems such as that of the Native Americans, Ayurveda and Traditional Chinese Medicine. In so doing, he has put the Western herbalist tradition on the same level with other great systems, and given Western herbalists a new access to the lost energetic system, such as the tissue states. In drawing clear parallels between the Western and other traditional systems, he created a language and thinking model that allows the practitioner to comprehend all traditional systems of the world as one. Wood is a forerunner paving the way to an intuitive and spiritual based planetary herbalism of the future.

In *Flowers that Heal* (1998), Patricia **Kaminski** attempts a systematic classification of the signature of flowers pertaining to flower essences, discussing the basic colors and shapes of flowers themselves, also considering the healing properties of flower essences by plant families. An anthroposophist, she follows the tradition of Goethe and Steiner. In the same year, Isla **Burgess** wrote an herbal workbook *Weeds Heal* (1998). In it, she guides the student of herbalism through a process of using all of the senses to detect keys and signatures pointing to the medicinal properties of the plant.

With the advent of modern materialistic reductionist biology and the decoding of the genome, science thought to have unveiled the mystery of nature. Just as the discovery of the atomic sub-particles did *not* make the world entirely mechanically explainable, but pushed "hard science" into an ever more mystifying realm of elusive quantum physics, decoding the human genome has only led biologists to realize that that does *not* hold the key to morphology: surprisingly, the genes as it turns out do not explain why we have the colors and shapes that we do. The platonic mechanistic worldview of the universe as a mechanical machine can no longer be upheld. Nature will not have herself unraveled fully by the analytic view! The Cambridge and Harvard trained cutting edge biochemist and plant physiologist Rupert **Sheldrake** (1942), father of the *resonance field theory*, has sought to comprehend morphogenesis, how shapes and colors arise in plants, animals and humans. Sheldrake states that in a constantly evolving universe, the laws of nature cannot be constant. Sheldrake, not so much interested in morphology as morphogenesis, proposes the existence of morphic fields, of which morphogenetic fields are a subcategory. They contain the information needed to shape the exact form of a living thing and may also shape its behavior. The nascent organism tunes into the information like a receiver and thus grows in resonance to the shape communicated by that field. The effect is transmitted across time and space, and the morphic fields are not electromagnetic fields of energy as we know them. These fields arise as a result of similar shapes having come into being in the past, and are constantly strengthened or changed by new, similar organisms. This is refreshing; since Plato we have had to contend with the *ideas* or archetypes being constant and unchanging, as would be fit for an entity in a mechanical world. Sheldrake argues that bodily forms and instincts, while expressed through genes, do not have their primary origin in them. Instead, his hypothesis states that the organism develops under the influence of previous simi-lar organisms, by a mechanism he calls *morphic resonance*. Rupert Sheldrake's work, like that of Paracelsus, spans from the exact science of the laboratory to the spiritual truth gleaned from careful observation, thus his work is at once accepted as scientific and condemned as magic. Sheldrake's research into causation of form in nature, *morphogenesis,* as put forth in his *New Science of Life* (2009) proposes that the natural laws are "habits of nature" and thus could change: things are what they are, because they were what they were. Sheldrake proposes the existence of organizing fields; such a field would remain after a limb is severed and explain phantom pain and sensations as well as the regrowth of severed limbs of reptiles: the organiz-ing field remains after the physical limb is cut. Growing trees are said to tune into the morphic field of previously growing similar trees to know what shape to take. While Sheldrake's theory gives a plastic idea of the causation of shape in nature, unrelated to genes and genetic expres-sion, it does not explain how similarities in shape outside of very close biological relatives can occur, let alone have similar medicinal effects. It is, however, making biology more in tune with quantum physics in that it allows for fluidity of the universe and takes the effect of the observer onto the observed into account. Sheldrake's theory could serve to explain the doc-trine of signatures if we were to propose organizing fields for things of similar morphological characteristics who are dissimilar in terms of species.

Since **Heisenberg**'s uncertainty principle, modern science has had to acknowledge that there is no such thing as the objective observer, or the objective observation. While this meanwhile not-so-new discovery has not made its way into the science of life, biology, this is where Hermes Trismegistos, Western philosophers such as Rudolf Steiner, Mahayana Buddhism, and quantum physics meet: what we perceive and how we perceive the world around us is at least in part determined by the observer, by the mind perceiving. The most modern scientific theory that validates what we could call a shamanistic approach to nature is the *implicate and explicate order* proposed by quantum physicist David **Bohm** (1917–1992). He proposes a holistic worldview in which things only become definable by time and space once the order unfolds, and not determined while the order is implicate, as if folded like a piece of paper. His thoughts are similar to those of the ancient *Mahayana Buddhist* teachings of the Middle Way Philosophy, *Madyamika Prasangika.* The latter describes things as void of definable characteristics for as long as they have not been locked into these by a mind perceiving them as having those. All of these philosophical approaches acknowledge the importance of the mind and perceiving individual in creating reality as we perceive it, acknowledging the paramount role of our mind and its conceptual limitations in what we perceive in nature.

In this book, I will attempt to unite all the material available, which under the perspective of life force or energy can easily be recognized as the same phenomenon taking different labels in different cultural circumstances, thereby bringing it to a planetary level.

CHAPTER TWO

THE DOCTRINE OF SIGNATURE TODAY

"The natural tendency of medical experience is toward the development of intuitive and deductive skills which provide insight into medical conditions."

—MATTHEW WOOD (1992, p. 66)

"The practice must not proceed from the theory, but the theory from practice."

—PARACELSUS (Wood 1992, p. 74)

DEDUCTIVE VERSUS INDUCTIVE, OR THE RATIONAL VERSUS THE INTUITIVE

The philosophical underpinnings of natural science as it is practiced today is logical empiricism, a system where the theory is formulated in response to the observed data, and changed whenever the findings call for it. Surprisingly, herbalism and the art of signatures are no different—even when knowledge of an herbal use or signature came to a medicine man or woman in *dreamtime*. Frances Densmore reports in 1918 about the Chippewa that the Indians say that they receive knowledge about medicinal plants in dreams, "but the response of the physical organism was the test of the plant as a remedy" (p. 322). All innovative herbalists the world over with common sense have acted that way.

In our day and age, most people—especially scientists—are far removed from nature. Today, we analyze nature by way of technological imaging. Before, nature was what you saw in front of you with your very own eyes, eyes that were not overcrowded by a flood of colorful media images, with minds still and slow, ready to behold and take in details. It is not surprising that such people when unearthing a root that resembles themselves—Mandrake root or Ginseng, called "man-root," had to ask themselves the question: does this root that resembles me in shape also resemble me in other ways? If we were to meet another human who looks like us, our double, would we not also be compelled to ask: does he or she resemble me in character?

It has been said that the doctrine of signature is not scientific, because it is not causal. Kinder statements call it pre-scientific. The attempt to classify it as such shows that the authors do not understand the doctrine of signature from within it's own context. The doctrine of signature is found the world over in all traditional cultures. It is equally found in all systems of traditional medicine, systems that did not yet ban nature from medicine, and did not yet have a separation between doctor and pharmacologist. The person giving the medicine was at the same time the one gathering the herbs, drying and processing them into the preparation to use on the ailing person. This traditional doctor was also the nurse, sitting by the sick person's bed hour after hour, watching the course of the disease and the result of the administered preparation—a preparation of which the person could recall where it was gathered—it's environment, the weather conditions of the region, the year, and the particular day it was gathered, all circumstances of preparation and so on. This person had a living knowledge of plants, their energetic qualities, a sense of the quality of the raw substance as well as of the prepared batch, and a lifetime of experience in administering to the sick. Some of these doctors from traditional medical systems will see as much as about a hundred patients per day—I am thinking of the crowded consultation room of Doctor Yeshe Donden, a world-renowned Tibetan herbal doctor in Dharamshala, India.

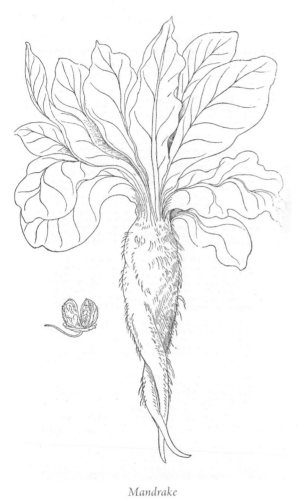

Mandrake

It is easy to dismiss such knowledge and experience as unscientific and having no real effect; it is nevertheless rich, living knowledge. It is arrogant to call it "mere clinical anecdotes." We could also call it "a lifetime worth of professional experience," which is worth gold in the real-life job market. In another profession, we would not hesitate to call such a person "world's leading expert." The doctrine of signature in the context of such a medical system served to organize the qualities and characteristics of the medicinal plant into patterns. These patterns allowed the healer to understand and predict their course of action when administered to the sick. In much the same way as the categories of Traditional Chinese Medicine or Ayurveda, such as yin and yang, Spleen (as an energetic pattern, not as the anatomic organ), or *Vata* and *Pitta,* are categories that group clusters of symptoms into a recognizable and predictable whole, rendering the symptom pattern predictable and manageable. The doctrine of signature is the same thing applied to the medicinal plant, to pharmacology. Thus, the doctrine allows capturing and organizing the countless characteristics of a healing plant into a *gestalt,* of which the interaction with a given set of symptoms in the person will interact in a predictable, clear and precise manner. This point, of course, will escape all ethnobotanists or researchers from the medical establishment, who research the doctrine of signature from the outside, and not from the point of view of a highly skilled and knowledgeable insider of the craft. The experienced herbal doctor knows without a shadow of a doubt that a Kidney yang deficiency will be cured by a Kidney yang increasing herb, and that the flame-shaped peach leaf with it's cooling, moistening properties will remedy a hot, dry stomach in a person with a flame-shaped tongue. Why? Because it makes intuitive sense and it works, verifiably so. Verifiable to clinical experience. "An intuitive method is used, since the intuition comprehends patterns that unite separate phenomena into a whole" (Wood 2005, p. 1)

It is interesting to note in this context how many of the supposed rational scientific discoveries came to those scientists in a vision or a dream—that is, in a non-rational non-analytic but holistic state of mind. One of the famous examples is that of the German chemist August **Kekulé**'s (1829–1896) vision of the benzene ring that came to him in a daydream on a bus. He saw the molecules spinning around and biting its own tail like a snake. A Native American would call this *dreamtime,* a state of mind in which the countless bits and pieces of analytical information are synthesized into a sensible whole. While this is common knowledge, it is not commonly known that Kekulé actually systematically trained himself in this kind of imaginary visualization, which is what led up to and enabled him to discover the benzene ring in this way.

The doctrine of signature is furthermore said to be a mere aid of memory, applied to the plant in hindsight—"Well, I need to remember that Horse Chestnut is a liver herb—so in order to better remember, let me remember that it's fruit looks liver-shaped." It has been written that the doctrine of signature has never led to medicinal discoveries, nor that the medicinal properties of the plant can be predicted based on it. That is wrong. While knowing the signature helps in retaining the medicinal properties, it is not its only function. As all herbalists who are actually practicing with the doctrine of signature can attest, it *does* lead to medicinal discoveries, and the medicinal properties *can* be predicted based on it. Furthermore, it is a great aid in diagnosis—by way of recognizing the correspondence between the disease and the healing agent, it leads to finding the perfect remedy. A classical example of a medicinal discovery by way of a signature would be the story of the discovery of *Ho Shou Wu* (Chinese Knotweed), literally "Ho's head (turned) black (again)." Old man Ho was in ill health, grey haired, with little energy and infertile (all signs of kidney yin and essence deficiency)—but receptive to plants. He prayed for help about his condition. One night, Ho saw the "nocturnal comingling" of the prolific vine *Ho Shou Wu*, which spoke to him about its properties regarding health and fertility—the night being the most yin part of the day. So he started taking the herb, which enabled him to recover his health, his hair turned black again and he fathered many children. The herb has a big root described as being the size of a baby. It is useful for premature ejaculation and spermatorrhea.

To take some examples from recent history, Rudolf Steiner recommended the use of Mistletoe extract as a cure for cancer based on the doctrine of signature—Mistletoe growing in the tree as a tumor-like parasite that eventually kills the host tree. It was not until some fifty years after his death that scientific research showed that Mistletoe contains a peptide that punctures cancer cells upon contact with them, leading to their death. Herbalists trained in the doctrine of signature do not need such molecular validation; they know this must be so, given the energetic constellation. Today, the Minnesotan herbalist Matthew Wood, a good example of a contemporary herbalist who makes the medicines with which he treats his clients himself, has come up with numerous new uses for herbs based on the doctrine of signature. His sizable contribution to the herbal literature bears witness thereof. For example, he pioneered the use of Peony for head injuries based on the signature of the bud looking like a skull. In anthroposophic medicine, the two medical laboratories Weleda and WALA (Dr. Hauschka) have implemented Rudolf Steiner's alchemical teachings. These international companies for holistic natural medicine from Germany base their research and product development on reading the plant's qualities in terms of life force, planetary correspondence and so on. Wilhelm Pelikan, author of the monumental work *Healing Plants* and *The Secrets of Metals,* a work on the healing properties of the seven metals correlated with the seven planets, was a direct disciple of Steiner and the head of the German Weleda laboratories for forty years. These laboratories have developed numerous medicinal and cosmetic products based on the doctrine of signature—in many cases pioneering new uses of well-known medicinal plants, such as using Horse Chestnut as a sunscreen or *Solum oliginosum* (peat moss extract) to protect against radioactivity. In fact, the entire anthroposophic pharmacology along with its innovative thrust is based on the law of correspondence and the doctrine of signature. The Weleda and WALA companies have furthermore used the method of sensitive crystallization

Mistletoe on a silver Birch

to render visible and subsequently quantify and describe those formative forces. Ehrenfried Pfeiffer, who developed sensitive crystallization, was thus able to show the similarity of the crystallization patterns between certain organs and plants. For instance, the crystallization images of extracts of Chamomile and the small intestine are very similar (*The Healing Plant,* vol. 1, p. 28 [German edition]), illustrating Chamomile's main sphere of action.

Since it is scientifically accepted that looking from the outside with a biased, maybe even judgmental attitude onto a system without learning the way it gives meaning to itself from the inside is considered unscientific, we should therefore establish the terms of this work—it is written by a practicing herbalist who makes her own medicine from medicinal herbs she grows and wildcrafts, and who was trained both by the folk tradition coming down through the ages, as well as several practicing herbalists, naturopathic doctors, and homeopaths. Incidentally, I have even attended medical school. I am an insider of the ancient tradition, and will be writing as such. My book is dedicated to the living craft of herbalism, in the hope that it may escape the fate of Traditional Chinese Medicine, which in the process of being streamlined to fit biomedicine had to drop much of what it once was—including the doctrine of signature from its pharmacopoeia.

The doctrine of signature is useful in working with any kind of plant substance or medicine—herbs, flower essences, homeopathic remedies, healing foods, and to a somewhat lesser degree essential oils, since they are plant extracts and as such no longer represent the plant as a whole. It also applies to fruits and vegetables, since everything that is nourishing is also a medicine.

CHAPTER THREE

WHAT IS A SIGNATURE?

"It is a fascinating approach, not only because of the satisfying symmetry of such correspondence, but because generally it is an accurate guide. I adopted the doctrine of signature as a teaching aid in identifying medicinal herbs."

—BEN CHARLES HARRIS (1985, p. 4)

DEFINITIONS

Paracelsus (1493–1541) saw the doctrine of signature as a proof of how microcosm and macrocosm where analogous—as above, so below. He says in *Astronomica magna:* "The expert must know how to recognize the virtue of all things thanks to the signs, be it an herb, a tree, a living being, or an inanimate object." While this thought originates from his alchemical studies that are pre-Christian, as a devout Christian he concludes by writing that this is because God created things as such, and that he left signs for us to discover the virtues He has hidden in all of creation. It is quite noticeable in his work how, throughout his work, entire passages are free from any Christian notions, while others attribute everything back to a creator God.

To Paracelsus, **signatures are the knowledge of the inner essence based on outer characteristics** (Jakobi 1991, p. 53). He said, "Thou shalst know all internal [characteristics] by looking at the outside." "God does not want things to stay hidden, which He created for mankind's benefit and which he gave man as his property into his hand.... And even though He Himself hid it, so did He mark upon it outer, visible signs, that are special marks. Not different from One, who buries a treasure and does not leave it unmarked, because he puts a sign onto the spot, so he himself can find it again." Calling it the "art of signs," he writes. "As you see, every herb has been brought into the shape that is akin to its inner nature [by God]" (ibid., p. 169f). Due to the law of correspondence, the universe is established lawfully enough for him to base his knowledge of medical plants upon it. He writes: "There is a further necessity that you know such shapes in the anatomy of herbs and plants and that you bring them together with the anatomy of the disease. The simile, according to which you should treat, makes healing understandable." And, "Who writes about the power of the herbs without the signature, is not writing from knowledge. He writes like a blind man" (Wood 1992, p. 21). Thus, tumor-like plants such as tree fungi treat tumor-like diseases. Today, the reishi and chaga fungi, for instance, have been proven to have strong anti-cancer properties. His definition might be paraphrased this way: "Like colors, shapes and other characteristics in the plant cure those same or corresponding colors, shapes and characteristics in the body" or "that which looks like a body part or disease in the plant cures that body part or disease in animals or humans."

Paracelsus' law of similes "like cures like" applied to herbology means that specific characteristic of the plant will cure the thing similar to it in the human body or mind. It looks like what it cures. Likeness or being similar here are another way of talking about the analogy contained in the doctrine of signature.

Paracelsus saw the innermost essence or essential properties of a substance as something like a secret, hence *arcana*. It was not secret in the sense of something one has not been told, but of something ineffable, beyond words. Who or what we ultimately are cannot be expressed in our limited language, and trying to put labels to it brings us away from the secret—the truth (ibid., 1992, p. 25). Unlike his contemporaries, he did not believe in the rational or analytical way of matching correspondences, such as curing the right eye of a human with the right eye of an animal. This did not work, because it was not magical, not in keeping with natural magic, and this beyond-rational magic of healing with natural substances meant that a flower with a luminous look such as Eyebright, something that was not an eye but eye-like, by way of that correspondence would cure the eyes as if by magic—Eyebright is one of the most efficient remedies for conjunctivitis.

The doctrine of signature is the practical application of the doctrine of correspondence. It is also the practical application of the law of contraries, since the signature of the plant, it's quality, can be matched with the signature of the disease either by way of correspondence, or by way of contrary. While this might seem confusing and contradictory, it is not when one understands that the law of action and reaction as a healing principle encompasses both of these seemingly opposite laws. For more details, see below in the section *Plants as Teachers.*

As much as one can say that the doctrine of signature is the applied form of the law of correspondences, one could also say in reverse that the doctrine of signature is the ancient foundation for the law of correspondences. The more modern version is the homeopathic like cures like based on the pathology created by a poison.

While to Paracelsus, "it looks like what it cures," Hahnemann took the law of similar to mean "it causes what it cures."

The contemporary herbalist Matthew Wood explains that **signatures represent configurations of energy or patterns, archetypes in plants and these correspond to similar patterns in people**. "We are not looking here for superficial resemblance, but for one that operates on the level of essence," the being-ness (Wood 1997, p. 21f). "The law of correspondence, the doctrine of signature, and the law of similars point to the existence of a core essence, configuration, or identity-pattern at the root of every natural substance" (Wood 1992, p. 25). He sees true signatures as more profound and

Wood Betony

magical, if they are less rational in keeping with Paracelsus' understanding of natural magic. Ferns do not really look like spleens, yet their leaf pattern is the spleen signature, and that holds true like magic even in non-ferns such as Sweetfern (*Comptonia*) or even Wood Betony.

I would define a signature of a plant as a characteristic that can be detected by one of the senses—the eyes, ears, nose, tongue/taste, tactile sensation, in concert with the mind giving it meaning. These give rise in turn to the signature of the colors and shapes, of the sounds, smells and the taste pharmacology so well developed in ancient Western as well as Indian and Chinese herbalism. Unbiased, skillful observation of nature is crucial. It does not extend to the molecular structure of the plant tissue, since to identify this in the scientific sense, we would need a microscope and other gadgets in a laboratory. The doctrine of signature is in this sense—positively so—"pre-scientific." It is a short-cut to plant knowledge when we do not want to wait for decades for the lab results—most of which become distorted by looking at isolated substances, rather than the vast orchestra of molecules playing in concert inside of herb tissue. The molecular signature is not part of our direct experience of the plant. It is a mental construct that we reach with the help of technology, and that we believe based on scientific authority. Instead of anthroquines, we taste bitter and see yellow. Bitter and yellow is the signature, "anthroquines" a mental construct. However, we will not be surprised to find heart glycosides in a plant with such a strong and unmistakable heart-healing plant signature as Foxglove or Lily of the Valley. I see the molecular structure as the expression of the signature on the molecular level. If we are right that the macrocosm resembles the microcosm, such as a characteristic of a planet and the plant, then it should also apply to the next levels down, as in the plant and their cells—and so it does.

We are entering an era when things are understood within the context of their energy or energetic fields. In this view, the doctrine of signature is the recognition that similar energetic patterns giving rise to a similar shape and unfoldment in two different things—in this case, a plant or plant part, and a person or body part/mind set. This is the *correspondence of energetic pattern*. It is with this in mind that we understand why the big, heavy peony buds that in their spherical compactness look so like a skull with sutures will yield a medicine for trauma to this hard, dense, heavy body part—especially helping to open up the blocked sutures, as verifiable in sacro-cranial treatment.

My Haitian folk herbalist friend Jacquelin Guiteau put it succinctly: "The doctrine of signature is how the medicinal plants introduce their healing powers to the healer." So it is, above all, a means of communication, a language.

A POETIC LANGUAGE

The doctrine of signature is really a poetic language describing a multidimensional reality in which different facets of signature are simultaneously true, and in which the interplay of the countless elements cannot be exhaustively and finally interpreted. Since it is the human mind that gives meaning to nature, naturally the signatures and their categories shift from one cultural context to another, one adding to the other without contradiction but rather contributing another piece to the larger picture. I was challenged by my brother, thoroughly trained in natural science, when trying to explain to him the doctrine of signature: "But if you say that a mushroom growing on a tree is like a cancerous tumor, then, because a mushroom has mycelia, the tumor should therefore have them, too." I did not know what to reply in the moment, however an easy misunderstanding might be that we are in the realm of mathematics, where if A equals B, then therefore B equals A. We are, however, in the realm of similars. If something is similar, it is not same. There is a corresponding underlying principal, but the two corresponding things are not identical. The mushroom reaches out via mycelia, the tumor via chemical signals. If they were the same, they could not be a plant and a human disease condition. So since the doctrine of signature helps to draw parallels between a plant on the one hand and a human condition on the other, it can never be a pair of identical things. It can only be similar. We are entering a realm of analogies, and sometimes our modern minds have become so attuned to natural science that we lose sense of what an analogy is—it serves to make the point by one or more parallels, but if stretched too far, will stop working. We should therefore always remember that the doctrine of signature is in the truest sense an art, and not a science reducible to mathematical formulas. As much as it is an art, it is a science of observation in the sense that Goethe formulated for his approach to natural science. It was his idea, later promoted by Rudolf Steiner, that we should train our senses to a point where our mental force of observation of nature becomes like an organ.

The art of interpreting poetry means that there is never just one meaning, and that one can never find all the meanings. It would be impossible, for instance, to make a complete list of all the possible interpretations of Goethe's *Faust*. In poetry, while a word might appear in the line, and the meaning of the word by itself is such and such, we might expect it to take the same meaning in the context of that very line. It is the beauty of the oscillating imprecision of language that the context, intonation, diacritical marks used, and even background of the listener can alter the meaning of that very word. In the very same manner, the context in which one doctrine occurs in a plant with regard to its other characteristics can alter or override its meaning. In that sense, the doctrine of signature is an art of interpretation of the direct encounter with the plant, making thorough use of the associative function of the brain that engages both of its halves fully.

Within poetry, the same word or grammar structure also does not always mean the same thing. Depending on the context, the same word will mean different things in different lines. Similarly, a flower being yellow will also means different things in different plants. In Oregon-Grape it means that it is a liver healing plant; in Dandelion that it heals the solar plexus with the associated fear and power issues; in Yellow Day Lily it mean that it bestows happiness and joy, dispelling depression; and in Sunflower it means that it strengthens the inner Sun archetype, the inner father.

Being a poetic language, it is also sometimes cryptic—it escapes us. We do not understand. It is too profound yet for us to decipher. While this book seeks to be something of a dictionary for this language of plants, it is not only a foreign language to learn, it is also a language that requires us to change our minds: to the degree that we still our mind chatter and become calm, allowing nature to talk to us, we will understand clearer. To the degree that we tune more into nature herself, she will speak up.

Herbalist David Winston considers the doctrine of signature part of something much larger that he also calls the "language of plants." He regards the doctrine of signature as we know it as the last remnant of the European tradition of the language of plants, which includes as its physical aspect the doctrine of signature, then knowledge of the plant's personality, and finally of its "is-ness." This can only be known through well trained intuition, in direct communication with the plant. These three aspects together make up the full language of plants. I would add that the language of plants is part of the larger *language of nature,* which includes geomancy, palmistry, face reading—the same principals used here can be used to decode the underlying characteristics of anything in nature, including landscapes, minerals and stones, animals, and humans.

Art and poetry engage the right brain, while science uses the left. The doctrine of signature is a thoroughly holistic approach, engaging both brain halves. In our analytical culture, "it's a mystery" means that it cannot be understood nor known. However, as Wood suggests in *The Magical Staff*, mystery *can* communicate (p. ix)—not to the analytical mind, but to the holistic view, to intuition. What *mystic* and *cryptic* really mean is that we have not yet found words that abide in the realm of duality, to describe it. Thus, nature and plants' unfolding cannot ever be pinned down in one finite definition of the truth, but remain forever mystical and elusive, forever spurring us on to new visions of multi-dimensional layers of truth from a realm beyond words.

THE GRAMMAR RULES

Besides being a poetic language, it is a language similar to the language of dreams in that there can be no negations—no "yes, but" and so on. Interestingly, Native Americans sought to acquire plant knowledge in *dreamtime*. It is a language of associated characteristics, all of which are positive statements. The flower cannot be "not red"; simply, it is red. It is a flow of simple, straightforward positive statements; "I am like this and this and that," simultaneously true all at the same time. In this language, adjectives play the main role: "I am soft, straight, yellow, cool and bitter." "I like humid, acidic soil." So it is really those adjectives we should pay attention to. If in tuning into a tree someone comes up with "I just feel beauty, simply beauty," then this is a good hint that one has tuned into something other than the plant itself—perhaps the abstract idea of beauty or love and light. Sometimes, instead of tuning into the plant and its essence, we tune into the something else, such as the landscape or the atmosphere of the moment. For instance, stately trees in general emit a sense of serenity and peace. That is due to their size and age, and not specific to the tree species. While it is alright to get a sense of peace from tuning into a plant in true plant attunement, it would not stop there but be precise and qualify the sense of peace. Sedating healing plants, or relaxing nervines, can bestow this feeling. So it can feel like "peaceful, cooling," or "peaceful, relaxing." Plants are not abstract. Not "out there." They are earthy, juicy, and real. Right here!

These positive statements can seem to be contradictions. A plant such as nasturtium might be shade-loving and watery, thus cooling, and at the same time pungent in taste and warming. Cooling and warming are contradictory, but here, the plant is saying that it contains both these in harmony. It can teach us about maintaining moderate warmth while staying moist.

Another example is the inflated seedpod of *Lobelia inflata*. It has been taken as a signature for the alveoli inflated in an asthma attack; or as having the form of a stomach. Being a stomach and alveoli are contradictory, but looking similar in shape to both of them is not. Hence, lobelia continues to be an excellent herbal remedy for both, asthma *and* ills of the stomach.

In this context, it is worth pointing out that in holistic case taking as well as psychotherapy, it is precisely those adjectives our clients use to describe their conditions—"I am heartbroken, discouraged and down"—that are the most noteworthy thing of what they are telling us, since it is them that will lead us to the right remedy. Thus we ask: *How* do you feel? It is telling that this very description of subjective symptoms is given no value in orthodox medicine (whose language abounds with nouns: "proliferation of streptococci in the trachea . . . ").

The truth about nature is multidimensional and multifaceted. So whenever we find ourselves becoming dogmatic about it being only one way or another, we can be sure that we have fallen away from the ultimate truth about Mother Nature, who simply cannot be pigeon-holed.

THE RULES OF COMMUNICATION

The first rule is that you can only hear what you allow to filter through the constant chatter of your mind. Meditators trained in stilling and calming the ongoing flow of inner talk are very good at perceiving what is out there in a calm, unbiased manner.

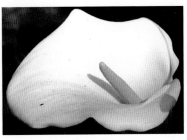

Calla Lily

The second rule is that we can perceive correctly only what does not get distorted by our layer of neuroses. It is well known in the realm of psychotherapy that any neurosis we might have will distort the inner messages we receive. A simple example is a woman who got very upset and offended at the mere sight of a Calla Lily, calling it "an ugly monkey penis." She had been sexually abused. Our neuroses quite literally become colored glasses we see the world through—it would be best to at least know we had them on our nose, or better even which color they were.

The third rule is to let reasoning and interpretation come only after the direct communication with the plant; before or during it will cut the communication. This requires some mental effort. It is to restrain ourselves once we found the slightest inkling of a signature, to run and want to write it down and talk about it, rather than to stay with the experience and let it unfold.

The fourth rule is that we forget when we go from one mental state to another. It is commonly known that people remember what they experienced while drunk when they become drunk again, but not while sober. We suddenly remember last night's dream when slipping into sleep the next night. In the same way, as we "go under" into a meditative state to do the plant attunement, we tend to forget the images and message as we come out of that state and back into our everyday mind. It is therefore helpful to learn to come across the threshold slowly and mindfully in order not to interrupt the link of memory.

Thus, the calmer, clearer, and more unbiased you are, the better. For a long time, I tried not to read anything about a healing plant before I would go to sit with it to feel its essence. I found that not having read other people's comments left my mind fresh and free. In Zen Buddhism, this is called *beginner's mind*. It was also very helpful to go back and check my findings against those of others to see how much overlap there was. It is a way of checking back later with oneself about whether one is indeed tuning into the plant and reading the signature, or just tripping. This all ties in with the principle known in psychological testing, as well as quantum physics, according to which the observer, especially the observer's intention, influences the outcome of the experiment—furthermore, that objects under observation, even inanimate objects such as electrons, behave differently under observation than when not observed.

"The doctrine of signatures operates through at least two different subjective faculties, the intuition and the imagination" (Wood 1997 p. 23). He explains the difference as follows: intuition is the ability to see patterns in the world; imagination is the ability to see images.

Ayurveda takes this into the context of direct yogic perception, a kind of insight gained based on perfect concentration, a completely still mind with an unmoving focus, a state in which the observing mind and the observed object are said to merge into union like water poured into water (Losang Gyatso 1998, p. 31ff). "The human being transmutes life into consciousness through perception. Through direct perception, the seer is the seen, the observer the observed" (Frawley and Lad 1986, p. 5).

> The sages of ancient India approached healing and herbs with this same consciousness [of total communion with the plant]. Theirs was not a science of experimentation, but a form of direct participation. Experimentation implies distance, a division between the observer and the observed, subject and object. As a result, it is mediated, measured, translated. In dissecting the corpse, the penetration of the soul is missed. Direct perception, or meditation, is the science of yoga. Yoga allows the essence, the thing-in-itself, to disclose itself. When this happens, a full revelation of material and spiritual potential occurs.
>
> The seers, through the yoga of perception, let the plants speak to them. And plants disclose their secrets—many of which are far more subtle than a chemical analysis would uncover. Approaching plants in the same way today, not as objects for self-aggrandizement but as integral parts of our own unity, the true value of a plant will flourish for our unselfish use.
>
> To become a true herbalist, therefore, means to become a seer. This means to be sensitive to the being of the herbs, to commune in receptive awareness with the plant-light of the universe. It is to learn to listen when the plant speaks, to speak to the plants as another human being, and to look upon it as one's teacher." (ibid., p. 5f)

THE UNIVERSAL LANGUAGE

In a realm free from human culture and language stuck in the limitations of dualism, we can imagine a world made from energy—in the physical sense of its definition, as something immaterial that functions to do work. Energy has received all kinds of labels through the ages and times—the Chinese call it *chi,* the Indians *prana* or *vayu,* it has been called *life force* in the West and *medicine power* by the Northern Native Americans. It matters little what it is called—it is the dynamic immaterial aspect of life that propels things, making them function. It is the difference between a living body and a corpse, a live herb and a dried one. In Ayurveda, *prana* or *vayu* (wind) as it is called is said to be the flow of energy that courses the body in set patterns, in part following the nerves and blood vessels, and that propels physiological functions, such as breathing, urination, or blood circulation. It is called wind to illustrate its beyond-matter nature, as well as its dynamic, mobile characteristic. In Traditional Chinese Medicine, *chi* and blood are said to be like two sides of a coin, that is: go together. So the blood flow and flow of *chi* are coupled, again giving *chi* a dynamic, non-material aspect. In the Greek humoral medicine, the humors or body liquids were thought of in a similar fashion, and this is how holistic practitioners of today use the term *energy*. Energy language is becoming a universal language and accepted principle, surprisingly uniting such disciplines as quantum physics and chakra healing.

In this universal language of energy, we find that we can establish the doctrine of signature based on a universally observable correspondence of underlying energy patterns and their development.

These can occur at any level: ginseng roots looking like little persons and therefore being the supreme tonic for humankind as a whole; resins oozing out of injured barks, healing and sealing them, hence being powerful antiseptic wound healers; Wild Snapdragon with yellow flowers shaped like huge jaws helping with digestion and temporomandibular joint disorder (TMJ, tight jaws and teeth grinding) .

⚘

CHAPTER FOUR

PLANTS AS TEACHERS

While the doctrine of signature can point to a correspondence by way of either contraries or similars, some point to both. When a plant works by way of contraries, that is brings about the opposite state of what is, we can think of them as teachers teaching something new.

While the doctrine of signature is the practical application of the doctrine of correspondence, the plants from their side are not partial as to which correspondence should be right—the one by way of contraries or the one by way of similars. In fact, within a plant, some of the characteristics might be a signature by way of the one, others by way of the other. One single characteristic also may be interpreted one way or the other. This is the multi-dimensional, non-linear logic of nature. For instance, red can stand for increasing or decreasing heat, a brown flower can stand for a state of being sullied and denote its cleansing properties. Also, a white flower might denote that it will purify a sullied state. None of the ways of correspondence are more right than the other.

Plants often heal opposite qualities: sporting a blood signature, they stop excessive bleeding and bring it on when not enough. Or they heal diarrhea when needed, and constipation when that's present. I once committed the heresy of pointing out to one of my homeopathy teachers that countless plants described in the homeopathic *materia medica* showed this phenomenon, and asked whether that meant that they really rebalance what is out of balance, rather than heal by way of "like cures like." He became furious at me saying such utter nonsense. The fact is that if we dig in our heels, insisting that a plant should heal only by way of one paradigm (as if it had gone to dogma class), we will be hard-pressed to explain why so many plants heal polar opposite states. I therefore suggest that the healing powers of the plant, viewed as an energetic pattern, has some inherent intelligence as such that knows when to act one or the other way: "Tighten the loose tendons, relax the tight ones"; Solomon's Seal knows how to do this simultaneously even within one joint. So, was that by way of similars or contraries, then? It is, perhaps, because the healing plant is a wholeness operating, carrying all the healing possibilities within it. Burdock root will lubricate dry skin and reduce oiliness in greasy skin. Even if we were to argue the existence of two different kinds of chemical substances that trigger either one of those reactions, how come out of those two only one is set in motion, and not at random, but rather unfailingly the appropriate one?

The way that a healing plant can adapt its healing effect to the person's need is through neither contraries nor similars. In this, I would like to invoke the spirit of our time. Herbalism originated in a time when the world was understood as living nature, *anima mundi*. Later shaped by the Newtonian mechanistic reductionist worldview, for almost one hundred years now physics and astronomy has moved beyond that mechanistic view, entering into the ever more mysterious realm of quantum physics with multitudes of dimensions. Neither modern biology nor herbalism has been updated in the light of those findings. Quantum physics now talks about the enfolded or implicate order, in which our linear notions of time and space become obsolete. In the quantum vacuum field, all electrical and magnetic forces are the result of virtual photons that appear out of that field and disappear back into it. All of nature, with all its biochemical processes, "depend on virtual photons appearing and disappearing within the all-pervading vacuum field of nature" (Sheldrake 2009, p. 15). In light of this, why would it then be so outrageous to say that the energy within this herbal tea is not yet completely defined, that the virtual photons giving rise to the final healing effect have not yet arisen and taken a defined shape and path, and that this happens only after the tea is inside of us. Once we drink it, the order becomes explicate and unfolded and we find ourselves in a three-dimensional world with what appears to be linear time. Then, it would be easy to accept that the same generic herbal infusion gave rise to contradictory healing reactions depending on the actual situation. One of the challenges of modern energetic herbalism is not to wait for reductionist molecular biology to come around and integrate quantum physics, but to do it before they do.

Since for the plant, similars and opposites are not diametrically opposed but naturally one, herbs can teach us synthesis and integration. This becomes blatantly clear when working with flower essences, which generally helps us find a higher level of soul truth above the one or other polar opposite. Madonna Lily flower essence helps bring our sexual expression into balance, helping promiscuous people to stay put and sexually inhibited ones to open up. The higher integration is to see that sexuality is part of our spiritual development, is spiritual practice. Snapdragon flower essence does relax a tight jaw and tone a drooping one. Ultimately, it teaches balanced jaw pressure, and beyond that balanced verbal expression of anger.

Snapdragon

We could think of it in a more imaginative, holistic way: The plant is the teacher, teaching me to do what I do not understand or do not know how to do. There are two ways that plants can be my teacher, teaching me what they have mastered. They can either show me the way back to find my natural balance once I have lost it—such as when catching a cold—or inspire me to change my way of functioning to include ways in which I did not function before—such as cure an eczema I had since birth, or increase my digestive fire in a way I never had. This can extend to healing constitutional and inherited weaknesses. They can thus be my guides back home to myself, or to as yet uncharted new territories, pushing me on to evolve beyond my *status quo.*

For example, if my skin is dry, I do not know how to maintain the humidity content of my tissue in dry—or even moist—environments. Aloe can be my teacher. This desert plant has mastered survival in a desert environment, while maintaining "moist skin"; Aloe has very succulent leaves that store moisture for long periods of dryness. When cut, we see what looks like a cross section of the human skin. The leathery outside of the leaf parallels the horny tough outside layer of the skin, and the gel filling the leaf the subcutaneous tissue. We should not underestimate how familiar the ancients were with live anatomy, given their experience of hunting and slaughtering animals, not to mention dealing with warfare battle wounds. From my experience of being in an operating room and in the dissection room in medical school, I can say that there is no more striking likeness between a cut-open Aloe leaf and human skin tissue. We find that Aloe is probably the best skin moisturizer in all of nature, making the subcutaneous tissue as moist and plump as the Aloe itself. It teaches and shows the way. Aloe is at its healthiest in an arid climate, yet becomes sick in humid air. What better teacher could there be then for perfecting the art of retaining moisture in dry air than Aloe? The homeopathic provings of Aloe say: The patient is ill-humored on cloudy days! In classical terms, it heals by way of contrary (wet to dry), but the outward appearance is one of like cures like.

Plants can teach what they themselves have mastered to survive. Certain plants have mastered an ability to survive with their roots in soggy, wet soil their entire lives; so they can teach us to deal with excess humidity, internally or externally. Others need frost or chill to spring to life, like Echinacea seeds, which will germinate only after the frost has gone over them. They are at their happiest and healthiest when chilled thoroughly: they can teach me to throw off a chill or a fever with chills from having gotten too cold.

The cross section of an Aloe leaf reveals how much it looks like a cross section through the skin with the underlying fatty tissue.

Another example would be Artichoke. It is a *Compositae*, with large, branching leaves and huge magenta flowers. The flower buds are used as a food. The entire plant is moderately bitter and surprisingly succulent for a plant so closely related to the thistle clan. All thistles have a healing affinity for liver and gallbladder, and the bitterness of Artichoke also points to this. Its specialty, however, is the moistness of the plant—it is thus not simply a cholagogue, but a *moistening* cholagogue. This is easily observed from the fact that the leaves dry unwillingly, and once they are crispy-dry, rehydrate immediately in an environment with normal levels of air humidity. They thus have a hygroscopic property. This they impart to the liver and gallbladder tissue. One can literally feel the dried-out gall duct remoistening and reopening to release the gall flow under its action. It teaches the tissue its ability to hold moisture.

Plants can either teach me what I do not know to do—such as produce less stomach acid (Meadowsweet)—or give me what I need—bind the stomach acid that is too plentiful (Marshmallow). As such they are not only teachers, but also Givers, who bestow knowledge to the tissue and mind, as well as give me what my body lacks.

This principle of healing is common to the mild, nontoxic plants. Understanding plants as teachers and letting ourselves be guided by them is an approach that surpasses the mere classification as

Thistle

law of contraries, expanding their range of healing action beyond a mere matching of opposite categories. It includes the spiritual lessons we can take from our green neighbors: thistles being probably the most upright and best defended of green citizens, they can teach weak children to be courageous and upright, facing threats with calm poise (especially given in the form of a flower essence).

There are four ways that the plant relates to our inner state in healing. It can either be my very opposite, so different that it can balance me by shifting my balance like a weight being put on the opposite side of a scale. Or it can be just like my state, so in harmony with my being that it nourishes my balance like a tonic, without changing it. Or else it can represent within itself a perfect balance of opposites that I have slipped away from or am struggling to maintain, thus rebalancing me. Last, it can provide an impetus to advance in a way that I acquire a new level or state of being beyond what I ever reached before. This is the spiritual dimension of healing, in which we change our constitution, inherited tendencies, character traits and stride into the realm of wisdom: Healing does not just take place on a line between two polar opposites that need to be rebalanced. It can also advance upward, to form a triangle, a new level looking back down and in insight and wisdom integrate the two seemingly opposites under a new understanding. The battle between light and dark becomes just shades of luminosity, and even death can be seen as an ultimate form of healing back into the non-physical. Wisdom could be presented as the polar opposite of ignorance, but that does not do justice to explain the shift in dimension: this spiritual dimension can get lost in the business of analyzing the plant chemicals that are its ingredients, or long lists of symptoms treated. Many medieval observations such as the anti-witchcraft indications for St. John's Wort and Wood Betony have been lost from herbalism. In modern days, the spiritual dimensions are most clearly described in the flower essence pictures, as well as preserved in the Ayurvedic descriptions of herbs.

PLANTS AS HEALERS

When a plant works by way of similars, healing in me the symptom it can cause, we can think of it as a healer. This means that rather than teaching me a skill they have and I do not, they will cure what they caused me—the French herbalist Dominique Lepage uses an infusion of Stinging Nettle to cure the nettle rash caused by falling into a nettle patch. Homeopathic Stinging Nettle heals burns and *Urticaria*, skin rashes as if of Stinging Nettle. As we have seen, this principle of healing is common to noxious, toxic plants, and the healing effect often depends on the dose. The real healing genius of plants spans much wider, which is why I think Paracelsus called it magic.

Stinging Nettle

We should not attempt to squeeze all of plant healing into the human laws of similars, contraries, or even action-and-reaction, the latter of which reduces all healing to cause and effect, as though speaking of opposed directions, which explains somewhat poorly the spiritual impulses of herbal medicines. As many great healers of the past have noticed: whereas these laws most definitely exist, we can observe far more than they explain in the realm of plant healing. Matthew Wood remarked that many plants heal by both the law of contraries *and* the law of similars—not separate conditions, but one and the same disease. He gives an example:

> How are we to make sense out of these conflicting "laws"? Some herbs work according to several approaches. *Chelidonium* (Celandine) is bitter and heating. Used according to the law of contraries, it will warm up and dissipate congestion, and that is what it does in the liver and gall bladder. However, the location of its work is only specified through the doctrine of signatures: it is useful for problems with the bile because it has a unique yellow, bile-like sap. It has received a homeopathic proving (Celandine is fairly toxic), producing symptoms of congestion in the liver and gall bladder, so it works on the same basic conditions whether it is used as a contrary (hot to cold), a similar or by signature....
>
> The important point from the perspective of vitalism is that every herb and poison ultimately has a primal essence or identity pattern and this, whether delivered in a gentle or a toxic envelope, possesses curative power. The essence shines forth through the chemistry, qualities, toxicity, and signatures to show how the agent is to be used appropriately. It teaches the sick, disabled body how to rule supreme in its own environment, to add or expel, dry or lubricate, cool or warm, to maintain natural balance or homeostasis. (2004, pp. 71–76)

Beyond that, Celandine also imparts a spiritual lesson; it imparts inner sight and the courage to advance on one's path unbound by fears of social convention and authority (flower essence). Being a gall bladder remedy, Traditional Chinese Medicine would call the gift of strengthening the gall bladder "augmenting daring."

A more general way of explaining how plants heal is by way of energetic resonance. Their shapes are the result of formative energetic forces, and if one spills the tea or tincture that carries their energetic imprint, one can clairvoyantly see or clairsentiently sense that a similar energetic form arises. When I ingest or otherwise come in contact with the plant or plant medicine, it stimulates my energy bodies to resonate on the same energetic wavelength, and also take a similar shape. For instance, tall towering Mullein will cause me to stand tall and straight. Teasel with its distinctively shaped flower *head* will energize my head and open the chakras there. Like a guitar string that starts swinging when another in the same room is struck, my energy field is vibrating along with the plant medicine. Like a dancer, my energy body follows the movements the plant makes. This energetic understanding of healing is holistic and transcends the dualism of similars and contraries.

> By magically changing our lives, our green friends restore physical health, psychological happiness, and spiritual purpose. A little miracle occurs and the magical level clicks in, in fact, whenever an herb cures in a real and radical way. This is a sign that something great and new has come in from a different world to enrich and develop our lives to their fullest and most beautiful potential. (Matthew Wood)

Plants as healers have their own intelligence that sets right the wrongs of the disease. This is insufficiently explained by the law of contraries versus similars alone. Boneset, for instance, is the bone-setting herb *par excellence.* It sends an intelligent energy into the bones that shifts them back into their natural position. Sporting several bone signatures, I feel that it is its strong rhythmic build, echoing the clear rhythmic build of the skeleton, that is the "bone-setting signature." There is nothing about Boneset that is out of alignment. The bone setting movement it induces comes from within the bones, and not from the tension of the ligaments onto the bones being balanced, allowing the bone back into place. This is the unique medicinal power of a small herb.

PLANTS AS SPIRITUAL GUIDES

In the process of healing, plants can become our spiritual guides. This can be by way of changing our awareness, giving us a sense of nature imbued with wisdom, or any other way. Contemplating how a tree sheds its seeds and leaves in autumn, letting them be carried away by the wind, can teach us profound lessons of detachment, calm, and trust in the process of life. The tree does not cling to its leaves, nor does it try to control the destiny of its offspring. Contemplating plants and nature can help us find our place in the cosmos—not the one promoted by Christianity, in which humankind is asked to dominate nature, but the interconnected and interdependent place we actually hold. This can lead us to actualizing our highest potential: in Ayurveda, the yoga of herbs is no different from any other yoga (Sanskrit for *yoke*—what binds or ties us to Truth), a path to enlightenment. It is, of course, a medicinal system developed by yogis for yogis:

> In the outer world, a central sun is the source of light and life. In the inner world, a central sun is also the source of life. This inner sun is our true Self.... Plants bring us into communion with the energy of the outer sun [having built itself up from light through photosynthesis], while our inner plant, our nervous system, brings us into communion with the inner sun. Establishing the proper link between the outer plant and the inner plant thus completes the circuit of light and life, establishes the free flow of awareness in which the mind is liberated—unites the sun with the sun, merges the outer with the inner, creates a festival of delight in living.
>
> The proper usage of the plant or herb, during which its true power is released, implies a communion with it. The plant, when we are one with it, will vitalize our nervous system and invigorate our perception. This means giving value to a plant as something sacred, as a means of communion with all nature. Each plant, then, like a *mantra*, will help to actualize the potential of cosmic life of which it is a representative. (Frawley and Lad 1986, p. 5)

When we use healing plants, our energy is infused by, and merges with, their energy. They often strongly increase our life force or energy. In that sense, by way of merging with something other than ourselves, we are having a transcendental experience, transcending the limits of ourselves.

Seeing Plants as Equals

While it may seem naïve to talk about plants in an anthropomorphic way, it actually serves an intelligent purpose. By thinking of the plant as a fellow person, I am dropping my human pride and prejudice about my innate superiority, which interferes with a naked, raw encounter with the plant. Thinking of it as a character I am encountering helps me to make an inner map of its being, as well as to remember the different character traits by association to the whole image. It lets the plant spring alive to our imagination, opens up mental communicative with it, and makes the encounter a memorable event. By thus mentally taking the herb as my fellow human being or teacher, it can become one. This is mental interdependence with herbs as teachers. By perceiving the plant as a person, I can enter into a personal relationship with it. Wood writes, "We are not used to thinking of plants like this. We do not think of them as being individual entities with specific traits. This makes it sound too much like the plant has or is a 'personality.' This, however, is exactly what we need to learn. The plant is not a bundle of separate chemicals, but is an intelligent being that directs all of these constituents in an integrated, self-maintaining, self-healing fashion. The separate parts are bound together by an entity-like core, and this, as director of the parts, has characteristic habits and expressions, just like a personality." He equates the terms *energy, essence,* and *personality* (2005, p. 2f). An advocate of talking to plants, he says, "Probably the most profound learning comes from actual communication with the plant, as an equal—it can tell us for what it is medicinal." This particular practice is much easier for those with a proclivity for clairaudience.

It is also helpful to identify oneself with the plant. When I used to teach basic classes on flower essences, I would sometimes lead the class in a visualization whereby I asked them to see themselves as a specific flower or plant. It was surprising how profoundly the students understood the plant and its healing properties after such an exercise. I specifically remember one student after identifying with Clematis, a climber that is used for a Bach flower remedy. The student was astonished: "I felt myself getting longer and longer, and then I fell over because I could no longer hold myself up [as a long, thin climber]. Is that right?" This *is* the point; she discovered that Clematis, like all climbers, lacks the power to hold itself upright. Clematis is for dreamers, who lack positive Ego, or "I," strength—who, rather than being present to the challenges of everyday life, retreat into a dream state of reality. If we ponder how a vine overruns shrubs and trees, smothering them to death, then we see the manipulating character of those who need vine flower essences manipulating and suppressing others with their ego power. If we ponder more deeply, however, we come to see that the very need to manipulate and suppress, to dominate others rather than sharing as equals, stems from a lack of true positive "I" strength, fueled by the fear of not being good enough. So—never judge a plant unless you have walked 1,000 steps in its moccasins (to paraphrase a Native American saying).

᛭

CHAPTER FIVE

THE DOCTRINE OF SIGNATURE IN PRACTICE

"Many ancient people have had reverence for the plant kingdom. It is not a superstitious awe, nor a mere sensitivity to beauty, but a reception of the power plants bring to us. The force is not received simply though ingesting the plant, but in our total communion with it."

—FRAWLEY AND LAD (1986, p. 5)

NATURE ATTUNEMENT

Our ultimate aim is *holistic* plant study. Without the use of technological aids, we are free to meet the plant on nature's ground. "Technological devices make true intimacy in meeting the plant impossible," says Haitian folk herbalist and electrical engineer Jacquelin Guiteau. The use of technological gadgets is, in that sense, an expression of a sick society incapable of true intimacy, both among its members and with nature. This means we use all of our senses and all of our brain, the rational and the intuitive, to encounter the plant. Based on a calm, clear mind, free of chemical disturbances and distortions, such as from drugs or neuroses, we look at the plant in detail, listing and analyzing its characteristics (left brain). We take in the *gestalt* of the plant as a whole and tune into the essence of its *is*-ness (right brain), careful not to superimpose prefabricated ideas. Then we combine the two by using the associative fibers of the brain that connect the two brain halves. Having brought the entirety of ourselves into the encounter, we can form a whole, a holistic, picture of that plant-being in front of us. In reality, of course, this process is not linear, but rather the mind vacillates back and forth between these modes.

Steiner outlined a systematic path of spiritual training for the study of truth throughout his work. For him, like philosophers who came before him, truth can be found in nature and learned to be perceived there by those who learn to unveil it, so to speak. He clarifies the steps as going from sensory perception to *imagination*, to *inspiration*, and finally to *intuition*. Without careful study of what Steiner means by those terms, as well as the steps of evolution in the development of true clairvoyance to which he refers, one can easily misunderstand his work.

While spiritual realization transcends mere sensory perception, careful and mindful sensory perception is the gate to higher knowledge. Based on what is present in the here and now, and based on human incarnation with human senses, Steiner advises seekers of truth to train systematically in *imagination*. Images are one step before clairvoyance. For the field of plant study, this would be the kind of imagination that pictures every step in the metamorphosis of one plant as it grows from a seed to the moment it dies, and from one plant species in the same plant family to the next, like a movie. This imaginative perception of things is distinctly different from visions and hallucinations, or what we would call trips today. The prior is a sign of a heightened sense of perception, while the latter points to a lower level.

Steiner names Goethe as a perfect example for someone who realized this step. "He was always endeavoring to achieve a vivid, plastic image" like a sculptor (1986, p. 33). This is akin to what I call "the dance of plants in time." The image in this stage of imagination is still removed from the truth of nature, in that it is still an image of what truly is rather than a direct perception. At this stage, the images are still just that for the trainee—images. Once he gains the level of *inspiration* (not in the usual sense of the word), the images become reality. This should not be confused with deluded people who believe in their visions, such as a schizophrenic. "Imagination first presents a picture of suprasensory reality. *Inspiration* shows the way beyond, to the reality" (ibid., p. 38ff). We achieve this level by diligent meditation and concentration practice. As this is the second step, "this must lead to the ability to reject and, in the final instance, wipe out the imaginative life, the life in images, as we have acquired it. Anyone merely able to have *Imaginations* cannot yet penetrate into spiritual reality.... These *Imaginations* appear like a realization of imaginative faculties only initially and have to be erased, for they are something we have produced more or less ourselves" (ibid.). The progress from one level to another comes through increasingly energized, heightened states of consciousness—higher levels of inner perspective that grant a much broader vision of things. At that stage, one becomes a vessel for impulses from the spiritual world, which is what Steiner calls Intuition. "Then we advance to *Intuition*, and in the *Intuition* we are not merely touched by the spiritual truth that is outside the physical world...but live into it, become one with it" (ibid.). Steiner thus understands sensory perception and *intuition* (as explained here) as polar opposites, with *imagination* and *inspiration* as the spectrum between them.

With sensory perception, spiritual truth is entirely outside of our experience, whereas for *Intuition* it becomes who we are. Steiner's use of the word is quite different from that of an "intuitive hit." These terms actually outline a lifelong path of spiritual training. These four steps have been applied in anthroposophic plant study, but I think it wise to remember that, for Steiner, they refer to advanced steps of spiritual realization. Wright calls these steps *exact sensory perception, exact sensorial imagination, seeing in beholding,* and *intuitive precognition,* followed by *intuition* and *being one with the object,* suggesting they be used in a circular fashion to apprehend plants. While this is certainly fruitful, trained herbalists who have not undergone the training path outlined by Steiner find that to go through those five with relation to one plant in this particular order is somewhat artificial, and that they naturally spontaneously shift between one another. They do most likely not, however, occur at the level of insight aimed at by Steiner. Little known in the West, from personal familiarity I would like to point out that this entire topic is covered in detail in the ancient Mahayana Buddhist scriptures on logic and cognitional theory, as well as in the teachings on how to train in the path of meditation.

Freed from all cultural superimpositions and what-we-prefer-to-believe, plants are patterns of unfolding energy that we can detect with our senses, with colors, shapes and tastes taking a predictable and distinct course of coming into being, existing, and fading away. As witnessing bystanders to their mysterious dance, we are invited to listen to their song-beyond-concept, and will not receive their secrets for as long as we try to make them march to our tune.

WHAT THIS MEANS IN A PRACTICAL VEIN

The doctrine of signature is a holistic system of making sense out of countless, otherwise seemingly arbitrary facts about an herb. It is a way of communicating about its "personality," its essence. Just as we figure out some people fast, and others not in a lifetime, we will find ourselves understanding and reading certain plants much faster than others. Some plants have been "read" for their signatures in great detail, while about others nothing has been said so far. It is not necessary to understand the signature to know how to use the herb well in healing. The signatures are a way of matching the essence or personality as it were of the plant with the essence or personality of the person or disease.

It does take time and effort to decipher a plant. Even I have not yet had the time to sit quietly with all the plants I use as medicine, and although I understand some of them very well for their healing effect, I could not explain how that is expressed in the signature. Whenever I find the time, however, I do find that the below explained principles hold true and the signatures are there waiting to be discovered.

A single plant has many signatures, and one alone—especially if it is not highly special or bizarre for the plant kingdom, such as eating meat—is not necessarily highly significant. In a practical sense, we should be able to find at least three signatures per plant that point to the same thing, such as "calms the nerves."

Reading plants based on signatures is something that we can become masterful at, but I would caution my fellow herbalists that in order to avoid hubris, we should always double-check the accuracy of our interpretations of nature; when I prepare a new medicine based on a signature I think I discovered, I observe very closely whether it has the desired effect in the person to whom I administered it. Only when it does—and in more than just one person—can I claim to have developed a new medicinal use based on the doctrine of signature. Otherwise, it is easy to fall prey to our wishful thinking.

Sometimes it is a matter of working out the specific indications—the plant might have a joint signature, such as Teasel. But how exactly does it help the joints? It is for torn muscles and tendons attaching to the joint. This might take a while to work out, either by way of the signature, or through clinical experience.

If you wish to use the doctrine of signature to make or create medicines, you should have in-depth botanical identification skills and be able to identify all poisonous plants and plant parts by heart! Don't forget—it was a tool used by the *master herbalists, pharmacologists,* and *botanists* of time gone by; they were people who knew their plants. The doctrine of signature is not a free-for-all. Suffice to say that there is also a signature for poisonous plants, as worked out by Wilhelm Pelikan (1958, p. 148). (See "The Signature of Poisons," beginning on page 285.)

THE LANGUAGE OF PLANTS

Ben Charles Harris advises, "However, again and again we do find countless examples of medicinal herbs on which are "stamped" an indication of their healing properties. The inquisitive novice herbalist need only apply his powers of observation to evaluate clues to the herbs' therapeutic powers, the remedial qualities, or the disease for which these qualities are indicated. If at times the examples seem far-fetched, let me offer as warrants of the doctrine's usefulness some fifty-five years of living with and experiencing the healing herbs, as well as close to four decades of professional pharmacy and teaching of herbalism" (1985, p. 38).

WHICH PLANTS HAVE SIGNATURES?

Important signatures are all that deviates, all that is unique or special, about a plant— for example, the fact that it survives the most severe ice or drought or grows at extreme altitudes. The Edelweiss, for instance, grows at extreme alpine altitudes, where sun exposure is harsh. Based on the principle of signatures, the researchers at the Weleda laboratories inferred that the Edelweiss must therefore have a special ability to protect itself from sunburn. (This is not meant to be humorous; plant tissue can be badly scalded by the sun!) They decided to test Edelweiss extract for its ability to protect human skin from ultraviolet rays and found it serviceable. It is so efficient that it was developed into a whole line of high-factor sun protection cremes and lotions.

Each plant family in itself also has its own signature. It is the specific way the clan deviates from the imaginary blueprint of the archetypal plant, or Goethe's *Urpflanze*. These have been worked out beautifully by Wilhelm Pelikan in his three-volume *Heilpflanzenkunde* (The Healing Plant). An example would be flesh-eating plants, which even deviate from the plant norm of "eating" only light.

Another strong signature is a characteristic by which a plant clearly deviates from the rest of its botanical family. An example would be Celandine, one out of two poppies in the sun-loving Poppy family that grows in the half-shade and does not have showy flowers; it does not invest much energy in blooming, as Pelikan would put it. Instead, it invests in making the Poppies' usual white milk sap bright yellow; its succulent leaves are jaundiced, as it were. Hence, it is one of the best remedies for jaundice we might find. Its other half-shade-loving cousin, Bloodroot, produces blood-red sap; it controls blood rushing to the head, one of the finest migraine remedies

60

to be found. The Opium Poppy by contrast, a showy flowered "standard" Poppy, is not a liver herb, nor is it useful for migraine. We can think of it for inducing sleep. These healing gifts are acquired by Celandine and Bloodroot by their unique characteristics, their personal signatures.

Once we become astute in the reading of signatures, we see that there is no such thing as a plant with or a plant without a signature. By then, nature lies before one like a book, asking to be read. Then, there are only various remarkable signatures to be discovered.

THE SIGNATURE OF HUMANS: PHYSIOGNOMY

> No mountain, no rock is so large as that it could cover or hide what is inside of it, so that man could not know; all of that is possible by way of special signs. Because every fruit is a sign, and it shalt be known by it, what is inside, and whence it was created. Equally there is nothing in man that was not marked on the outside, by way of which one could not recognize what is inside him who carries that sign. (Paracelsus, in Jakobi 1991, p. 170)

No book on the doctrine of signature would be complete without pointing out that physiognomy is the law of correspondences applied to the human form. Just as the doctrine of signature helps us to correctly and meaningfully read the colors and shapes of plants, physiognomy is the art of reading the colors, shapes, and so on of the human body. We find different schools of this in different traditional medicinal systems: Traditional Chinese Medicine points out the predominance of which of the five elements gives which shape and color; Ayurveda phrases it in terms of the tree *doshas,* the three groups into which it condenses the five elements; in the West, the physiognomy tradition goes with the four temperaments, based on the four Greek humors, which are in turn based on the four elements and so on.

To give an example, *Pitta* or people with a fire predominance, have reddish or copper-colored hues, generally bright and shiny colors, and have strong smells, sulfurous, malodorous. The same is true of plants with a strong fire element.[2]

---

2 Works on this for further reading include *Prakruti* by Robert Svoboda; *Reading the Face,* vols. 1 & 2; *Die Hände offenbaren den Menschen,* about reading the hands; and others by Norbert Glas; *Your Face Never Lies* by Michio Kushi; and the unpublished "Herbal Diagnosis" by Matthew Wood.

Then, of course, who says that only plants look like human organs, and not human organs like plants? Who says (outside of an anthropocentric worldview) that plants cannot be matched to human shapes to indicate their inherent human qualities? The Native North Americans match plants to animals to infer their inherent animal powers, while Western tradition relates them to the signs of the zodiac.

CHAPTER SIX

WHAT IS NOT A SIGNATURE

THE TRUE AND THE FALSE

My friend and master teacher, the Minnesotan herbalist Matthew Wood, pointed out that one should not compare plants to technological items when referring to signatures. This makes a lot of sense; nature existed and prevailed for billions of years before human beings arrived and came up with satellite dishes or antennas. How can we compare something so ancient and organic to a mechanical or electrical device. We can compare technology to nature, but not the other way around. A flower is not like a satellite dish, but rather a satellite dish is like an ear receiving waves. Passion Flower, discussed later in more detail, is called "Clock Flower" in some cultures, because it reminds people of a clock face. It is an important nervine and a calming, sleep-inducing remedy, but I have yet to hear that it helps people be on time.

Channeling the angel of the plant about its properties equally has nothing to do with reading the plant's signature, since it uses extrasensory methods. The art of reading the signatures involves being in the here and now, awake and able-minded, and using the five senses along with one's intelligence. Wood remarked on channeling angels as a method to discover a plant's medicinal virtues: "It's not like the plants themselves don't have wisdom." They do. They unmistakably know who and what they are. Incidentally, I would like to point out that channeling the plant angel to find out about the plant's usefulness in healing adds a whole other dimension. Before, we were dealing only with having to translate the plant's language of colors, shapes, and so on into human language; but here, we are dealing with an angel's perception of a plant, translating the plant language into angelic language, which we then channel, but it can be very cryptic, and we then need to translate it all into human language. Quite complicated. Deciphering the plant's own signs is far more straightforward—not to mention the loss of subtlety in meaning and accuracy with each translation from one language to another.

SIGNATURES AND SYMBOLISM

A signature is not a symbol that represents something else, like an assigned code, but a direct expression, or *is-ness,* of an energetic state. There are true and false symbolic associations with the signatures. A popular example for a signature is that of the Passion Flower, which

is in fact a good example for two layers of false symbolic associations. The first is based merely on its name, "Passion Flower," for which it is marketed in all kinds of sexual passion-evoking drinks and such. Far from being an aphrodisiac, the plant is in fact calming and sedating. "Passion" in the name of the flower has nothing to do with sexual passion. The name is not a characteristic of the plant, but attributed by Spanish conquistadores, who named it after the Passion, or the suffering of the Christ. This association (see below for details) is also a false signature. For instance, one would be hard-pressed to explain to people foreign to Christianity why

Passion Flower—a symbolic representation of the Christ's Crucifixion

they should see in the petals surrounding the flower center the apostles standing close to the Christ in the moment of his suffering. They do not look more human or tightly surrounding than the petals of any other flower.

- the pointed leaves represent the Holy Lance
- the tendrils the whips used to beat him
- the petals and sepals the faithful apostles closely surrounding the Christ
- the radial filaments the Crown of Thorns
- the chalice-shaped ovary with its receptacle the Holy Grail

- the three stigmata (this is the botanical term here) the three nails, and the five anthers the five wounds

It is clear from this list that the creators of this name forced some of the associations to fit the story. In fact, the symbolism is superimposed onto the preexisting reality of the Passion Flower. The doctrine of signature does *not* mean to put our trip onto nature, but rather to forget about our agenda and listen to *her* heartbeat!

The true reading of the signatures of Passion Flower would be like this: It is a flower genus with about 500 species, most of which are quite similar. They are slender vines that use their tendrils to climb up on other plants, and the main stem eventually becomes woody. They can form great tangles. The tendrils appear to grip, gradually tense, and seem to spasm. The stem is square in cross-section, the leaves five-lobed and hand-like, and the flowers open with many radial petals and florets. They are white with blue or purple for most species, and bear plum-shaped, sweet and sour edible fruits. The overall impression of the plant is that it is fragile, with sprouts that metamorphose from a relaxed look to a cramped appearance, with open and inviting flowers. The flowers and fruit seem large for it's fragile build.

- *climber*—anxious persons lacking the power to stand up, dependency
- *finely cut plant parts*—sensitivity, over-excitability
- *hand-like leaves*—associated with power, empowerment, ancient symbol of magic
- *tangles*—getting entangled
- *tendrils*—clinging to others, tendency to dependency and weakness, convolutedness, convulsions
- *gripping and tense tendrils*—nervous, muscular, emotional and mental tension, gripping, spasmodic pain
- *square stem*—nervine (nerve calming remedy)
- *white*—purity, calmness, spirituality
- *blue*—calmness, clarity, cooling
- *purple*—spiritual opening
- *radial flower shape*—open, centered personality
- *radial floral filaments*—overly open and sensitive, radiant personality
- *very fine florets*—sensitivity, over-sensitivity

- *big, top-heavy flower buds, fruits heavy, pulling downward*—this top-heaviness and falling appearance could be taken as a signature for the falling disease, epilepsy
- *bitter herb*—cooling, calming to the nerves, stimulates digestion
- *sweet, edible fruits*—nurturance
- *sweet and sour taste*—grounding, sedating, nurturing

The herb yields a medicine different from that of the fruit and is the part most commonly used. So if we look at this picture, we see that Passion Flower herb is a nerve-calming remedy for anxious people who cannot stay calm and clear and open, but whose thoughts form tangles. It is an excellent herb for gripping pain and spasms, as well as mental, emotional, nervous or muscular tension and convulsions. Passion Flower herb tea calms and opens them up. It is well suited to sensitive or oversensitive, easily over-excitable people. "It is one of the most important remedies for insomnia from overstimulation of the mind, excessive thinking, and chatter of the brain" (Wood 2009, p. 263). It is helpful for any disturbance involving high nervous tension.

The Passion Flower is one of the tensest plants around, and it cures states of tension, even convulsions, epilepsy, and tetanus (Murphy 2000, p. 1,322). The heavy flower buds and fruits, which make the plant "top-heavy" and pull the vines down with a crash should the support fail, could be taken as a signature for epilepsy, the "falling disease." In Ayurvedic terms, a thin climber such as Passion Flower would be considered a *Vata* plant, as having a predominance of the air and ether elements. If *Vata* predominates in the body, we get insomnia and all kinds of nerve disorders, including cramps of all sorts. It is classified as a cooling nervine (Frawley and Lad 1986, p. 209), thus well suited to insomnia due to overactive thinking—overactivity being associated with excess heat. Five-lobed palmate leaves take the shape of the hand and stand for power and magic (actions of the hand). *Cunningham's Encyclopedia of Magical Herbs* lists Passion Flower as an herb to use for peace, sleep, and friendship. Cunningham recommends placing it in the house to calm troubles and problems and bring peace. One can also carry it to attract friends and enhance popularity. A practicing magic herbalist I met at Flower Power Herb Store in Manhattan explained to me, "I use it when I do white magic to attract opportunities. That can often create such high energy that I do not recognize the opportunity when it presents itself, but only in hindsight. Passion Flower allows me to stay calm enough not to miss it." The magical use is thus in harmony with the herbal indications. We see from this example that a true understanding of signature is not culturally limited; it is nature-bound.

Going back to the example of divinities being superimposed over a plant's medicinal actions, we easily see how Passion Flower—on the one hand so lovely, open and radiant, on the other so intensely cramped up—could be a good plant onto which to project the agonies of the Christ's passion, during which he kept his heart and mind calm and open. I am sure that he would have much benefited from a cup of Passion Flower tea at the time!

There is also a different kind of symbolism related to the use of plants that is not the doctrine of signature, either: the symbolic use of plants in healing rituals in Southern Africa, for example. Here, the cure is enacted as if in a psychodrama—to cure sharp, cutting period cramps, for instance, the *nganga* or shaman of the Shona in Zimbabwe might ask the woman to eat red millet porridge that has been stabbed with a knife during the healing ritual as her medicine. The redness here symbolizes the period blood, and the stabbing the stabbing pains. The millet is used merely for it's red color, not for a signature of the plant pointing to period pains, or any true herbal use. This use is theatrical and as such very effective (Hoffmann, 1990).

THE VICTORIAN LANGUAGE OF FLOWERS

In the Victorian era, flowers were used as a code language, much like the Morse code, to send messages between lovers. It served to convey messages through bouquets or flower arrangements that could not otherwise be spoken. While some of them carry forth the folk wisdom associated with the plant, and hence some herbal wisdom, others are mere bases for a concept they had to convey. While it is not surprising to find rose standing for love and violet for hidden love (since shyness is the personality trait going with the "shrinking violet"), I personally cannot say I ever noticed that coquetry was part of the action of Bluebell, nor can I understand how Anise can stand for "promise"; Oats for music (other than resembling wind chimes—but "music" is not a medical keynote); or purple Lilac for the first emotion of love more than other heart opening flowers. The Victorian language of flowers is not the language of flowers as discussed in this book, but a secret code between two parties in a rigid, moralistic society. (See *Flower Power* by Anne McIntyre for more details.)

CONCLUSION

We could say that, if we wish to apply a signature label to a plant, then we should take it from a basic ancient language that is common to all of nature and humankind and, in a sense, transcends culture. This is why categories such as the four elements, the *element signature,* work; they might be clad in a cultural context, but the direct experience of the four states of the aggregates is common to all cultures.

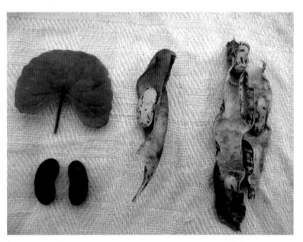

Left to right: Gotu Kola leaf, Kidney Beans, bean pods broken open to show the way the beans attach to the pods. As a kidney remedy and brain tonic, Gotu Kola has a kidney-shaped leaf that also looks like a cross section of the brain. Red Beans look like the organ itself, and opened pods show that the beans are attached in a way that recalls the pelvis of the kidney running down along the spine. In Chinese medicine, Beans are seen as a kidney-strengthening food, while the pods are a fine diuretic.

An example of a true symbolic signature is that of the heart-shaped Rose petal taking it to mean it is a heart remedy, which indeed it cools an excited heart and allays many difficult emotions related to the heart. Once we look closely, we see that all true examples for symbolic signatures are really once again cases of likeness in form or energetic situation; kidney beans are not symbolic of kidneys, but directly similar to them. Once breaking open the hard shells of the dried pods, we find the seed inside, colored and shaped exactly like the kidneys. They curve toward the spine of the pod just as the kidneys curve toward the spine. Moreover, they are attached to the pod the way the pelvis of the kidneys attach. The shape and rigidity of the opened, dried pod echoes the shape of the rib cage. Thus, eating beans or drinking a tea of the dried pods have been valued from time immemorial for their diuretic properties and against gravel in the urine.

It has been said that the doctrine of signature is a mere mnemonic tool. Quite contrary to being *merely* that, once the herbalist or nature lover beholds the innate holistic sense in the signature, the truth of this so strongly impresses itself upon the mind that it becomes unforgettable. One might forget an indication for an herb or chemical constituent, but one never forgets a signature once it makes sense.

Outlook for Part Two

What I will attempt in the second part of this book is to create an overview of the doctrine of signature as such, covering any aspect of the topic that I can. I will be doing this as an insider of the herbal craft, as someone having spent her life living with, growing, and harvesting herbs, making them into medicines and using those on others and myself for healing.

If you the reader are not a plant person or an herbalist and are unfamiliar with plants and the doctrine of signature, I would like to suggest rereading part one of this book on theory after reading the remainder of this book. It will make far more sense then.

My intention is not to write a book that lists every single example of the doctrine of signature. That would be impossible, given the countless number of plants with all their billions of characteristics. Rather, I am attempting to introduce as many different ways of looking at a plant as I can think of while illustrating the signatures with examples. My aim is to inspire the reader to become an apprentice of nature and—based on the examples—become enabled to apply the ideas to whatever plants one encounters. The doctrine of signature does not mean an art of sensing a plant's characteristics clairvoyantly. Rather, it is an art of precise observation of what *is,* of what resembles. May this sharpen the reader's senses.

PART TWO

THE DOCTRINE
OF SIGNATURES
IN PRACTICE

In this part of the book, I will go over every angle of the doctrine of signature I know. Some of the characteristics might surface in several categories, since they may belong to more than one. Because this part is intended as an encyclopedia in which to look up specific aspects of the doctrine of signature, such repetition is needed for the sake of completeness. I hope that this repetition under different angles will leave an indelible impression in the reader's mind. Since the main way in which we assess plants is to look at them, the main part of the doctrine of signature falls under the category of color or shape. We will then explore the other senses, such as taste and touch. The reader might be surprised by the large size of the section on the elements; however, the elements have been the traditional underpinning of all great energetic traditions of herbalism. They are therefore crucial for understanding the art of herbal medicine.

It is important to recall that each of the characteristics of the plant are a signature, and that the overall healing essence of the plant is the sum of all of those plus its wholeness. It is similar to the way an artist mixes colors—some crimson, some scarlet and magenta, with a hint of yellow and orange, to give an overall red. Even a splash of black or blue will not change its overriding redness. Thus, the doctrine of signature as a holistic form of medicinal art requires our minds to remain open and flexible.

⚶

CHAPTER SEVEN

COLORS, THE LANGUAGE OF FLOWERS

The Earth laughs in flowers. —E. E. CUMMINGS

Colors exist on this earthly plane as a gift of sunlight, which—breaking into its rainbow components—enriches life by bestowing all the visible hues. We can clearly see that even in plant and animal life, the coloring of nature depends on the contact with sunlight to come into being. We will observe that the sunnier the location or climate in which a plant grows, the more vivid and flamboyant the colors of its flowers.

The first and easiest approach to the doctrine of signature are the colors of the plant, the most colorful part of it being its flowers. We will therefore begin the discussion of colors with those of the flower. In this section, we need not worry whether the color appears in what botanically are true petals or not; it will suffice to apply it to what we apprehend as the flower of the plant. What we call the petals of the dogwood flower, for example, are technically bracts, but they can be treated here as petals, since it is only the color that concerns us. As a general rule of thumb, the bigger and more showy the flower, the more it is significant as the signature of the plant.

There are several ways of looking at the colors. There are three types of correspondences: the most esoteric is the correspondence of the flowers to chakras and their color, second is the psychological effect of the color and its symbolical meaning, and then there is the correspondence between the body color and that of the plant—black heals black and purple heals purple. Last, of course, we can interpret how the different colors of a multicolored flower interact.

There is—not surprisingly so in a world of correspondence—a lot of overlap between those three categories: the chakras and their colors are related in their psychological functioning to the psychological keynote and symbolism of their color. Also, the chakra colors and their assigned body parts correspond: the root chakra is red, often healed by red flowers and plants; its functioning influences the blood, which is red; and both blood and the root chakra have to

73

do with emergencies and threats to the life, as well as seeing red with rage. The solar plexus chakra is yellow, named after the nerve web that bears the name of the yellow sun, and rules the yellow-most substance in the body, the bile and its flow. The examples for the correspondence between tissue color in human and plant bodies is stark: red plants heal the blood, yellow plants the bile, black plants necrotic black tissue, and purple ones livid stagnant and toxic tissue states.

As always a word of caution— while the color of a flower might mean this or that, it does not mean that therefore the medicinal effect will be such—it has to been seen in the context of the totality of the plant, and might be overridden by another aspect.

As we move into the examination of different aspects of the plant in the light of the doctrine of signature, we are well to be reminded of the fact that none of this will make sense unless we engage in a direct and living dialogue with nature. Broken down into its facets, the signatures may lose their most essential ingredient: the holistic context of all the parts being aspects of one whole. And always remember: the whole is greater than the sum of its parts. Bearing this in mind, we may begin.

THE COLORS AND THE MEANINGS WE GIVE THEM

In the context of the doctrine of signature, one way of interpreting the colors of a flower is by way of their symbolic and psychologically associated meanings. Yellow, for example, stands for joy. The Yellow Day Lily has long been known in Asian medicine to "brighten the *chi*," hence to counteract depression. These qualities are felt subjectively, such as:

> *blue*—cool, calm, clear, clean, distant, calming, water, sky, space, distance, expansiveness, retreating to the background
> *examples:* cooling blueberries; calming Chicory flower essences giving a sense of inner space
> *red*—heat, fire, warmth, intensity, anger, aggression, rage, passion, intense feelings, proximity, coming to the forefront, in one's face, danger
> *examples:* Scarlet Monkeyflower for screaming red anger; warming red beets
> *yellow*—joyful, gay, sunny, radiant, luminous, light, young
> *examples:* Chamomile flower essence for a sunny inner disposition; Yellow Day Lily against depression

purple—spirituality, refinement, brooding

>   *example:* Purple Gentian for hope in the spiritual sense

The yellow Sunflower—joyful, gay, sunny, radiant

Purple has different shades that take on different meanings. Dark purple, or blackish purple as in some *Pulsatillas* (Windflower, Pasque Flower), *Pulsatilla nigricans,* can mean dark emotions and depression. Light purple or reddish purple as in Harebell or Bluebell can mean spirituality, spiritual opening, sense of abundance and oneness. Purple is the color that depends more on how the hue strikes one than any other—the most important question is whether it is heavy or light, meaning depression versus spirituality.

orange—upbeat, energetic, warm, radiant, fire, glow

>   *example:* Aloe Vera for burns and burn-out or exhaustion

green—calm, calming, cool, nature, vitality

>   *example:* Lady's Mantle for nature awareness

pink—vulnerability, tenderness, loveliness, love

>   *examples:* Pink Yarrow for emotional vulnerability; Wild Tulip (*Tulipa bakeri*) for opening to love

magenta—basic life force (Kaminski, 1998)

>   *example:* Echinacea flower essence for vitality

golden—while not really a color present in flowers, some shades of yellow can best be described as golden: pertaining to the noble emotions of the heart and spirituality

>   *examples:* the golden spots on Wild Tulip, or Toad Lily; in golden California Poppy, it takes the connotation of falling for glamour and glitz versus knowing what has true value

silver—while flowers are not really silver, leaves and petals may have a silvery hue. Sometimes, white takes the roles of silver: related to the night, Moon, dreams and daydreaming *examples:* white Clematis, a plant that embodies the Moon archetype, for daydreaming and dreaminess; *Artemisia* leaves for access to dream memories and conscious dreaming

iridescent—transcendence into a non-material realm (by this I do not mean variegated or having several colors, but the sunlight being broken and reflected in rainbow colors such as on the surface of Lotus leaves and petals)

example: Lotus for transcendence and spiritual advancement

white—light, clean, purity, neutral

examples: Madonna Lily for physical, emotional, and spiritual purity; Basil for detox

grey—twilight, between the realms, neutral

example: a rare color in flowers, Star Tulip (*Calochortus tolmiei*) has a purple white that oddly strikes one as light grey. It is for remaining conscious between realms of consciousness.

black—darkness, dirt, night, density, heaviness, death, decay, lack of awareness

example: black center of Borage denotes its use for depression

brown—earth, earthen, groundedness, dirty, sullied, death, lack of awareness

examples: the black brown velvety center of Black-Eyed Susan indicates its use for bringing awareness to the shadow parts of the self, one's blind spots; light brown Chrysanthemum for fear of death

red brown—blood, earth, groundedness, instincts, lower emotions

example: Wakerobin (or red-brown Trillium) for menstrual hemorrhaging, giving birth, and being stuck in lower emotions

Earth colors depend on which metals or other substances are forming the soil. Most shades of orange, red, brown, black and grey are due to the presence of iron. Copper can give a green hue, sulphur yellow. The bauxite rich soils of the tropics can be of a very warm red due to the presence of aluminium, and other places have yellow soil. So different colors can have the connotation of "earth." I never understood why in ancient India the color symbolizing earth is yellow, until I saw the yellow soil there. However, it is not a luminous yellow of a flower, but greyish and faded.

Often, flower shades of color are somewhat vague—one person might call it golden yellow, another orange; someone blue, someone else violet. The main thing is to feel the color's effect.

Does it look vibrant, coming to the foreground? Or is it shy, fading into the background? Does the color look clean or murky? How does it strike me?

Colors in flowers come into being in relation to sunlight. For instance, apple blossoms are red on the parts exposed to sunlight while still a bud, while Borage flowers turn sky blue from pale pink under the morning sunlight. On the other hand, flowers on the forest floor tend to be white from the lack of the color-forming sunlight. In their case, being white is not highly significant. This is different with a pure white flower growing in bright sunlight. This is a stronger signature of purity.

Borage

THE COLOR OF FLOWERS AND THE CHAKRAS

> The Plant Kingdom exists to bring feelings into manifestation. On the plant level, feelings exist in a pure and passive form. The animal and human kingdoms manifest this more actively, more separately, but often with less beauty. Consciousness in plants is on a primal level of unity; therefore, it is more psychic, telepathic. (*The Yoga of Herbs,* Frawley and Lad, 1986, p. 4)

I will start the presentation of colors of flowers with their relationship to the colors of the chakras, because this is in a way the most medicinal and scientific approach. Clairvoyant people see the chakras and aura in rainbow colors, the colors going from red to violet, from bottom to the crown, with the lowest vibration of energy equalling the lowest energy carrying light—red—and the highest the color that carries the highest energy—violet. Each chakra is linked directly to a set of physiological functions, glands and inner organs, thus connecting the color to a state of health, as well as to emotional states.

I have found a very close correlation between the color of the flower and its effect within the human energy system. When working with flower essences, we can see that the color of the flower will guide its energetic effect within the aura to the charkra of the corresponding color. I like to say that *the color conducts the energetic effect in the aura*. It determines to which area the effect will gravitate. This becomes especially clear when working with the same flower in different colors, such as Roses or Snapdragons: a yellow Snapdragon flower essence will gravitate toward the solar plexus, while a pink one will gravitate toward the heart. This occurs, of course, only as long as no other signature dominates over the color.

CHAKRA	COLOR	BODY PART	POSITIVE INNER QUALITY
Crown	white	central nervous system	inner peace, bliss, sense of oneness
Third Eye	violet	nose, ears, sinus	wisdom, clairvoyance
Throat	blue	throat, chest	knowledge, communication
Heart	green	lungs, heart	unconditional love, forgiveness
Solar Plexus	yellow	stomach, liver, gallbladder	personal power, authority, discipline
Navel	orange	sexual organs, small intestines	sexuality, procreation
Root	red	survival, instincts, groundedness	bones, blood

It is interesting to note that when the human aura is seen in auric vision, the chakras within the aura look very similar in appearance to flowers on a flowering plant. In this sense, the association between the colors of flowers and those of the chakras is a true signature. As we will see in the section for shapes, this correlation becomes even stronger, if the flower also has a typical chakra shape—that is: looks like a funnel or energy eddy, or else groups of small funnels/eddies.

We should not be surprised to find that the flowers and their colors have a strong relationship to the realm of emotions. We intuit this by adorning emotional events with flowers: weddings, anniversaries, enthronements, burials. Endowed with a heavenly touch, all cultures talk of rains of flower petals released by happy gods, who, naturally, always appear adorned with blossoms.... The flowers are of course the part of the plant we feel opens to the heavens. To express love and other fine emotions, we offer a bouquet of flowers. This seems so natural to us, we forget how special the flowers as a plant part are. Just think how your loved one would feel if you offered her or him a bouquet of freshly plucked roots to ask for marriage.

The examples of this section pertain most clearly to the preparation of flowers as a flower essence, since made from flowers only and not another part of the plant, they carry the flower healing potential in the clearest and strongest form. The flowers are not as preeminently important in herbalism, since most of the material is herbaceous—hence *herb*alism.

Black, Brown and Red

Starting at the bottom, the root chakra is associated with these earthy colors. The root chakra is our energetic center that rules survival, fight and flight and the lowest instincts, the blood, muscles and bones, as well as the colon.

Black

While black flowers are rare, many flowers do have some black in them. Borage, for instance, is a star-shaped flower that is pink upon opening and turns sky blue as the sun starts shining on it, sporting a pitch black protruding center. Borage is a flower for heavyheartedness and depression, the blackness here standing for the darkness of mood at the center of one's being. Black can indicate any of the dark moods. The psychological meaning is also one of darkness, as well as of death, which could also be positive in the blackish-purple of *Pulsatilla nigricans,* Wind or Pasque Flower, where it has to do with integrating inner darkness or shadow aspects of one's Self. Another example would be Black-Eyed Susan (*Rudbeckia hirta*). This *Compositae* has a black center surrounded by golden yellow florets. It helps us shed light into the darkness at the center of our being—our blind spots.

Brown

There are true brown flowers such as brown Chrysanthemum or Lilies. Their effect is the acceptance of impermanence and death for the former, and first chakra issues such as lower instincts and cleansing of the lower organs for the latter.

Reddish brown

Some of the *Trilliums*, such as Wakerobin, are reddish brown, a wonderful signature for the preparation of giving birth, an activity that involves the lowest part of the body, as well as muscles, blood, uterine hemorrhaging and giving birth—more illustrating the root chakra still—they are famous for "bringing down the baby." Coming down to us from the Native American traditions, herbalist David Winston specifies that it was the red *Trillium* under discussion here that was used to stop postpartum bleeding in Cherokee medicine. Wild Ginger with its odd reddish-brown, uterus-shaped flowers heals uterine spasms and cramping of the lower back, as well as excessive menstrual cramps and is useful in cases of weak labor.

Trillium, or Wakerobin (photo by Sandra Lory)

Burgundy

Herbalist Matthew Wood teaches that burgundy-colored plants build blood. He names Sumac berries, Rehmannia, Beets, and Elder juice. By contrast, red treat heat in the blood or the lack thereof.

Red

Bright red flowers include Waratha from Australia, a flower essence that heals survival trauma, or Scarlet Monkeyflower, which helps to integrate aggression—screaming red anger (it looks like a screaming mouth). Sturt Desert Pea from Australia is both bright red and black at the center. Aboriginal legends connect it to deep hurt, pain and grief, and the flower essence is used in the same way. These are the kind of hurts that touch our ability to survive and live on—or else, if not overcome might make us feel like we want to die.

The root chakra governs the blood. Harris offers "Those plants with reddish flowers, such as Red Clover, Burdock, Rose, Raspberry, Bee Balm, and Pimpernel, have long been established as blood purifiers or alteratives, and may still be used as such today. A reddish color may also suggest the astringency or healing effect of a plant in external or skin disorders arising from blood impurities. (The active principles of plants are today considered 'antibiotic.')" (Harris 1985, p. 43). It is remarkable in this context that in the wake of battles, blood red Corn Poppies tend to cover the battle fields, giving rise to the idea that they spring from the blood of the fallen in Europe (McIntyre 1996, p. 177). Corn Poppies are either plain blood-red or sport black spots at the petals' base, the colors of survival trauma such as combat. As a flower essence, it is useful for those who are scared of expressing strong emotions (fear being one of the emotions associate with the root chakra), and helps us to "show our true colors." Poppies are remedies for blood, circulation and excruciating pain. It

is remarkable that this innocent plant in the form of the Opium Poppy is indispensable not only to quell the pain of terminal diseases (death and survival), and for the treatment of pain from battle wounds, but has led to tremendous amounts of international warfare and criminality—both root chakra issues (ibid.).

The list of remedies pertaining to the blood as alteratives, blood thinners, hemostatic, circulatory or other that are red or reddish brown includes Alkanet, Amaranth, Bloodroot, Barberry (berries), Red Beet, Burdock (stem and flowers), Red Clover, Echinacea spp., Cranberry (ber-

The red Hawthorn berries are precious medicine for the organs touched by red blood: they calm histaminic overreactions and heat in the tissue, free the arteries of plaque, and rebuild tired heart muscles (photo by Sandra Lory).

ries), Figwort (flowers), Wild Yam (extract), Fumitory, Hawthorn berries, Wild Geranium (leaves), red Grape (leaves), Rose, red Peony, Madder, Rosehips, Red Root, Scarlet Pimpernel, Poke, Elder, Sheep Sorrel, Soapwort (root), Strawberry, Raspberry, Staghorn Sumac, *Trillium* (Wakerobin), and Wintergreen.

Orange

Orange flowers energize the sexual chakra and sexual energy. We may think of Tiger Lily and other wild orange lilies similar to Tiger Lily, such as *Lilium henrii*, the Wild Himalayan Lily, or the wild North American Lilies. They are helpful in gynecological disease, as well. Some of them are orange-yellow, such as Safflower or Hawkweed, and extend their action to liver and gallbladder (see also the entry for yellow and for liver and gallbladder under organ signature). Another example is Calendula, the orange flowers used in herbalism. Their healing powers gravitate to the pelvic area and the skin, healing vaginal candida among other things, and being one of the most wonderful teas for a woman to heal after giving birth. William Coles considers the orange-yellow of Calendula flowers a signature for their action in jaundice (Coles 1657, p. 183).

Yellow

Yellow flowers gravitate and energize the solar plexus chakra and the organs of the upper abdomen, particularly the gallbladder and liver. Good examples here are Dandelion, Celandine, Safflower or Oregon-Grape as liver- and gallbladder-healing plants with yellow flowers. Some of them also have yellow sap (Celandine). They have to do with group and leadership issues, for instance Golden Yarrow and Yellow Star Tulip flower essences protect the solar plexus when too oversensitive in group situations. Celandine as a flower essence helps to empower oneself and become one's own authority over one's life. The list of common liver and jaundice remedies that are yellow or yellow-orange in preparation, flower, root, fruit, or seed is impressive. In addition to the above-mentioned plants, we may think of Saffron (pistils), Agrimony, the inner bark of

Calendula (photo by Sandra Lory)

Black Alder, Aloe rind, Buckbean fruit, Butter and Eggs, carrots, Yellow Dock, Barberry (root), Elecampane (flower), Fennel (seeds), Sweetflag, Fringetree, Fumitory (root), yellow Gentian, Goat's Beard, Goldenseal, Goldthread, Hawkweed, Henna (flowers), Jewelweed, Madder, Papaya, Parsnip (flowers), Quassia (heartwood), Queen's Root, Tansy, Turmeric, False Unicorn (roots), Woad, and Wormwood (flowers).

Light Green / Yellowish Green

I have found that light green flowers tend to energize the area of the diaphragm—right between the heart/lung and solar plexus areas. This is an illustration of light green being a mix of yellow and green, so they energize the area between the heart and solar plexus chakra, deepening the awareness into the space below the heart, helping to take deeper breaths. Since we often cut the lower part of our body off from our body awareness at the level of the diaphragm, flower essences such as Lady's Mantle and Linden can aid in breaking through such a block, the former in keeping with the rest of the signature also opening the heart and connecting the life force into the limbs, while the latter calms the nerves that innervate heart, diaphragm, as well as the solar plexus. Green and light green are colors said to go to the heart chakra. However, I have found that pink is more powerful for opening the heart chakra itself than light green. Light green or crème white can also be neutral color for a non-showy flower, the grey of the flower realm so to speak, the "non-color."

Green

According to the rainbow model, green is the next color and attributed to the heart chakra and the lungs. In practice, I have found this to be true, but pink, gold and white are more powerful to open the heart. When making and taking the essence of Lady's Mantle (which has green flowers), I became intensely aware of the nature spirits around me, meeting them face to face. I was intrigued to hear years later that Patricia Kaminski states that green flowers help us to connect with nature as a living being (*Flowers that Heal,* 1998). She has since developed a whole line of flower essences from green flowers to this end. When the sunlight is broken up into colors on its way through a prism—or in a rainbow—green is the color of the middle. "Green flowers

Hellebore (Corn Lily)

are unusual: they remain aligned with the life mantle of the Earth. As a mid-point in the color spectrum between light and dark, they have many unique and significant qualities for balancing and healing the heart and opening the heart to compassion, awareness and sensitivity for the Earth."

A green flowered plant that, as a flower essence and homeopathically, acts on the heart is Hellebore, also called Corn Lily (*Veratrum viride*). Mistletoe is a curious example of a green flower—this ancient botanical creature does not really form what we would call a flower, it looks more like a tiny unripe green berry. Mistletoe is a useful remedy for heart and circulation, and as a flower essence helps to overcome codependence—an unhealthy symbiosis, a fusion of our heart with another person in a way that we cannot exists without them. This illustrates the green color mixing with the other prominent signature of mistletoe, of it being a parasite of the host tree.

Pink and Gold

While not on the rainbow chart, pink and a golden yellow that strikes us as golden such as in the flower essence of the Greek Wild Tulip (*Tulipa bakeri*) energize and open the heart chakra. Many other pink flowers that are heart remedies can be named here—Bleeding Heart, Mallow, Motherwort, Wild Rose, and Silktree (*Mimosa*), to name a few, all as flower essences and the latter four also from herbalism.

Gold has been associated with the heart since the times of the alchemists. The homeopathic provings of *Aurum*, potentized gold, affirm the healing action of the precious metal to the heart. Hence, a golden hue in a flower is a heart signature. An example would be Yellow Day Lily, antidepressant and opening the heart chakra.

Blue

Truly sky blue flowers open the throat chakra. We can think of scillas or Grape Hyacinth as a flower essence. This chakra governs breath and breathing also, and Chinese Bellflower (or Balloon Flower) is healing to asthma. Blue Flag Iris holds a position between blue and violet, and is also multicolored. However, as a flower essence, it strongly opens the throat chakra (artistic expression) and heals energetic blocks in the neck area (or chakra), as well as neck pain and problems. In the homeopathic preparation, the blue Wild Hyacinth previously called *Agraphis nutans* is chiefly used for swollen throats and tonsillitis (Murphy 2000, p. 50f).

Bluebells are not truly blue, but rather lavender color. Being merely blue in name, they therefore belong to the next section.

"Brilliant blue is one of the most reliable of the color signatures. It almost always indicates an antispasmodic: Lobelia, Skullcap, Blue Vervain, Chamomile (the oil is blue), Blue Cohosh" (Wood 1997, p. 26). We might add Speedwell (bronchial spasms), Rosemary (cramps of the stomach), and Periwinkle (calf cramps).

Harris writes that blue flowers might be indicated in cyanosis, where the skin is bluish due to a lack of oxygenation of the blood (Harris 1985, p. 44).

Purple, Lavender, Violet, Indigo

These colors energize the third eye chakra. The third eye chakra is connected to the functioning of the hypothalamus, and *Pulsatilla* or Windflower, purple in all shades, is homeopathy's prime balancing agent for that gland. Bluebell flower (lavender in color) essence opens the third eye chakra, thereby overcoming fear of feeling of lack and reconnecting us to a sense of greater abundance. Meadow Saffron as a flower essence also opens the third eye and increases intuition and clairvoyance. Dr. Bach researched purple Gentian essence and found it to restore hope in the spiritual sense. Violet Lilac flower essence is one of the most useful in opening the head chakras to allow the flow of life force to reenter the body.

See also the fruit entry on purple.

White

White is the color that contains all other colors in the spectrum, and the color of pale flowers growing in the shade. So we would need to expect there to be another signature in a flower to make it pertain to the crown—white being the color of the crown chakra, the one that connects us to the sense of being all-one. Here we can think of White Lotus or Yucca, both also having other signatures pointing to the head or crown. White flowers can also have an effect throughout the entire aura system and effect all chakras. An example are many white Lilies, such as Madonna Lily, that have a purifying effect throughout the entire system. White is sometimes associated with mother's milk, such as in Milkthistle (the variegated leaves) or Milkweed (the white sap).

Magenta

Patricia Kaminski suggests that the basic vital force of the aura is magenta in color, and that therefore magenta flowers are energizing to lack of basic vital force. An example here would be Fireweed. "Magenta combines qualities of red and purple and unites the color circle in the reverse direction of green. Magenta flowers stimulate the soul's consciousness for the etheric world" (1998, color plate after p. 58). She classifies Self-heal as magenta and therefore enhancing awareness of the etheric body. The important point here is to understand that magenta is a color that is a mix of red and purple, hence mixing the qualities of those two, as well as bringing together the root and crown chakra qualities—the two chakras connecting us to heavens and Earth, thus playing a major role in life embodied on this planet. Magenta being the complementary color to grass-green we can only understand in the light of the relationships of colors with their complementary colors—Rudolf Steiner taught that, when exposed to one color, one's soul responds by giving rise to the complementary color. Likewise, the afterimage in our retina would be of the complementary color, or also the negative of a photo would show that. Therefore, magenta has an intimate link to grass-green, the very color of lush nature connected to the etheric forces in plants according to Anthroposophy. I would like to point out that red being the color of the lowest, and violet also being considered the color of the highest chakra along with white, the mix of these two in magenta makes it a color of integration of highest and lowest, of Earth and cosmos.

Dirty Colors

Dirty colors that look mottled, ominous or dark can point to toxic plants, as is the case for many blossoms in the Nightshade family.

MULTICOLORED FLOWERS

Many flowers have more than one color. In this case, we would consider the combination of colors as a combination of attributes. We can also look for a progression of color in the lifespan of a flower as in our above-mentioned example of Borage (evolving from pink to blue—tenderness of the heart yielding to calm spaciousness), or consider which color is above, which below—are they in rainbow order or reversed? If in rainbow order, from dense to light, then the flower helps to overcome the material and become more in-spirited, if from more light to dense, then it brings us down into matter, into physical existence. An example here would be Shooting Star, in which a pink with a lavender hue is on top (spiritual), followed by a golden ring (middle/heart), and tipped black at the bottom (root chakra, matter). Thus, it helps those who do not want to be here in an earthly existence (Kaminski and Katz 1996, p. 377). A different Shooting Star follows the same pattern: above is white (spiritual, highest), then a yellow ring (middle), tipped brown red (root chakra, matter). The color order here also follows the form gesture of the plant which comes down like a shooting star.

Another wonderful example is that of Toad Lily. This small shade plant has flowers that are white with golden and purple spots. These three colors have of old been considered the most spiritual of colors. However, viewed from a distance, they blur into a dirty brown. Thus Toad Lily is the flower essence to purify the low and "dirty" emotions, to transform them into a more spiritual attitude.

Shooting Star

Compostiae flowers of course have their colors displayed as concentric rings, so the question here is what's at the center, what's at the periphery. A famous example is that of Black-Eyed Susan, where the sunny yellow petals ring around a velvety black center: This is the flower essence of becoming aware of the shadows of the soul, our blind spots, surrounding them with the light and joy of awareness and acceptance.

Spotted Flowers

The mottlings of the blossoms of the Foxglove and the Cowslip, like the spots on the butterfly wings and on the tails of peacocks and pheasants, were said to mark where the elves had placed their fingers, and one legend ran that the marks on the Foxglove were a warning sign of the baneful juices secreted by the plant, which in Ireland gain it the popular name of "Dead Man's Thimbles." (Grieve 1982, p. 323)

Spots seem to be a pattern more akin to animal life. Tiger Lily and Foxglove are not surprisingly named after animals. Tiger Lily is the Lily of the wildest temperament (see the mental indication of flower essence and homeopathy), and Foxglove is even toxic (see the relationship about

Foxglove

animal characteristics in plants and poisons below). Orchids are the botanical family maybe closest to animal life of all by way of their bonds with their pollinating insects.

The colors might also indicate the *range of action* within the chakra system: a red and white flower might cover the range from the root chakra to the crown (Asian Lily), a yellow and red one act on the lower three chakras (Aloe Vera).

Goethe's Theory of Color

The German poet and natural scientist Goethe did a lot of research on colors, working with prisms and watching how the light divides into the rainbow colors as they pass through them. In his work *Theory of Color*, he writes about the psychological effects of color and their relationship to light and dark. He noticed that when going toward the light or dawn, the colors of red/orange/yellow appear, while going into the dark or dusk, green/blue/purple prevails when watching sunrises and sunsets on freshly fallen snow. He talks about the joys and sufferings of color in this context. We may note that the joyful colors of yellow, orange and red are *yang* colors, while the suffering ones of green, blue and purple and considered *yin*. Thus according to Goethe, the former colors convey joy, while the latter are more the colors of sadness and gloominess.

The Color Correspondence between Body and Plant Tissue

As mentioned above, there is a strong and direct correspondence between the color of the human or animal and plant tissue—the color in the plant indicates a healing herb for the corresponding condition:

> *red* points to blood, inflammation and heat in the tissue;
> *blue* to coldness and air / lack thereof as in cyanosis, as well as the nerves associated with air in *Ayruveda*;
> *yellow* to liver and bile as well as the solar plexus;
> *purple* to stagnation and toxicity, even beginning necrosis;
> *orange* to liver and bile as well as sexual fire;
> *yellow-black* to stagnant bile;
> *white* to pallor or bone, teeth and nerves;
> *black* to necrosis and tissue death;
> *blue-grey* complexion calls for Sage, the leaves of which are blue grey.

Colors of Fruits, Roots, and the Plant in General

Red

"If roses were red, then to the Chippewa medicine man red signified the bloodstream; the reddish flowers and fruits (hips) of the herb were to be consumed as a food and as a tea. A weak infusion of the flowers helped greatly to soothe irritated or bloodshot eyes. Other eclectic practitioners placed thin scrapings or a powder of the stem within the wound and bandaged it, with the amazing result that there seldom remain even the least trace of a scar. Various species of roses possess decidedly antibiotic as well as astringent properties" (Harris 1985, p. 32). "The reddish fruits of Bearberry, Mulberry, Strawberry, Hawthorn, and Squaw Vine indicate these herbs in diseases of the blood" (ibid., p. 43). The Cherokee also took red to be a signature for blood (David Winston). Rose-petal water is also the Ayurvedic mainstay for inflammation, inflamed eyes, and other hot, red (excess *pitta*, or fire) tissue conditions. Cayenne pepper calms fevers by causing the person to break into a sweat, and heats the skin as a counterirritant for rheumatic or arthritic pains. Cayenne is an excellent circulatory remedy, pointing further toward the theme of heat, inflammation, blood, circulation, and heart of the color red.

In macrobiotic diet, it is thought that any red food is good against the common cold. So red here is seen as the universal warm color. We find that a number of red fruits are indeed classic for curing colds or throat aches—Rose hips (sour and sweet), Pomegranate (sweet, sour, astringent), Red Vine (a common home remedy for colds in the French countryside—I will admit that I am not sure how much of the efficiency is the heating effect of the alcohol and its disinfectant action!), and Elderberry juice (dark red). Red Root is useful for thinning the blood, as is the red Madder root, as well as for slow coagulation and thick, viscous blood or sluggish portal circulation (Wood 2009, p. 104ff). Another example is the use of leaves of red Grapes as a circulatory remedy in France. The leaves of green Grapevine is never used. And it is red wine that has the protective effect on the coronary vessels.

See under yellow for Coles' distinction between red and yellow.

Purple

"Purple, indigo, lavender, and purple-red usually indicate low-grade, septic, toxic heat and fever. When the stalk is red or purple-red we often have a plant which will pull out toxic heat" (Wood, 1997 p. 26). Purple-red is magenta. He gives Burdock, Gravelroot, and Echinacea as examples.

> Plants with purple or blue flowers have been considered good for improving the complexion of the skin. Joe-Pye, Red Clover, Verbena, Burdock, Gentian, and Chicory are good examples and, though generally categorized as blood purifiers, are also suitable remedies for a pathological condition known as cyanosis. This is a blueness or purplish lividness of

the skin's surface arising from a deficient oxygenation (respiratory-blood malfunction) which causes an impaired arterial flow of the blood stream. (Harris 1985, p. 44)

Blue

Blueberries, blue being cooling, are quite refrigerant—the present Dalai Lama of Tibet, having included them into His daily diet to strengthen His eyesight, fell seriously ill as an effect of them having too much diminished His digestive fire. Eating a bowl of blueberries on a hot summer day will leave you with a cold stomach, indeed! So how would it strengthen the eyesight? The crushed berries are also deep red, hence strengthening to the capillaries. Wood says that "blue cools fever" (1992, p. 20).

Blueberries look like blue eyes and strengthen the eyesight (photo by Sandra Lory).

Yellow

As for flowers, yellow points to the solar plexus and liver/gallbladder. Harris names Mandrake or Lemons as yellow fruits with a healing action for jaundice or the liver. In Traditional Chinese Medicine, yellow rice wine might be used to guide the effect of other herbs to the liver. Papaya heals the liver and aids digestion. Herbalist David Winston confirms the same understanding of yellow for the Cherokee, and adds that **yellow-black**

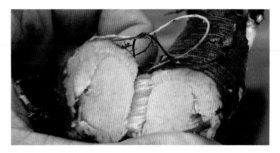

Yellow Dock root (photo by Sandra Lory)

points to symptoms such as headaches and migraine, dark circles under the eyes, general biliousness, and jaundice in Cherokee medicine—quite similar to the ancient Greek concept of *melancholia,* meaning "black bile."

William Coles distinguishes as follows: "The reddish and yellowish color of the inside of the roots of divers *Docks,* do signify that they are good for *hot Livers,* and the *Jaundise;* the red that is in them representing the *Liver,* and the yellow, the *Jaundise"* (1657, p. 286).

This is also true for roots. Orange sweet potatoes are said to strengthen the digestion also by way of their color in the Caribbean. Carrot juice detoxifies the liver. The intensely yellow roots of Goldenseal and Oregon-Grape are among the best liver remedies available. Even the heartwood of Quassia, so valuable as a liver remedy, is yellow.

Peach

Ripe peaches are of course peach-colored. They are soft, and covered with soft down like a baby's skin. They are a well-reputed remedy for all kinds of skin ailments. Ancient Chinese texts describe perfect beauty in a woman as her having cheeks like peaches. Apricots, so similar in looks, have similar properties. (Wood, 2008, p. 406).

Black

In Western herbalism, the color black is associated with putrefaction and necrosis, a tissue state in which the tissue turns black. This can be treated by alteratives such as Black Elder. "Wild Indigo has beautiful green leaves and pods, which on ripening or injury turn completely black. This plant is for necrosis, gangrene, typhoid, putrid deterioration" (Wood, 1997, p. 26). Black and blue are the colors that are associated with water and the kidneys in the Chinese five-element model. Black beans can be added to a formula to guide the effect of another herb to the kidneys.

White

White, especially of roots, may point to bone healing (Wild Yams, Solomon's Seal, Comfrey, Black Cohosh—for the latter two it is the inside of the root that is white), and Boneset and Black Cohosh with white flowers (Wood, 1997, p. 26). Similarly, the Haitian bonesetter and herbalist Oliama Derivière uses a chalky longish root that forms ropy strings when ground into a poultice for bone and tendon healing.

COLORS IN THE GREEN PLANT PARTS

Green plant parts are the stem and the leaves, and they are not always green. Sometimes, the leaves close to the flower take on colors and start to look like petals. In this case, we can speak of a flowering process that has descended into the green part of the plant. An example would be Dogwood flowers. Dogwood flower essence does not have an emotional effect so much as it does a physical; it helps to overcome energetic blocks in the limbs from having been beaten (Kaminski and Katz 1996, p. 310f), in that sense acting on the physical more than the emotional represented by a true flower.

When those green plant parts become woody, they mineralize and in a way become like the earth, they "earthify." In so doing, we should not be surprised to find that they don earth colors: the browns, greys, and blacks.

They may be tinged **red**, especially if other plant parts are red. This may indicate a degree of warmth. Traditionally, it was seen as a signature of the medicinal effect pertaining to the blood. How so depends on the shade of red. Peach leaves turn a light scarlet red, and peach leaf is a wonderful remedy in heat afflictions if the person shows this hue on tongue, lips, cheeks or ears. I once had to treat a desperate case of chronic nightly fevers, ongoing for almost two months. After several other herbal doctors failed, I noticed that the man had cherry red tongue and lips. I gave him Wild Cherry bark, a wonderful heat-reducing remedy, and the fever was promptly cured. This taught me that it is not naïve to use one's artistic sense of matching the shades in the plant to the shades of the tissues. If the stem is tinged pure red, "there may be a relationship to the blood and the heart: Blood Root (congestion of blood to the head, migraine, menstrual problems), red-stemmed Melilot (congestion of blood), Red Clover (mildly thins the blood), St. John's Wort (nutritive, blood building), Raspberry (nutritive), Hawthorn berry (heart)" (Wood 1997, p. 26). Derivière showed me a Haitian plant, with red stem and leaf veins, as one of his hemorrhage remedies. Herbalist and acupuncturist Peter Schell points out a captivating image: Spreading Dogbane, a slightly toxic plant that treats arrhythmia of the heart, has very rhythmical leaves held together by a red stalk—image of regular heart beats held together by the arteries flowing through them.

When it is **purplish**, this may indicate necrosis or blood poisoning. *Echinacea purpurea*, aptly named after this hue, is the Native American medicine for sepsis and necrosis such as of snakebites. *Eupatorium purpureum,* Gravelroot or Joe Pye Weed, has been of greatest service in septic conditions, and are indicated by purplish discoloration of the tissue (Wood 2009, p. 153). These medicinal actions were confirmed in the homeopathic provings. Red-stemmed with purplish blackish berries that look very glandular, Poke is specifically suitable for toxic stagnation and pussiness in the glandular system. Garlic, tinged purple throughout and sporting a dirty purple flower, is another example for a plant antibiotic of the highest quality, with great antiseptic abilities on top of that. In general, there is a steady spectrum from orange via scarlet and crimson red into purple to black meaning increasing heat turning into sepsis and finally necrosis. This thought of increasing shades of red standing for increasing levels of inner heat is also found in Chinese tongue diagnosis.

Hawkweed (*Hieracium venosum*), also called Rattlesnake Weed, bears purplish-red veins that mark the leaves with a pattern resembling that of a rattlesnake. In Cherokee medicine, the purple veins are seen as a signature for various veins and hemorrhoids (David Winston).

Poke

It is a traditional Native American snakebite remedy against snake poisons causing the kind of heat and sepsis with necrosis this color indicates. A similar reasoning applies to Lion's Foot, also called Rattlesnake Root (*Prenanthes alba*), where the purple markings occur on the stem (Harris 1985, pp. 107ff and 123). Wood says that when the plant's stalk is purple or purple-red "we often have a plant which will pull out toxic heat, detoxifying the interior, perhaps working through the portal vein and often on the liver: Dandelion, Burdock, Gravelroot, Plantain, Wild Indigo, Echinacea" (1997, p. 26).

Some plants are **variegated**, a term that means that there are whitish patterns on the green leaves. This is true of Milk Thistle, and the white pattern has been seen as a signature for milk. Milk Thistle does indeed increase the breast milk supply. Legend has it that Mother Mary spilled some of her breast milk onto the leaves, causing the plant to have these health benefits. I am not aware of a general meaning of this variegation, and a lot of them are artificially induced by horticulturists.

The color of the ***latex***, the milky juice, can vary. Red milk sap as in Bloodroot stands for its ability to rule the motion of the blood and other diseases arising from the blood, such as cancer; yellow milk sap as in Celandine stands for its liver and jaundice curative properties; white milk sap is usually cooling to the liver such as in Dandelion and Chicory. Latex is often rich in protein-digesting enzymes, and thus useful for "digesting" warts if applied locally— the latex of Celandine, Dandelion and Milkweed (described as having a "warty" seedpod) have a reputation thereof. This protein-digesting ability is another characteristic that points to latex being a signature of strong astrality, or closeness to animal life; it is animals that mainly consist of proteins, not plants, and it is carnivores that need to digest it more than anyone else! Pelikan (1958, p. 111ff) gives a cosmological explanation of the latex being a remnant of a long bygone cosmic developmental stage in which it was part of a nutritive outer atmosphere as it were. Thus, it is not surprising that it looks like milk and is called thus, the association with the nurturing liquid even carried forth into the name *Milk*weed. As a flower essence, Milkweed is for people who lack ego strength and regress in their development, and who tend to have opiate addictions. Lion's Foot (*Prenanthes alba*) has white latex and was used not only as a lactogenic remedy by the Native Americans, but also for white vaginal discharge (Foster and Duke 1990 p. 80; Harris 1985, p. 122f). Opiates are, of course, found in Poppy "milk."

According to Rudolf Steiner, during primordial cosmic times, human beings had more of a dream-like consciousness. It is therefore not surprising that latex is associated with sleep and dream states; Poppies have long been used to induce sleep (Corn Poppy, Opium Poppy, California Poppy). From another plant family, all Wild Lettuce varieties are also powerful sedatives. Both also can cause hallucinations, a state of exaggerated dream life. Matthew Wood called Celandine "the controller of the bile" and Bloodroot "the controller of blood." Having witnessed the healing powers of Celandine in deadly nausea and headache due to blocked flow of bile, or of a blinding migraine with Bloodroot, one comes to appreciate those truths. Cherokee medicine men and women recommended Bloodroot to promote menstruation, having observed its red sap oozing out of the plant (Harris 1985, p. 71).

Leaves marked by a spot such as in Lady's Thumb, a tongue-shaped leaf with a reddish sopt (thumb mark) at its center, has been found to be the signature for a tongue with a red or black spot at the center, often denoting unresolved heat at the center of the organism (Lise Wolff). Harris sees the spots on some of the Knotweed leaves as a signature for a remedy for skin eruptions, ulcers, gangrene, and so on. (Harris 1985, p. 141f). Oswald Kroll thought that Waterpepper (*Polygonum hydropiper*) heals wounds by signature, taking the reddish spot on their leaves as the sign for the wound, felon, or bruises or other marks on the skin (Coles 1657, p. 613). **Spotted leaves** such as found in some Orchids can be a signature pointing to a strong "astrality" of the plant, as the followers of Steiner would say, pointing to an animal-like characteristic of the plant. Coles notes of Pimpernel that the spots on the backside of the leaves are the signature for the bite of a mad dog, snake or scorpion bites (ibid., p. 625).

Evergreen plants have always been regarded as special to the peoples of the temperate climates. If we imagine ourselves in Europe a thousand years ago in the depth of winter, with maybe some snow on the ground, we will see how in that age before the advent of chemical color, everything was pale, brown-grey-yellowish-light green. Europe originally covered in deciduous trees for the most part was also stripped barren in that season. So, to walk in the forest and encounter something like a Holly Tree with lush glossy-green leaves and bright-red berries was something very unusual. No wonder that this mysterious ability of the tree to hold on to its leaves even, in the frost, caused it to be associated with immortality. All European evergreens—Holly, conifers, Ivy, Mistletoe and Periwinkle—have this connotation. They defy seasonal change, do not "die" in winter, nor are they reborn in spring.

Plants without Chlorophyll are white (Indian Pipe), pale, sometimes yellowish or orangy (Dodder) or taking other shades. They are always parasites, since a plant cannot live without chlorophyll. Refer to the section on *parasites* for more details on how this makes them medicinal for parasitic illnesses such as cancer.

Warm and Cool Colors

As we have seen in the section on the psychological and symbolical meanings of colors, we experience red as warm and blue as cool. Accordingly, speaking scientifically, infrared rays are warming whereas blue rays much less so. We can see an echo of this is the plant world. I have often noticed that, if there are spring flowers of the same kind but varied colors, in cold weather the ones with the warmer colors open before those with the cooler colors. It is as if they carried more internal warmth.

Similarly, White Peony is classified as less warming than **Red** Peony in Traditional Chinese Medicine. In northern Europe, Red Cabbage is traditionally cooked with warming spices, such as fried onions and cloves, into a warming winter dish, while pale Green Cabbage is allowed to ferment into cooling sauerkraut. It is unthinkable, as though forbidden by law, that someone would make Red Cabbage into sauerkraut or cook a Green Cabbage with the same warming spices; it's counter-intuitive. Red Onions are preferred in herbalism, since they are more pungent than their yellow cousins. Pungency is a fire and heat signature; thus, they are therapeutic for the first stage of acute colds and hay fever with sneezing, red-hot inflammation, and fever. Apart from that, they fire up the metabolism.

The bright **blue** Cornflower and Bachelor's Button were used in Europe as an eye remedy, especially for people with blue eyes. Since blue eyes tend to be more fragile and more easily inflamed, it makes sense that these blue flowers were used for hot, inflamed conditions and to sedate heat such as in conjunctivitis, insomnia, and rheumatism. For more examples of blue, see the paragraph below.

THE COLORS OF DRIED HERBS, TEAS, AND TINCTURES

It has been said that using the color of an herbal product in a processed stage is not a characteristic that can be counted as a signature. That is wrong. While Saint John's Wort releases a pale-red sap when a leaf is ripped off (blood and wound healing signature), the tea, tincture, oil and salve are equally pale or bright red, and that's a signature. The root of the Wild Yam, used by the Maya women for gynecological issues, is bright orange, yielding a bright red tincture. This is taken as a signature for blood. The Wild Yam is used for uterine and heart disorders (Kimberly Hart).

Some colors appear only in the preparation. During the process of extraction, Chamomile tea and tincture have a fleeting phase of a vivid, light blue hue, owing to its azulene content being extracted. Blue is a signature for a cooling herb, and azulene is anti-inflammatory. It is also only in the extract of the green parts of Horse Chestnut that we can find the blue fluorescent aesculin. This substance reflects ultraviolet light. It's cool hue illustrates the cooling properties of the tree, and explains why Horse Chestnut trees can be worked into a sun lotion. (The seeds do not contain aesculin, and are warming.) There is a French saying: "Do not sleep under a Chestnut tree lest you catch cold."

China has had an herb delivery and processing system in place for at least a thousand years, so a significant amount of the signatures are about describing an already-dried or processed plant. Five colors are assigned according to the Chinese five-element theory. For instance, the primary functions of *gan cao,* Licorice root, begin with the heart and the spleen; accordingly, the outer bark is reddish (heart) and the inner wood is yellow (spleen). Licorice root also effects all twelve channels, but most of those functions can be explained as radiating out from the central position of the heart and spleen/stomach. This is describing a sliced dried herb, not a living plant, but it is a signature.

CHAPTER EIGHT

SHAPES

The topic of a plant's outer form is probably discussed most within the area of the doctrine of signature. In this chapter, we will look at the outer shapes of plants. The physical shapes of plants are a result of energetic patterns giving rise to those forms. Since it takes time for those shapes to manifest, we will also consider the time of day of blooming and the development of the shape over the plant's lifetime. The shape of the plant is the primary focus in most of this chapter. The influence of the elements on the shapes will be discussed in detail in "The Elements and the Environment" (chapter 10), followed by considerations of environmental and seasonal influences on the signatures. "Organ and Physiological Signatures" is the subject of chapter 12. In "The Energetic Signature" (chapter 15), we will discuss the energetic aspect of the signature and plant shapes in greater detail. So the consideration of form as it pertains to the doctrine of signature will stay with us throughout the remainder of this book, though the chapter titles might not contain the word *shape*.

There are four basic plant parts—root, leaves, flower, and fruit or seed—and a few basic energetic gestures in plant signature. They are ascending, descending, expanding, or contracting. They can occur in combination, such as ascending and expanding, or descending and contracting. They can even be combined between the pairs of opposite: ascending and descending (lengthening); or ascending, then descending; or simultaneously ascending and descending while contracting—giving rise to a long vertical axis. Whenever the movements occur successively in time, they form what I call the "dance" of the plant in time. (See also the section "The Dance of Plants as They Unfold in Time," beginning on page 181.)

The shapes of the flowers, roots, and leaves interact with one another in a kind of dialogue fashion, negotiating between themselves the main signature. Each detail is a signature, but when considered as a whole plant, a larger picture emerges in which some of these might be drowned out.

Basic Plant Shapes

In considering plant shapes, we might look at how they unfold in time. They all start from a seed, a tiny roundish thing. So then, where do the formative forces take them from there? The sprout always stretches out in a polar fashion, sinking the root pole into the ground, and stretching the leaf pole toward the light. However, the force is not the same in different plants. If we were to draw the main forces at work in the form of vectors, we could come up with something like an upward or downward pointing arrow. For those who are familiar with the *vayus* or pranic winds in *Ayurveda,* this indicates on which of them the plant will have a medicinal effect:

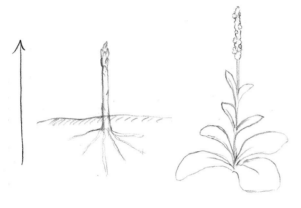

Asparagus (left) and Mullein

A simple upward-pointing arrow would represent Asparagus, especially in the sprouting stage. It has a soft tangle of underground roots that give rise to a much larger perpendicular upright sprout that sports no leaf. Other plants with a very strong and clear upright energy are Mullein and Sunflower (while still growing higher), or Hollyhock.

Other plants grow along a vertical line with vectors pointing up *and* down: Thistle and other upright plants with tap roots such as Teasel represent this kind of formative force. These plants growing strongly along the vertical line have a *yang signature* (see section below) and reinforce our *yang* qualities, such as our uprightness or spinal alignment or integrity as in the sense of honesty. The downward vector reinforces our stance, or groundedness. I like to say that Thistle is the best-defended plant, even taking a "warrior" stance: Don't mess with me or I will spike you with my spines!

In other plants, the vectors go mainly up or down, fanning out as they do. Blue Vervain plants grow up and outward; they are one of the finest herbs for dealing with *up*-tightness, an overly tense mental, emotional, or physical state of being that holds all of one's tension in the upper part of the body. It exemplifies too much energy flowing upward.

Other plants spread out immensely underground in a way that one would not expect looking at the above-ground plant part. Turkey Rhubarb is a prime example; it has huge roots that burrow deep into the soil. The dried roots release our blocked downward flow of energy that lead to troubles such as constipation, powerfully moving things downward and out of us. Ayurveda calls this downward energetic flow in the body *apana vayu*.

A mixed example would be Carrot or Parsnip, wild or domesticated, which grow straight down with their tap roots and fan out above with their leaves: They exemplify drawing the air element— so well embraced by the feathery leaves (see "The Elemental Signatures" beginning on page 215)— down into the soil, giving rise to aromatic, aerating and aerated (containing air pockets) roots. They help to aerate various tissues of the body.

Some plants hold a middle position (the vectors concentrate in the middle); for example, we could name Celandine, with its small roots and flowers, and abundant foliage; it is organ-specific to two organs in the middle of our body: the liver and the gallbladder.

We begin to get a feeling that the healing effect in the body follows the energetic pattern of the formative forces that created the plant: **it will move the energy within us up, down, or to the middle according to its own form.**

The next kind of basic consideration is to ask whether the shape expands or contracts. It was Goethe in his natural scientific works who

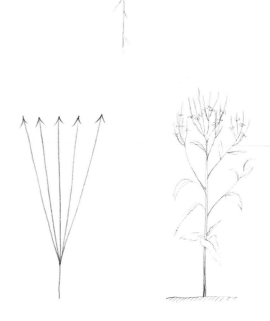

Thistle (above) and Blue Vervain (below)

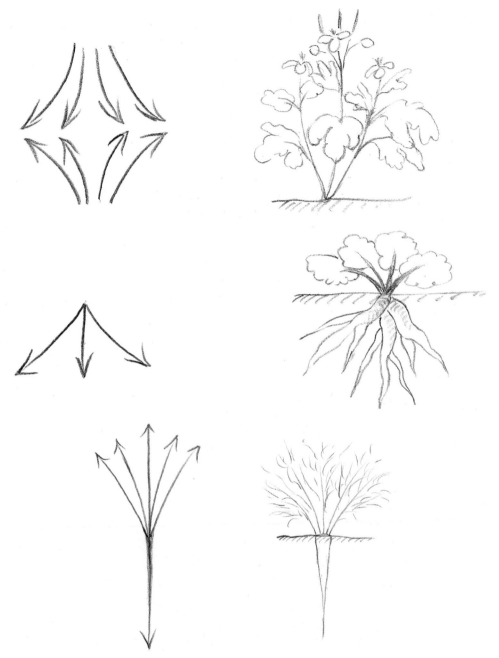

Top to bottom: Celandine, Turkey Rhubarb, and Carrot

first explored botany in this light. Plants in their life cycle expand upon germination, contract into a flower bud, expand in the flower, contract into pollen, expand in the fruit, to contract into a seed—and the whole cycle continues. So we can detect expanding vectors in an expansive flower such as a Hibiscus or Lily, and contracting forces in the bud or seed formation. A generally contracted plant would be Yucca, with its narrow, blade-like leaves and long, thin stem. A generally expansive plant would be Rhododendron bushes or Fig trees, which explode equally in all directions, or uncontainable Wild Blackberry canes crawling in all directions, as desperate gardeners can attest. Blackberry flower essences bring energy, awareness, and willpower back into the limbs (Kaminski and Katz 1996).

Yet another kind of basic shape is that of rhythmically structured plants. The leaves and flowers occur rhythmically patterned along the main stem, alternating between expansion and contraction. Pelikan (1982, p. 171ff) points to this as a signature for plants of our rhythmical system, the heart and lungs. This play of forces between expansion and contraction is akin to systole and diastole, and inhalation and exhalation. We may think of Foxglove, Mullein, and Lily of the Valley, to name just a few.

Sometimes the rhythmical change occurs over time. We find this pattern quite often in **biennials** such as Evening Primrose, or the above-mentioned Foxglove and Mullein, adding to their rhythm signature. These plants form a dense basal rosette the first year. The second year, they suddenly push upward to make towering, long plants that one could never have expected looking at the low growth of the previous year, after which they dry off and die. So here, we find a two-year-rhythm.

Foxglove (top); Mullein (center); and Lily of the Valley

The Shapes of Flowers

If we continue to ponder the forces at work in the shaping of a plant and look at its flowers, we will see more complex patterns than discussed above, with all kinds of combinations of upward, downward, expanding and contracting forces. The shape might fortify, neutralize, or override the meaning of the color in a flower or plant. Shapes evolve from simple to increasingly more complex. The ground-breaking work about flower shapes was done by Wilhelm Pelikan,

This plant family (Papilionaceae, or Butterfly Plants) is exemplified by the Sweet Pea. Its flowers look like butterflies. The flower essence is for the fugitive souls of people who do not feel at home on Earth (Kaminski and Katz) and have difficulty incarnating properly in life. The roots of the plants bind nitrogen to the soil, making it a fertile place to live for all creatures.

and taken up for flower essences by Kaminski in *Flowers that Heal*. In the realm of flower essences, it appears to me that simple flowers also address more simple emotional problems, while the more deeply invaginated and complex, animal-like the flower becomes, the more entrenched and complex the emotional block. Let's start with the shapes of flowers. Considering the most basic shape, it is the ***star shape***.

Star shapes are simple and open, radiating to all sides. They denote openness and a cosmic connection, "lifting our consciousness upward," being themselves images of the stars on Earth (Kaminski 1998; photo inserts after p. 122). In energetic terms, the energy radiates out equally from the center. When the star shape makes a chalice, we have cup-shaped flowers.

Cup-shaped flowers form a receptacle and talk about containing our energy, as well as being receptive, receiving, and maybe being received. When the cup becomes deeper, it becomes a ***trumpet***.

Trumpets give out sound, and trumpet shapes talk about releasing energy to the outside. When they droop down, they can be a ***hanging trumpet***, releasing energy

Above, Mullein during its first year;
right, during the second year

Star of Bethlehem

downward, or close up to make a **bell shape.** See also the Lily of the Valley flower.

While trumpets denote openness, bells can stand for withholding. There is, however, a blurred line between bell and trumpet shapes. My definition is as follows: if the funnel is continually widening, it is a trumpet. If the funnel stays more parallel for the most part as in Bluebells, it's a bell. Bells toll and give off sound as do trumpets; thus, they can represent openness and release. Bell-shaped flowers can retain energy if the entrance is somewhat closed, such as in Grape Hyacinth or Lily of the Valley. Hanging bells such as in Bell Heather can at the same time stimulate energetic flow downward and prevent it from leaking out toward the earth.

Retroflexed petals in any of those shapes mean an exaggerated openness (Tiger Lily). In some of these cases, the **petals fuse** to make the funnel shape, denoting union

Shapes, top to bottom:
cup, trumpet, and hanging trumpet

Lily trumpet

or fusion. Or, to the contrary, the petals can be next to nonexistent, and the stamens form airy **tufts,** which stand for sensitivity.

The *Compositae* family of Sunflower and Daisy holds a special place. One could simply say that they hold a **center surrounded by a periphery** and thus talk about how our center is surrounded by our aura or about how our core personality connects to the world. *Compositae* flowers are named such because they are, in fact, composed of a multitude of single flowers which form the center. In that sense, they are highly structured groups of flowers. They denote the parts of the whole, the subparts of ourselves, taking their rightful place in the whole. Teasel and Scabiosa similarly group their flowers into heads, but do not have a circle of petals surrounding them. They do then have the organization of the parts into a whole, although geometrically it is less perfect of a mandala pattern than in the *Compositae.* Essence of the sunny Chamomile flower bestows a sense sunny disposition. Wood dubs Calendula "herbal sunshine," and both of these radiant, sun-like *Compositae* bring on a sense of inner centeredness and joy, a sunny mood. However, they make **flower heads,** a

Daisy (left); Compositae family

Top to bottom: bell shape; retroflexed petals; Silktree

signature for energy grouping into a head, and therefore the healing properties go to the head (see below under *grouped flowers* for more details). This ends the variations of open flowers, and before we venture into more complex shapes, let us look a little closer.

Borage (above) and Daffodil

One of the most basic questions is: **Which way is the flower oriented?** Does it look to the sky? Heavenward? Does it have a cosmic orientation, or does it look downward, earthward, to the ground? Maybe it looks sideward, horizontally, like we humans do? This orientation speaks of the basic direction into which the healing properties go. Borage, for instance, is a *star-shaped* flower which opens sideward but, within an hour or two, turns downward. It is a flower for being downcast, heavy-hearted and depressed. Feeling star-like, radiating and wide like the sky is the healing potential to which Borage takes us. Stars are simple and open, there is no place for hiding anything. The Star of Bethlehem plant is very simple and straightforward, as a flower as well as in its healing properties: it brings us back present into our bodies once we have joined the cosmic realms on a sojourn as a space cadet, having been shocked out of our body by trauma. An example for *cup-shaped* flowers are Tulips or Mariposa Lilies. They act on our sense of containedness, a motherly or *yin* quality. A classic *trumpet shape* is that of Trumpet Vine, a flower essence that helps people who have speech impediments and stammer. A hanging trumpet would be Angel's Trumpet, helping the soul to be released from its physical bondage at death. Looking at a combination, Daffodils (Narcissus) have a star shape with a trumpet. They stand for putting ourselves out radiant as a star to our fellow humans (horizontal orientation means face to face), while proclaiming what we have to proclaim. The trumpet also looking like an old-fashioned hearing aid; it helps communication in general. Daffodil flower essence facilitates people to become public speakers, helping them to feel that they are understood by the audience. Many **bell shapes** have to do with the infusion of the soul into the body, the process of incarnation: Blueberry, Bell Heather, Manzanita (all from the same botanical family), as well as Solomon's Seal and Lily of the Valley. They are hanging straight down, the opening facing the earth. Bluebells, facing horizontally, do not have this effect, but rather one of opening to the world. Bells can also denote a sense of enclosing something—in Lily of the Valley, the tiny white hanging bells enclose the sweetest of smells possible.

It is the flower essence for the refined, noble and sweet emotions of the heart. The cups, trumpets and bells can open by way of strongly **retroflexed petals**, meaning a strong sense of opening and openness: Tiger Lily, while maintaining the relationship to the earth as per the drooping flowers (hence invaluable in uterine prolapse), is also the flower essence for very outgoing people, lively people. While the petals of Tiger Lily stay separated in their retroflection, and the flower being about individuation, Bluebell or Lily of the Valley bells

Tiger Lily

are shaped by way of **fusion of the petals**. They point to a sense of all-oneness, which goes to the third eye chakra for Bluebell since it is violet (sense of abundance and oneness with the universe), and sense of oneness in love going to the heart for Lily of the Valley. Gentian has bells with fused petals that may even point heavenward, and thus purple (spiritual) Gentian as a flower essence bestows spiritual hope and belief. We can say that retroflexed petals make for the most extroverted, closed bells for the most introverted flowers.

Flowers that shape **tufts** such as St. John's Wort (a star with a tuft) point to nerve endings and sensitivity. St. John's Wort is one of the finest nervines available. All of its starry, sun-yellow flowers look up; they facilitate the prana flowing in through the crown. Silktree is used in a similar

St. John's Wort (photo by Sandra Lory)

vein. This flower probably best portrays "a bundle of nerves" in the plant kingdom. Its action, described by Traditional Chinese Medicine as being in the small energy channel, parallels the effect on the nerve endings, as we remember the correlation of the meridians and Ayurvedic energy channel concept to that of the physical nerves. As a flower essence, Silktree helps with over-sensitivity and "rawness." American Ginseng with its little flower tufts also calm nerves.

Within the Aster clan, the *Compositae* family, we find the theme of integrating the different parts of the self in their healing qualities. Possibly the most famous herb here is Arnica, helping us to come back together again when we are shattered by a psychological or physical trauma. Shasta Daisy flower essence aids "synthesizing ideas into a living wholeness" and Echinacea flower essence is appropriate when "feeling shattered by severe trauma" and bestows the ability to maintain "an integrated sense of Self" (Kaminski and Katz 1996).

It is remarkable that flowers take on asymmetrical shapes, mirror images along a vertical plane like animals, once they assume ***horizontal orientations*** like animals. Flowers that point up or down remain radially symmetrical (Grohmann 1989, p. 104).

Once we follow the flowers into even more complex forms, we come into the realm of ***invaginations***. Rudolf Steiner saw the plant as the primordially extroverted being, and the animal and human being as primordially introverted. He clarified this in two sketches. Anyone who has ever studied botany and zoology, and the blurred line between plant- and animal life, will immediately appreciate these sketches: while the plant in general opens up to the world with its first pair of cotyledons, or shortly thereafter the first pair of true leaves (left), animal life begins when the sea anemones form the first invaginations (middle), folding in on themselves to make the most primitive of stomachs. Plants open their leaves and flowers to the world; animals and humans close themselves off to form inner organs (right). Plants are completely extroverted; animals and humans introverted, giving birth to an "inner life."

This development is echoed in flowers. Once we move beyond the basic shapes, we find flowers with invaginations, even forming hollow inner spaces. Invaginations, inner spaces and closed off organs are something typical of the animal realm.

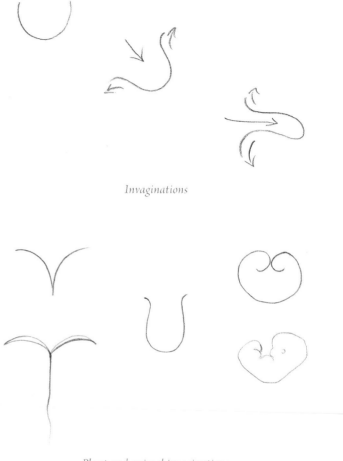

Invaginations

*Plant and animal invaginations
(after Rudolf Steiner's sketch)*

The axis of the flower transforms the direction of the sprout into the horizontal, and in doing so the *Labiatae* flower aims beyond the plant-like into that which is animal-like. That is so, because the horizontal is the form and movement orientation of animals. In the process, upper and lower lips protrude; throats, gorges are forming, counter forms to the insects, who frequent those blossoms. If one pours wax into these flowers, so is the cast form similar to the bee's head with stretched out proboscis [their tongue ready to take the nectar]. Stamen and pistil become organs that are mobile upon touch. The approaching insect is welcomed by the flower shape, enveloped, its movements even answered by a counter-movement that they cause like an echo of movement. A flow of sap of the plant streams forth toward the animal in the form of nectar, which flows the more they visit the flower. (Pelikan 1980, p. 46)

This elegant description of the Peppermint clan, or *Labiatae,* illustrates this point. Furthermore, the *Labiatae* are the plant family with the highest number of aromatic spice and healing plants high in warming essential oils of all botanical families. They are thus intimately related to mammals who have the ability to maintain a constant body temperature, as well as the insects who maintain warmth within their hive: the bees. This botanical family is very rich in nectar-rich bee plants that are called after their insect—*melissa* is Greek for "bee," and Melissa is, of course, a *Labiatae* much loved by the bees. Most of these herbs are healing to the digestion (the digestive fire requires warmth) and to coughs and colds—given the throat signature, and their innate warmth antidotes the cold. Sage is the most archetypal sore throat herb, and Hoarhound one of the most useful cough herbs. A more watery cousin, Self-heal, is a drawing agent, that is a healing plant that sucks poisons such as venom back out of the tissue—sucking like the "sucking doctor," a sub-profession among medicine men and women, would do with their lips and mouth

and throat....It was praised as the infallible remedy for mouth and throat by William Cole, and its German name *Bräune* means quinsy, as does Sage. Ground Ivy is for the neighboring invagination, healing middle ear infections. White Deadnettle remedies white vaginal discharge. Sweet Leaf (*Monarda fistulosa*) "has tubular flowers and is one of the greatest diaphoretics." In other words, it opens the pores (Wood 1997, p. 27).

Another big plant family with horizontal flowers is the Pea family (*Leguminosae*). They do not form a closed throat, but an open structure, within which the single petals enclose the air as if in pockets. Their main characteristic is their ability to enter into symbiosis with bacteria at root level which deliver the soil nitrate in organic form ready-to-use to them. If we realize that nitrate is the main ingredient in protein, and if there were to be a difference made between plants and animals, we would have to agree that plants are made up mainly out of carbohydrates, and animals out of proteins. The legumes make the seeds with

Throated Sage flowers, front and side views

the highest quality of plant protein, which earned them the

nickname "veggie meat." We think of soy, beans, peas, and lentils. They come even closer to this by way of being able to move their leaves and tendrils in a very animal-like fashion—*Mimosae,* for example, react to touch by folding their leaves. Such phenomena are otherwise observed far more often in the animal kingdom (Pelikan 1980, p. 302).

The *Scrofulariaceae* are also a plant family in which the flowers have sunk, following gravity to the horizontal orientation, and make mouth—and throat—like animal shapes. They do not share the warmth expressed in the pungency and essential oils found in the *Labiatae,* and in that sense do not come as close to the mammals as those.

Mullein has yellow star-shaped flowers, and it stands for the inner qualities of uprightness (as expressed in its tall growth) as well as honesty. The Mullein flower is oriented horizontally, looking us straight in the eye. The star shaped petals are fused at the center, forming a tiny invagination. The entire flower has a waxy look and can remind us of an ear; it is indeed one of the best remedies for earaches available. Another prime example is Snapdragon, which forms jaws so strong that, as a friend told me, as children they would trap flies inside the flower's "buccal cavity." As a flower essence, it is invaluable in treating TMJ, tooth grinding, and other jaw clenching tendencies. The tension held in the jaws extends to grouchiness and verbal aggression (Kaminski and Katz 1996, in the relevant sections), so I like to say that Snapdragon is for people who are "snappy" like dragons. The animal imagery in the name is also noteworthy.

Mullein flowers

The invaginations of the poisonous members of the Nightshade family are accompanied by strong, narcotic smells that are often unpleasant and animal-like, as well as dark, dirty, and spotted coloring.

Other examples of invaginations are Jack-in-the-Pulpit, a well-known throat remedy. *Impatiens* flowers are also invaginated, the entrance looking labia-like, and the color astoundingly like mammal mucosa. Herbally, it aids vaginal dryness. The outside of the flower looks like a *glans penis*, and the bud like an embryo. The seed pods are phallic and eject their seeds at the slightest touch;

Dr. Bach called, the flower essence for impatience, but the signature insists on premature ejaculation. Invaginations also cover the realm of sexuality. The flower of Thornapple looks like an ear tube, and it is for ear infections accompanied by obsessive thoughts (Wood 1997, p. 26). Wild Ginger flowers are deep red, uterine-shaped and a uterine remedy.

The invaginations can evolve toward **organ shapes**—for example hearts in Bleeding Heart, the flower essence for broken-heartedness; testicles in orchids, a sexual tonic; uterus-shaped Wild Ginger flower to aid in birth; and the throat shape of the many types of Sage, Thyme, the Bluebell Throatwort, and Tall Bellflower, denoting sore-throat remedies. The heart shape can also point to the hips (Gabrielle Simon); Bleeding Heart flower essence applied externally is one of the best remedies for sacroiliac pain and misalignment. The *Aristolochiacea* Contribo (*Aristolochia triloba*) of Central America has an odd, stomach-like flower, used traditionally for stomachache and gastric disorders by the Maya of Belize (Arvigo and Balick 1998, p. 83). Its temperate-zone cousin, Wild Ginger, also has stomach-shaped flowers, which are useful for a tense stomach and other problems of the stomach.

Certain Orchids have **moccasin-shaped** flowers, hence Moccasin Flower or Lady's Slippers. Paracelsus said that, if a remedy looks like a foot, it is a remedy for a foot. What does this mean in here? The foot represents a possibility of wandering, while the shoe represents protection for the foot (and for the wanderer). It also represents the idea of settling down. An old proverb says, "If the shoe fits, wear it." It is the flower for those who cannot figure out which one is the right

Bleeding Heart (above); Impatiens blossoms (center); and Contribo, or Aristolochia grandiflora (photo by Cynthia Thomas)

choice, especially with regard to partners and having children or not (Wood 1986, p. 114ff). In my experience, the flower essence helps to walk one's talk, as well as know whether the shoe fits: a friend ended her new extramarital affair after taking the essence—the new man was not right for her. Wood gives several case histories of Lady's Slipper flower essence healing foot pain (ibid.). He names it as the medicine for edema where the shoe does not fit right (1997, p. 27).

Coneflowers seem to form a suppurating ***boil-like protuberance***, the cone, in the center of their flower. Black-Eyed Susan (*Rudbeckia hirta*) and Purple Coneflower have always been used for skin diseases arising from the blood, especially in septic conditions such as boils and ulcers, as well as general sepsis. Black-Eyed Susan has been found to be a specific against *Staphylococcus aureus*, which causes nasty septic conditions and is golden yellow, like the flower (Harris 1985, p. 70). David Winston told me that Black-Eyed Susan, called fittingly *Deer Eye* in Cherokee, is used for Lyme disease in Cherokee medicine (see also below). The same logic applies to Burdock flowers (ibid., p. 74). Chamomile is so valuable as an anti-inflammatory that Chamomile lotion has even made it into modern day hospitals. Spilanthes is renowned as an anti-microbial. Harris calls Chamomile flowers head-shaped and relates that to their usefulness in headaches (ibid., p. 80).

Spilanthes (Paracress), a well-known remedy for dental abcesses; other useful cone flowers for abcesses and boils are Echinacea, Black-Eyed Susan, and Chamomile (photo by Sandra Lory)

A Black Eyed-Susan, showing the cone shape (photo by Sandra Lory)

Ring-like patterns are a signature for the circular bull's eye rash of Lyme disease, and found in Teasel inflorescences as well as Black-Eyed Susan. Culpeper recommends Teasel Root for "ring shaped skin fungi, even when these come from the French Pox [syphilis]" (Storl 2010, p. 167).

The **scaly pappus** of the seeds of *Scabiosa* corresponds to certain skin diseases where the skin comes off, like a certain kind of leprosy, dandruff, and so on, where the skin comes off in scales. *Scabiosa* comes from the Latin *scabere,* to scratch.

The *"everlasting" flowers* of some autumn blooming *Compositae* stir the string of eternity. First we find the asters with their very long blooming period—and by that I do not mean new flowers opening over a long time, but the same flower staying without withering for a long time. As a flower essence, they help accept the inevitable impermanence of life, hence loss. Tuning into the autumn as the life of plants draws to an end, Aster as well as Chrysanthemum essences teach us to accept death and to overcome fear of death (Chrysanthemum—FES). The latter hold the freshness of the flower well beyond the first frosts, as all other flowers have died. Last, we find the Everlastings. Sweet and Pearly Everlasting, as well as the other close botanical cousins such as Helichrysum hold on to "life" after death by remaining as beautiful dried flower heads that make them favorites for dried flower bouquets. Wood points out that the dried Sweet Everlasting flowers open and close with changes in weather, releasing their fragrance for a long time after they have died. He calls the plant by its Indian name *Rabbit Tobacco* and explains the signature "something like 'life' continues in rabbit tobacco after the death of the plant, so that it carries on a communication between the living and dead" (2005, p. 20). He gives examples to that effect, pointing out that sacred tobacco was always the Native American medium to enter into communication with the Creator. He calls it a plant that "walks the border of the world" (ibid., p. 19).

Drooping, nodding, or top-heavy flowers were seen as a signature for epilepsy. Examples of epilepsy remedies with this signature include Lily of the Valley, Wormwood (Harris 1985, 1985, under the mentioned plants), Peony, Passion Flower, and Gotu Kola. The nodding bells of Lily of the Valley have since antiquity been recognized as a signature for epilepsy. The Greeks believed that the disease was caused by "the drooping of the humors into the principal ventricles of the brain." Thus the drooping flowers of Lily of the Valley were much employed for this condition (ibid, p. 122). Coles explains, "It cureth *Apoplexy* by Signature; for as that disease is caused by the dropping of humors into the principall Ventricles of the brain: so the flowers of this Lilly hanging on the plants as if they were drops, are of wonderful use therein, if they be distilled with Wine.... Being drunk for fourty daies, it doth away the falling Sicknesse" (Coles 1657, p. 25). Top-heavy plants such as peonies, the big flower heads of which can literally fall to the ground, and also the heavy big buds of Passion Flower, and even more so its heavy fruits, are a signature for "falling disease," epilepsy. Anyone who has ever seen a person fall and crash their head to the ground in an epileptic fit will appreciate the image. It is interesting that since the dawn of time, Mistletoe has been used as a remedy for falling sickness; however, it is stated everywhere that under no circumstances should the cut branches

Lily of the Valley; buds starting to give in to gravity

be allowed to fall onto the ground during the harvest. The parasite hangs off of the branches of the host tree. "*Mistleto* of the Oak, and the *Bird-lime* that is made thereof, is very effectual for the curing of the Falling-Sickness, and it doth it by Signature: the viscosity and tenacious quality of the Bird-lime, representing those melancholy and phlegmatick humours, consisting of tough and clammy slime, by which it is caused" (Coles 1657, p. 27). This is a nice example of signature by correspondence of humours. Interestingly, the tiny flowers of the creeper Gotu Kola used in Ayurveda to combat epilepsy hang onto the ground. This becomes even more curious once one understands Gotu Kola to be an *Umbellifera*. They can also denote a strong downward flow of energy, and point to a prolapse, pregnancy or birth flower, as in the cases of Tiger Lily, *Trillium* (Wakerobin), Windflower, and Wild Ginger. They might point to uterine hemorrhage or profuse menstruation, as well as depression and sadness (they let their head hang down).

Finally, I would like to point to the **spurs and other bizarre structures** as in *Delphinium*, which look as if something were entering the flower. According to anthroposophic spiritual botany, plants consist only of a physical body, which is what's left when they die, and an etheric body, the basic life force that makes them grow and different from dead minerals. They do not have an astral body (somewhat equal to the aura with chakras), basis of feelings, such as animals and humans have. However, there is something called the *astral forces* of the plant. Unlike the aura-like body "inside" animals and humans, it remains a force "outside" the plant body as

Larkspur (Consolida)

such. It interacts, forms, and weaves *around* the plant. In some plants, it enters the plant somewhat forcefully. In the Larkspur (*Consolida*) and *Delphinium* families, for instance (both named after animals!), it creates the poisons. This forceful entering is visible in the spurs (see also Columbine, Monk's Hood, and so on). More on this process and poison formation can be found below in chapter 12.

The Number of Petals

The meaning of the number of petals follows the general meaning of numerology, which for the smaller numbers is agreed upon cross-culturally, since derived from observation of nature (see drawing).

one stands for oneness and union (few flowers have truly one petal, it is mostly the result of a fusion of several petals into one) and thus stands for union and fusion;

two for the division of the one into the primordial polarity, pairs and opposites;

three is the spiritual number denoting the higher union of the two polar opposites, and symbolic of the non-manifest divine, the divine principle of speech or thought, and the manifest divine; in *Trillium* and Lilies, three can stand for feminine sexually, as also in Lady's Slippers, which sports three petals arranged as a triangle above the "slippers." It can point to a gynecological remedy, as in Trillium and Wild Ginger.

four as illustrated by the solidity of the cube, square and cross shapes stands of the earth (element), the four directions, and solidity; as well as two pairs of opposites in a cross;

five is the number of man with his or her five limbs; it is equally relevant as the number of leaves or other part of the plant taking the geometrical shape of the five pointed star, such as the seeds in the seed pod of Cocoa. It often points to a general tonic for man, such as Ginseng or Cocoa.

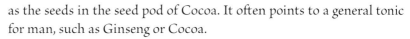

six is two times three and spiritual, sometimes the coming together of the two opposed triangles, this union is a profound spiritual symbol in several world cultures;

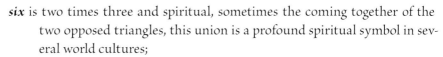

seven is the combination of the spiritual three and the worldly four, thus being an important spiritual number denoting integration in many traditions, sometimes standing for the angelic realm (adding their two wings makes seven limbs);

eight is two times four, stable, earthy, and so on.

Higher amounts of petals are either multiples of what is described here, as in Iris with **nine** (three times three, potentized spirituality), or simply **many**, meaning a multitude of aspects united. The number of petals is tied in with the geometrical aspect of the flower; radial flowers make triangles, squares, pentagons, hexagons, and so on as a result.

Many botanical families follow a numerological blueprint that applies to the entire family. For instance, the Mustard family, *Cruciferae,* is based on four petals per flower. Their healing virtues lie in firing up the metabolism, a very earthy aspect, indeed. We might think of Mustard, Cabbage, or Cress. The Rose clan, *Rosaceae,* is built upon five petals, and they act on the relationship of the center versus the periphery of our five limbs: many have heart healing properties and act on the blood and circulation. They bring us into our five limbs and thus into human incarnation. This is an image of *Vyana vayu,* and unlike the *vayus* or energetic winds that operate only upward or downward, this one governs the circulation to all five limbs, head, hands, feet and heart at the same time. The archetypal example here would be Hawthorn (flower, leaf, or berry). It teaches us to engage with our

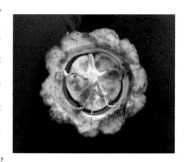

Cocoa star, showing fivefold signature of the human being (courtesy of Sandra Lory)

heart in the right relationship to our limbs, actions, and thus incarnation. The lilies, *Liliacea,* are built upon the number of six, which is clearly two sets of three petals. They have long been associated with spiritual purity. The classical example is Madonna Lily. Their sub-clan of the *Trilliums* has only one set of three petals and plays a less exalted, more earthy spiritual theme, largely because of other aspects of the signature. Most plant families have four, five, six, or many petals. (For an in-depth study of all plant families in those terms, see Pelikan's classic *Heilpflanzenkunde* in three volumes.)

The Shapes of Single Petals

Apart from looking at petals in the context of the whole flower, we can also look at petals and their shapes one by one. A form that has of old attracted much attention in our culture are ***heart-shaped*** petals. We might especially think of pink heart-shaped petals, sporting a double heart signature: we find them in Wild Roses, Mallows, and Primroses—all heart remedies, and also remedies to calm, soothe or open the heart. Many wild Primroses have yellow petals, some lavender, but all are heart-shaped, and all of them are heart remedies. Other petals are ***forked or frazzled*** at the tip; this indicates that their life force is also frazzled, and as in Madia or Indian Pink flower essences, they help us to focus our mind. We find ***flame-shaped*** petals in flamboyant and extroverted Tiger Lilies, denoting inner fire and intense emotions.

Some petals form ***hair-like structures*** or have ***fuzz*** on them. All very fine structures denote refinement and sensitivity, such as in the Cat's Ears among the Mariposa Lilies; as a flower essence, they help become more sensitive. I have found that they are of invaluable help in overly sensitive people, also. Silktree flower helps one not to be as sensitive as a *Mimosa* is. *Pulsatilla,* or Windflower, is covered in white fine hairs. These are made of organic silica, and thus share some of the silica healing powers known from homeopathy, all helping to calm overly fragile nerves and strengthen those too sensitive (see more on silica below under *Spines* and *Alchemy*). Hair and fuzz, when ***velvety,*** such as in Edelweiss or Pussypaws (*Cistanthe*), have to do with the hand being touched tenderly (see also *velvety leaves* below). Matthew Wood considers the Everlastings to be herbs that help tune into higher and finer levels of the spiritual worlds. He uses it for people who are too open and sensitive to "psychic or emotional vibes from others." He quotes it as a Native American remedy to mediate between the living and the dead, a "walker between the worlds" (2009, p. 169f).

For the shapes of the anthers and pistil, see following *Shapes of the Reproductive Flower Parts*.

Flowers Grouped in Umbels

I am not aware of a systematic analysis of the meaning of all the different ways in which flowers can be grouped as umbels,

Pulsatilla; the fuzz indicates a remedy for mucus (photo by Sandra Lory)

racemes, cymes, and spikes. The main point is that they are grouped and to see what impression that gives. This means a moving away from the individualization of the single, showy flower, toward a group of flowers giving an impression as if they were one flower. They therefore often have to do with our comportment in groups, or the unification of all our sub-parts, of self. For instance, in Goldenrod, the compound flowers are grouped into a panicle (the Northern American kind; the European kind is truly rod-shaped), thus being single flowers grouped into little flowers grouped into a rod, a double grouping process. It is the flower essence for children who seek attention from the group by acting in a negative way. It will enable them to act in harmony with the group without needing negative attention. Red Onion has a spherical inflorescence that looks like the negative of the heavenly star-strewn dome. The flower essence helps us connect to each of our parts, and each part to the whole. This is clearly shown in the symmetry of the flower stalks; via the stalks, each part is connected to the whole, and the whole to each part. This is in stark contrast to most of its botanical cousins which sport grand individual blossoms. These examples suffice to show that groups of flowers mean "the group and the parts." In whichever variation, grouped flowers play on the theme of the individual versus the larger human context. In the case of the onion, which is such a cosmic image, it is even the theme of the individual in the cosmos. In the case of

Quaking Grass flower essence, it bestows group consciousness and helps us to behave harmoniously within a group.

Spikes in their uprightness are of course another *yang* gesture. **Flowers drooping from hanging branches** are *yin*. See below under *Spikes and Thorns* and *Yin and Yang* for more details.

The **umbels** in the *umbelliferae* clan have a structure that resembles that of the milk glands and ducts in the *mammae*. Many of them enhance the flow of milk. The umbel-like **umbrella** or shield-like formation of Yarrow betrays its properties to reinforce the protective auric shield. "Lacy leaves and umbel flowers represent aeration of the lungs and blood stream: Elder, Sumac, Fennel, Dill, Angelica, White Pine" (Wood 1997, p. 27).

Flowers arranged into **flower heads** speak of a concentration of the formative forces in the head part of the flower, and many of them regulate too much or too little energy or blood in the head—Yucca and Artichoke treat headaches, and Lilac opens the head chakras. So does Teasel and Seapink, all flowers on a long, naked stem which form clear heads (with the exception of leafy Lilac where the purple color helps the orientation toward the head). "Sweet Leaf (*Monarda fistulosa*) has a crownlike ring of petals around the compound flower head, representing mental restfulness" (ibid.). We would consider this acting on the upward flowing *vayu* in Ayurveda.

In Cherokee medicine, the flower head of Snakehead (Self-heal) is seen as resembling the rearing head of a snake, and thus employed to treat snakebites (David Winston). This is doubly suitable if we recall its power as a drawing agent and the throat/sucking signature. The European counterpart is the slender, snake-like flower of Bistort, a famous medieval snakebite remedy. The flower or flowers making a head can also point to a head trauma remedy, such as Peony, Wood Betony, or, to a lesser degree, Spreading Dogbane. A great example of the coming together of the different signatures to make one meaning is the cluster of flowers of Pleusry Root. Making a head shape at the tip of the stalk, they are bright orange, a color that points to a medicinal quality of strengthening digestion. Hence, it is the herb for headaches due to gastric troubles! (Wood 2009, p. 80ff).

Some flowers uncurl from a tight **spiral** as they bloom—this is true of the Borage family from Forget-Me-Not through Lungwort. While Pelikan sees this as a kind of form-symbiosis with the unfurling proboscis of the insects that come to pollinate it (1980, p. 291ff), it is Viper's Bugloss that is famous as a snakebite remedy, and the flowers bloom one at a time on the uncurling branches in a motion of a snake rearing its head. The same is true of Forget-Me-Not, also called Snake Grass or Scorpion Grass. Harris names the flower spiral as a signature for the tail of a scorpion, whose bite it heals (Harris 1985, p. 99). It is worth pointing out that chemically, insect, scorpion and snake venom are closely related. Maybe this favors Pelikan's view of these plants being in symbiosis with the insect realm.

Another consideration is whether the **blossoms open** in an **ascending or descending** order. Most flowers along spikes bloom from the bottom up—from Aloe via Black Cohosh to Foxglove, they open their lowest flowers first (*yang*). With regards to that, it is remarkable that Goldenrod blooms from above down (*yin*), as if it took the light of its burning golden candle inside at a time when the summer is dying into chilly fall, giving ample provisions of honey to the bees for winter. The whole gesture is one of preparing to go in after the outward gesture of summer. Goldenrod is a deep acting herb for some of the deepest seating issues and organs, such as the *yin* organ of the kidneys. Remarkably, it is said in Chinese medicine that the kidneys have to catch the air as it comes in through the lungs and pull it down into them for proper function.

Flowers Below the Leaves or on the Ground

In the archetypal flowering plant, the flower towers above the leaves at the end of the stalk, with the leaves below it. However, there are many flowers that have flowers in between the leaves as the stem continues to grow, and in some cases, the flower is all the way on the ground below the leaves. What does this mean?

Self-heal (Prunella) and Bistort

Grohmann (1989, p. 30ff) points to the fact that when the leaves keep appearing along the stem while flowers come out from the leaf axils, the flowers will necessarily be smaller and less showy than if the leaves stop and metamorphose into a calyx to bring forth the flower. In a sense, this means that there is less of a flowering, and more of a leafy process: more water, more abundant life force, less air and fire. These statements are quite relative and have to be seen in the context of the individual plant and plant family. In the case of Solomon's Seal, the flowers hanging under the leaves denote the plant's ability to stimulate incarnation, our coming into our body and into our bones (a downward gesture).

Wild Ginger

Gotu Kola flowers literally hang on the ground. This is an epilepsy signature. The fact is even more remarkable if we bear in mind that Gotu Kola is a botanical relative of carrot.

If we consider plants with flowers that are hidden below the leaves on the ground, such as in Wild Ginger (*Asarum europeanum* or *canadense*), we find that there is a considerable "below" signature. Wild Ginger has a pungent, warming root and an odd, red-brown uterine-shaped flower. Talking about animal shapes and the accompanying strong astrality in anthroposophic thought being connected to cramps, we will not be surprised to find Wild Ginger to be a wonderful remedy for uterine cramps, and spasms of the lower back. It prevents threatening miscarriage and aids in weak labor (Wood 2009, p. 77ff). The European cousin *Asarum europeanum* which looks almost identical but does not have the ginger taste is a laxative, emmenagogue, purging and diuretic (Pelikan 1984, p. 210ff).

Shapes of the Reproductive Flower Parts

Looking at the plant's **reproductive organs** in general, we can see that they are either very obvious, or rather hidden. This is similar to people: some dress sexy, others hide their bodies. Some of the flowers most commonly associated with feminine (sexual) beauty are Hibiscus (no woman in the tropics is ever without one in her hair, and many tropical women's print dresses are adorned with them). In the old world it would be the lilies. Both flower families share a wide open, trumpet-shaped flower form with the reproductive organs protruding wide and happily. Greek lore has it that lilies spring from drops of Mother Goddess Hera's breasts. Aphrodite was so angry at this flawless image of purity, that she stuck the protruding sexual parts into their middle.

This story mixes divine purity and divine female sexuality. Both plants, especially as flower essences, can aid in sexual openness and are invaluable in treating gynecological conditions such as infertility. The pollen on lilies is so abundant, that they are commonly "castrated" in the

flower shops to avoid staining. Other flowers completely hide their reproductive organs inside of themselves: we might think of the Pea family, the flowers of which self-fertilize, or orchids, which lure the insect inside of them-selves to be pollinated. Others hide them under a petal such as Skullcap of Self-heal, or have them visible but almost unnoticeably so. Chickweed and Cowslip come to mind. None of the latter plants play a role in open-ing us sexually. Orchids owe their action in the sexual sphere to other very remarkable signatures, such as their mating behavior with insects. Many orchids imitate the shape of a bee or bumble bee with their external shapes of the petals in such detail, that the insect approaches to mate with the imagined partner, and in this way polli-nates the orchid. Others lure the insect into the inside of their puffy flowers where, as they struggle to find a way back out, they pollinate the flower. Orchids with their remarkably sexual behavior are a valuable sexual tonic. Vanilla "beans," the pods of an Orchid, are an emmena-gogue (a menstrual aid) and aphrodisiacal.

Easter Lily (above) and Lotus

On a side note; I would like to put forth a thought about the alarming rate at which human infertility increases. While environmental toxins have been blamed quite rightfully, we are also increasingly eating plant foods that stem from hybridized seeds—seeds that bring forth plants that cannot in turn reproduce fertile seeds. According to the ancient Ayurvedic wisdom, if a plant lacks the special *prana*-endowing fertile seeds with the potential to bring forth a new plant, how could it endow or aid our reproductive tissues with that potential?

The position of the ovary in a plant is telling: a position above the insertion point of petal and anthers (the corolla), which is above the receptacle, shows that the flower is oriented toward the cosmos (above); this is called **superior ovary**. A position below that leans toward the earth (below) is called **inferior ovary** (Pelikan 1980, p. 108). There are a few plants that have a half-inferior ovary, which really means it is midway, and thus balanced. The superior ovary could also be interpreted as *yang* (ascending), the inferior *yin* (descending). Examples of a superior ovary are Thistles and Dandelion, yang plants indeed, which release their seeds to ascend evermore heavenward with the wind. Examples of the inferior ovary are Lilies (very *yin* plants) and flowers from the Rose family. (For more on *yin and yang signature* see pages 209–215). We start to appreciate that Lilies, with open trumpets and protruding sexual organs but inferior ovaries, are *yin* plants. Lotuses carry their ovaries in a capsule that resembles a cone above the receptacle, as though held up to the sun. The Lotus is the plant of the seekers of en*light*enment.

Tiger Lily; the baby bulblets are the small, shiny black balls

Pollen is considered a potent health food in the West. Various minerals and other substances are given as the reason. In Tibetan Ayurveda, it is thought that pollen drifting in the wind in springtime is revitalizing, because pollen represents reproductive parts of the plant and, like our reproductive organs, is imbued with especially high life force that permit procreation.

I heard the story of an elder Tibetan man in American exile who was told he had cancer and little to live. He politely declined chemotherapy and returned home to his family to die. The social worker, a little concerned, asked him what they would do in his country to make him well. He and his wife told him that, in Tibet, deadly sick people should sit uphill from the spring flowers and inhale the pollen carried on the wind. The social worker suggested he ask a nursery whether they could sit there among the flowers. The nursery agreed, and even offered fans to blow the pollen toward the man. As they made visits to several nurseries in this way, the predicted time of death came and went, and our patient steadily recovered. Indian Ayurveda sees all reproductive tissue of the plant—that is, flowers and fruit—as especially healing to human reproductive tissues, and plants with abundant pollen have special potential.

Another surprising characteristic is finding ***baby bulblets*** in the flower. Bulbs and bulblets are usually developed in the soil and as such belong to the soil. In some Onions, however, as well as Tiger Lilies, we find them in the leaf axils as high up as above the flower (Tiger Lily), or after the flower is done blooming in some Wild Onions, the receptacle becomes crowded with a carpet of baby bulblets. These form roots once they fall to the ground. We find a root process that has ascended all the way above the flowering process. These plants heal the metabolic process that invades the head, and as flower essences increase our potential to bring our projects to fruition.

Time of Day of Blooming

The growth or comportment, as it were, of a plant according to the time of the day is also a signature. Carl **Linnaeus** (1707–1778) noticed that flowers open at specific times of day and made a flower clock, a circle in which twenty-four plants open and close their flowers at different times of day and night. Other flowers open any time of night or day, whenever their blooms are ready.

The most basic division is of flowers that open in the morning, at noon, in the evenings, and at night. Morning Glories open in the early morn and help to wake up with the rising sun. "Blood Root flowers open from morning to noon, then slowly fold back up again (used for migraine, worse from morning to noon, better from noon to night and relieved by lying in the dark)" (Wood, 1997 p. 28). Star of Bethlehem is called *Dame de Onze Heures* (Eleven o'clock-lady) in French, since it opens at eleven in the mornings. Morning Glory in its homeopathic preparation notes that the symptoms calling for Morning Glory (*Convolvulus duartinus*) are worse in the mornings, at the time of bloom (Murphy 2000, p. 543). If we understand the change of energy within a solar day, we will see that just before noon the exaltation and exhilaration is at its strongest. The energy increases from midnight up to noon, and sinks back from then up to midnight, when it has its lowest point. The research of Maria Thun and her colleagues demonstrated that this accords with the life force being in the above ground plant parts up to noon, and from noon to midnight it descends into the below-ground plant parts. Thus, at eleven o'clock, the energy carries us up. Star of Bethlehem is the flower essence for the soul that is shocked out of the body and needs to come back in. Evening Primroses open at dusk and fade with dawn, facilitating the subconscious and dream awareness, as well as addressing psychological issues from our time *in utero*—a very lunar plant, indeed. *Cactus grandiflorus* blooms at midnight, and is a heart remedy for nightly aggravations. Poison Ivy is more poisonous at night, and the poison-ivy patient is also is worse at night.

Day-blooming flowers might also be **sensitive to the intensity of the sunlight**, closing up when dimmed by clouds, such as Dandelion or Silktree (in which case, the leaves that fold up instead of the flower). Others have flowers or flower buds that track the Sun on its daily journey, such as Madonna Lily. This light sensitivity is a general signature for sensitivity. Dandelion as a cooling liver remedy helps with light sensitivity of the eye due to liver heat; Silktree is for the oversensitive type in general; and Madonna Lily increases spiritual sensitivity. Sunflowers and Topinambur (Jerusalem Artichoke) also trace the Sun, in this case it is their flower heads looking like sun wheels that confirm their *Sun signature*.

The Shapes of Leaves

As we will see in chapter 10 on the elements, the leaves are formed chiefly by a dynamic interplay of the water and air elements. The in-between spaces in toothed, lobular, palmate or compound leaves could be seen, as in anthroposophic plant study, as the air pushing into the solid leaf surface. So, the lusher and more spherical, the more watery the leaves. The more feathered and fine, the more airy they are. In a lot a of plants, the shape of the leaves undergoes a considerable metamorphosis from the first true leaves up to the last before the calyx. In general, the lower ones are more ruled by water, and the upper ones finer and more ruled by air; the longer the leaves' stalk, the more airy they are (Grohmann 1989, vol. 1). This is easier to understand once one sees the flowering plant as stretched out between the root (earth) and flower (fire) pole with the leaves (water and air) striking their balance between them. For instance, in the case of Basil, the lower leaves are quite watery in look, but already have the typical pungent (fire) aroma. The leaves become increasingly flame-shaped up along the stem, until they give way to the flowers: it is an image of fire from above penetrating the water below. Basil is one of the best plants to teach the body a perfect balance of fire in water.

Upright versus bending or low growth point to *yin* or *yang* forces in the plant (see the section on *yin and yang* below). *Cactus grandiflorus* sprouts grow up straight only to fall over soon. A prostrate plant, it is used for prostration. A creeping growths where the plant looks as if pushed down as in Thorn Apple (*Stramonium*) might be a poison signature (see the section on *Signature of Poison* below).

Lush, abundant greenery means that the plant has strong vital force, or etheric force as it is called in Anthroposophy. It can shape a **parasol-like canopy** as horse chestnut trees do, which illustrates the plant's ability to create its own energetic space, and protect itself from the drying-out forces of wind and sunshine. Willow's foliage, on the contrary, is completely open to its surroundings. A relative **lack of leaves**, such as in Chicory with its naked tall stem, interestingly translates into neediness as the main psychological keynote for the flower essence. We find the same reduced leaves and naked stem in Bluebell, a flower essence for fear of lack and a poverty mind-set.

The **invasive growth** of Periwinkle is seen as the signature for its anti-cancer properties, a condition where the aberrant cells show invasive growth and take over everything else (Harris 1985, p. 140f). Some other cancer herbs show invasive growth, such as Sheep Sorrel or Japanese Knotweed, and have a reputation as cancer healers.

The **birth song** of a plant is the unfolding of its set of seed leaves, or subsequent first set of true leaves. Quite often, the shape already sets the stage for the energetic gesture of the subsequent plant. For instance, Angelica and *Dong Quai,* Chinese Angelica, spread with a graceful set of leaf-like wings. Very appropriate for an angel plant, dedicated to aerate the tissues! Echinacea, the warrior plant that helps defend our integrity by enhancing our immune system, heals psychological traumas and wards off sepsis and snake venom, raising what seems to be a sword between its first baby leaves, ready to defend. Basil, on the other hand, lets the first true set of leaves ripple like the surface of water over an underground well, indicating its intimate connection to the water element.

The overall shape of the plant can sometimes be the signature—Linden trees once fully grown form the shape of an upside-down heart. Their leaves are heart-shaped, and a leaf upright on its stem has the same form as the outline of the adult tree. Linden flowers have a very sweet scent and produce ample nectar, another heart signature. Thus, we have three strong heart signatures in this great heart calming plant.

Heavy, large structured leaves point to a predominance of the earth element. We find this often in tropical plants. Energetically speaking, the tropical atmosphere is heavy and earthy, in contrast to the thin and cosmic air of the arctics, where the plants are tiny and thin, too. "**Large leaves** stand for surface area and gas exchange or breathing, hence the lungs and the skin: Burdock, Elecampane, Comfrey, Mullein" (Wood 1997, p. 27).

Round, broad leaves as in Lotus and Water Lily pads are shaped like water drops or puddles of water, and point to a predominance of the water element. Water Lily is a good candida remedy, which needs internal "sogginess" of the tissue to thrive. Lettuce is another fine example—the head needs abundant moisture to form well, and looks like water welling up over a fountain. Its properties are cooling, as one would expect from water.

I have always been struck by the fact that swords are a symbol of wisdom cutting through ignorance like the sharpness of intelligence undercutting nonsense in many cultures, as well as of oral expression. The **sword-shaped** leaves of Iris suit a flower well that enhances creative expression in words, such as through poetry or writing. I was struck that Calamus, of which the leaves in winter can be easily mistaken for those of Iris (called *Schwertlilie,* Sword Lily in German—its medieval name being *Drachenwurz,* Dragon Root, and dragons of course have to be overcome in a sword fight) is called *Vacha* in Sanskrit. This translates as "speaking," and stands for the power of the word and intelligence or self-expression, which Calamus is said to facilitate (Frawley and Lad 1986, p. 106). Gladiolus is even named after the Latin for sword.

Water Lilies

Harris points to the leaves as a phallic symbol (as is the sword), Gladiolus being an aphrodisiac for men (Harris 1985, p. 102f). Water Soldier is an aquatic plant with an overall shape like Aloe, hence it is also called Water Aloe; however, it is not succulent. The sword-like leaves which have piercing prickles were thought to be a reliable remedy for all wounds inflicted by iron weapons, such as sword blades. "Later, when firearms came to the fore, the leaves became a standard application for gun-shot wounds" (ibid., p. 190).

Just as the blade comes to a point, so does our mind when focused. Calamus is also used in Chinese medicine to heighten the intensity of mental ability and consciousness. It heals lack of comprehension as well as the inability to grasp words. Contemporary herbalist Lise Wolf uses it for senility. It counteracts the effects of alcohol and hallucinogenics on the brain, bringing about clarity of consciousness.

Blades are the thin and narrow leaves so typical of grasses. In true grasses, they are also very sharp and, as many a child can attest, can cut your finger to the bone. Blade-like leaves, shaped like light rays, can be a signature of silica-rich plants. Silica is what crystals are made of, and silica will make crystalline or needle-like shapes. Grass blades are so cutting because of their silica content. (For more on the significance of the tissue-strengthening silica, see the section "Plant Chemistry and Alchemy," pages 202–208.)

Contracted, narrow, or needle-like leaves, as a general rule go, with highly aromatic plants— from Chamomile and Yarrow via the conifers to Thyme or Rosemary, it is a signature for a high predominance of air and fire, giving rise to a high essential oil content. The only exception I am aware of would be the leaves of asparagus, which are finely feathered, but only airy, not aromatic. So this signature is very reliable. If we consider the *Labiatae* family so high in aromatic plants, we see that their degree of being aromatic is directly related to the contracted nature of their leaves. Sage, with a balanced oval leaf, has all five elements and tastes—so well balanced within it that it has become a panacea, able to rebalance every tissue state. While the bottom leaves of basil bear a water signature, the higher ones increasingly take on the fire signature. Basil helps the body in learning to contain fire (it is pungent) in water. The exceptions, such as Asparagus and Horsetail

Yarrow (Achillea millefolium)

Grass, are rich in silica (see *Blades* above). So, too, are Pine needles, and, like all conifers with needles, they are very fragrant. (See also the next section.)

Divided and **feathered leaves** embrace the air element and help aerate the tissues. Chinese Angelica, *Dong Quai,* helps in coughs and breaks up congealed blood. Wood considers "lacy" leaves as a signature for aeration of the bloodstream and names Elder, Sumac, Fennel, Dill, Angelica, and White Pine (1997, p. 27). Feathered leaves can be a signature for air or the fine blood vessels, since that's what they are: nothing but the veins of the leaf after the leaf's surface has gone. Yarrow is one of the best aids to stop bleeding and seems to act on the fine blood vessels. Coles interprets the signature as the leaf being "finely cut," thus the incisions into the leaf make it a wound remedy (Coles 1657, p. 556). My friends tell me it is the "carpenter's herb," which protects from cuts by sharp tools, and heals those cuts when they occur. Another example would be Chamomile, a keynote of which is "one cheek red and one cheek pale"—hence it is needed in vegetative dystonia where the capillaries in different parts of the body are not constricted or dilated harmoniously. In the case of Chamomile, this is due to irregular nervous tension not orchestrating the capillaries quite right, and the finely feathered leaves could also be taken as a signature for the nerves. While fine and feathered leaves can point to a nervine such as the case for Pine and all other conifers with needles, they are also a signature for sensitivity, which so often goes with fragile nerves.

Flame-shaped leaves are a fire signature. They are most clearly seen on peach trees—turning scarlet red in autumn   hence peach tree in all of its parts is one of the best remedies to sedate heat. It is indicated by a red, flame-shaped tongue.

Serrated leaves with a narrow row of round loops like an endless cursive *"m"* are considered a spleen signature by Matthew Wood. He points to Royal Fern, *Osmunda regalis* and Sweetfern, *Comptonia,* as examples. In the Middle Ages, many ferns were used in a similar way to shrink the spleen (see more under *Spleen*). Wood Betony has those same leaves, and Coles writes that it "openeth obstructions of Spleen and Liver" (Coles 1657, p. 14). The leaves of European Oak are not quite of that shape, but lobed in a wave-like line. The use of Oak bark or glands to reduce an enlarged spleen is ancient. If we look at the outline of the leaves of the American Oaks in an imaginative way, we can see that their outline is the negative of the shape of Sweetfern and so on— and their bark has been used to reduce the spleen in size. It makes sense to holistic thinking that the drying, astringent tannins in Oak would contract the spleen signature shape from a watery shape with a line welling outward to an outline resembling that to an evaporating water droplet curving inward. Ferns, Oaks, and Sweetfern (*Comptonia,* not botanically a fern) are also useful in re-mineralizing the bones and teeth, and their serrated outline looks like a line of teeth (Wood).

Truly *asymmetric* leaves are rare. Elm springs to mind. They point to mercury and healing properties akin to the mercurial principle (see under *Planetary Signature* for a complete explanation).

Succulent leaves such as of Aloe and Cacti speak of a special ability to store and withhold water. They can moisten dried or burned tissues, plump them up, and are helpful in treating or preventing heat stroke. Cactus cuttings in water are used to this end as a folk remedy in Haiti. *Cactus grandiflorus* is a well-known heart remedy helpful where the flow of blood through the heart is dammed up, in the same way that—as it were—the water inside of the succulent stems is bound in its flow. Flower essences of succulent plants such as Stonecrop help people break through inner stagnation

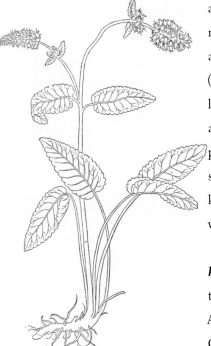

and feelings of isolation, while Aloe is for burn-out—not just regenerating burn tissues, but also worn out life force. Pelikan also describes *Cactus grandiflorus* as a plant of buoyant life force (it does grow quite rampantly) and names held back, abundant life force as a hallmark of Cacti (1958, p. 189ff); like Aloe, they are specifically helpful for burned-out and run-down, nervous people (Wood 2008, p. 90). Haitian herbalist Derivière uses the succulent leaves of the vining *Lougarou* for prostate swelling and kidney stones—a swollen leaf for a swollen organ, a leaf that withholds water for a disease of withheld water.

Wood Betony; the drawing shows the spleen signature of the leaves

Many of these succulents are remarkably **fast** in **tissue healing**, and unusually speedy tissue healing and regeneration in plants is a signature that the plant speeds tissue healing. Another example would be Houseleek, *Semprevivum tectorum*. Comfrey with its persistent root that can regenerate itself no matter how mutilated.

Trembling leaves as those of Aspen point to it being one of the best remedies for both trembling with fear and nightmares, as well as tremor caused by weak nerves, such as from excess *vata* or in old age.

Clasping leaves often point to remedies that heal the muscle or tendon insertions into the bones—examples are Solomon's Seal, Teasel, and Boneset (see under musculoskeletal organ signatures for more details). In the case of Teasel the clasping leaves create pockets around the stem which hold the rainwater. Gabrielle Simon teaches this as the signature that they help preserve the kidney *yin*, the essential water element energy of our body. And we can remember how the kidneys sit to both sides of the spine, just as the pockets attach to both sides of the stem.

Leaves covered by a mealy white substance, as found in the Lambsquarters family, and comes off at the slightest touch, is a signature for sores and ulcers. Arrach in particular also emits a foul odour, so it was used for sores and ulcers emitting foul odor (Harris 1985, p. 61).

Sage leaves have been described as looking "as if they were ***scorched*** by blasting," and thus taken as a signature for restoring man's body when it seems to be dead as if from blasting, restoring to it natural heat and vigour (Coles 1657, p. 16).

Sharply toothed leaves, as in Sweet Chestnut, "thus indicating a pain- or paroxysm-relieving effect" (Harris 1985, p. 81).

Visibly veined leaves as those of Plantain point to a nerve remedy—when pulled apart, the white "nerve" strands emerge. Plantain is one of the best trigeminus neuralgia remedies. The "nerved" leaves of Lady's Slipper point to it as an excellent nerve tonic.

The ***two-lobed leaves*** of *Gingko biloba* resemble the two bilaterally lobed organs, the brain and the lungs. Gingko seeds have a long history of being used to moisten the lungs in Chinese medicine, while modern pharmaceutical methods of creating concentrated extracts yield a leaf tincture which increases the circulation in the brain and treats dementia.

Narrow-leafed Plantain

Sets of three leaves occur surprisingly often in great gynecological remedies. *Trillium* (Wakerobin), Black and Blue Cohosh (belonging to different botanical families), Goldthread, and European and Chinese Angelica come to mind. While Matthew Wood told me he thought that Native Americans were lead to the discovery of this signature in *dreamtime,* I was struck by the fact that in many native cultures, the tripod or triangle stands for the female sexual organ, the entrance of which is indeed triangular.

Left: Dong Quai (Chinese Angelica) is one of the most valuable gynecological herbs. It shows the typical threefold signature of female remedies. Right: Goldenthread is another healing plant with threefold leaves. It yields a valuable female remedy. An extract of the root is useful for leucorrhea (photos by Sandra Lory).

Some cultures, such as the ancient Indian, consider the uterus to be a three-dimensional triangle in shape, like a pyramid standing on its tips. Herbalists Matthew Wood (2009, p. 338) and Jacquelin Guiteau see the three leaves as a signature for the torso with the two legs spread apart to give birth. On a side note, the equally parturient uterine-shaped Wild Ginger flower has three petals.

Sets of six leaves are a multiple of sets of three—Gravelroot has a whorl of six leaves, and makes a fine remedy for uterine prolapse.

Five-lobed leaves have an ancient connection to magic, since they resemble the human hand. A classical example would be Cinquefoil (Wood 1997, p. 85ff). We find here another echo of the five-petal flower, akin to the human being. This is not surprising, since human beings are indeed fivefold in limbs, hands, and feet. Ginseng also has fivefold leaves, as well as tiny five-petalled flowers. This, together with roots that can reach seventy years or more and be human-shaped should indeed yield an all-round general tonic for longevity.

The **palmate (hand-shaped) leaves** of Marihuana point to it being a remedy for arthritis pain in the hands (ibid., p. 27). Another example would be Horse Chestnut (a folk tradition says to keep them in your pocket to hold to prevent arthritis), Castor Plant (Rosvigo and Balcik 1998, p. 64ff) and Contra Hierba (ibid., p. 81).

Few leaves are **gland-dotted**, the famous signature of St. John's Wort, pointing to skin pores as well as puncture wounds, since the leaves look perforated. Another example is Bugleweed, of which the lower sides of the leaves are gland-dotted, marking it as a wound herb (Harris 1985, p. 73f).

The ginseng sprout displays the typical five-pointed leaf (photo by Sandra Lory)

Heart-shaped leaves stand for the heart and love. Linden is one of the best examples for a tree with a heart-shaped leaf, of which the bark (Native Americans used this part), leaves or flowers (the latter used in Europe) are a wonderful calming heart remedy which allays heat and tension in the heart. Other examples are the leaves of Heartsease, or Wild Pansy (*Viola tricolor*), and Wild Ginger. Harris names *Oxalis acetosella,* "Trefoil "(Harris 1985, p. 183). Coles recommends the latter, which he calls Wood-sorrel, for defending the heart from the plague and other pestilential diseases (Coles 1657, p. 180). He considers the leaves of Lemonbalm, so good for heart palpitations, heart-shaped (ibid., p. 181). Heart shape can also be a hip signature (Gabrielle Simon), since the iliac bones take that form. An example would be the heart-shaped leaves of Wild Yam, a good remedy for hip pain (no lying position feels right) and osteoporosis.

Scarlet Pimpernel (kidney signature)

Hepatica, or Liverwort (Liver signature)

Kidney-shaped leaves can point to a kidney remedy as in Self-heal (*Prunella vulgaris*), a wonderful kidney *yin* tonic, and Wild Ginger which produces the kidney-shaped leaves, often in pairs of two, another warming kidney-healing plant. This is also true of European Wild Ginger (Fuchs, 1543, chapter III). Ground Ivy and Marsh Marigold are other examples.

Harris gives the example of Partridge Berry, with **pairs of opposite, ovate leaves** said to resemble the kidneys in pairs on opposite sides of the spine (Harris 1985, p. 137). Another example is Scarlet Pimpernel (ibid., p. 143).

The **pitcher-like** leaves of Pitcher Plant that are often filled with water point to it as a kidney remedy. Harris cites these being used by Native Americans to enhance memory—since the leaves trap things inside them, they were used to "trap" memories in the mind (Harris 1985, p. 145). I am not sure this is not an example of postive magical thinking, rather than an actual medicinal effect. The flower essence supports digestion, as one would imagine given such a stomach-like, digesting plant organ (Kaminski and Katz 1996, p. 167). Native Americans also used it for lung (looks like a sack) and liver (digestion) ailments (Foster and Duke 1990, p. 142).

Organ signatures are also found on green leaves—the heart-shaped Linden leaf that calms the heart, the liver-looking leaf of Liverwort, *Hepatica nobilis,* as well as the lichen Common Liverwort, the leaf of Lungwort that so oddly resembles pulmonary tissue, to name a few. Harris (1985, p. 65) offers an original example of the doctrine of signature: a cross-section of the evergreen Bearberry leaves, famous for chronic cystitis and other kidney and bladder ailments, reveals at the microscoptic level two masses of kidney-shaped, thick-walled cells to equidistant to either side of the central vein of the leaf, which represents the spine. For more examples, refer to the single organs under *Organ Signature.*

Galls are the result of insect bites on leaves, such as the gall wasp on Oak leaves. Oak galls "are, and do, represent excrescences." They are used for skin disease (Harris 1985, p. 133). Grieve names swollen tonsils and hemorrhoids (swollen tissue heals swollen tissue; 1982, p. 597).

Lungwort (above), showing lung-like mottling on the leaves; Wild Yam leaves (below), showing the heart signature (photo by Sandra Lory)

Mullein shooting up (photo by Sandra Lory)

Cactus grandiflorus, *also called Snake Cactus, displays the typical rhythmic structure of a heart remedy*

Rhythmically-Arranged Leaves

Pelikan elaborates how the rhythmical organs of heart, lung, and uterus are strongly linked to plants with a clear rhythmical form. Examples are Foxglove, Lily of the Valley (the flowers), Spreading Dogbane, Motherwort and *Cactus grandiflorus* (in this case, the leaves have metamorphized into spines) for the heart and the latter two also for the uterus, and Lily of the Valley, Pleusry Root and Mullein for the lungs. Pelikan points out how, as it were, in its ascending growth the plant expands and contracts as do heart and lungs (1977, p. 235ff). The *Labiatae* family is also of rhythmical built, and maybe richest of all plant families in respiratory remedies. Most of them also being nervines, they calm the heart. Another rhythmical organ is the uterus shedding blood in a monthly rhythm, and plants such as Motherwort (which translates as "uterus herb") and the lilies show a pronounced rhythmical structure.

Rhythmically or ***symmetrically arranged leaves*** are also common in plants that heal the musculoskeletal system, which in turn is arranged strictly rhythmically and symmetrically. Plants that are important here are Solomon's Seal, Boneset, Motherwort, Pleusry Root (dry joints and muscles) or Horsetail Grass. For more details, see *Spine Images* below.

One way of detecting a *rhythmical signature* is to see the plant's rhythmic structure in the fully developed plant before us. Another way is to watch the rhythmic movement occurring stretched out over time. This can happen in the form of an ascending and descending movement alternating. Pelikan (1958, p. 354f) exemplifies this for Lily of the Valley. We find the same phenomenon in *Cactus grandiflorus*. Lily of the Valley is a flower that shows a balancing act between polar opposite forces. Growing in the shade, the flowers emerge as spike of buds along the stem. The buds first point upward, against gravity, and are equally distributed in all directions. Soon, they all point toward the light, only to drop down, giving in to gravity, and falling back toward the dark earth. While Lily of the Valley in flower is another example of the above-mentioned rhythmic structure, in which each flower is like an expansion, and the stem between them like a contraction, the plant also dances between dark and light and gravity and levity. It is a wonderful healing plant for heart and lungs, where blood and air are not only moved by expansion and contraction, but also sucked in and expelled following gravity and levity. Another example is the climbing snaking *Cactus*

Ground Ivy; the image shows the earache signature (flowers), the lung signature (rhythmically arranged leaves), and the minor kidney signature (opposing pairs of kidney-shaped leaves). It's odor is metallic, showing that it draws heavy metals from tissues (photo by Sandra Lory).

grandiflorus. It lifts long, snake-like succulent stems straight up. They have rhythmically occurring nodes with potential buds and spines, as well as airborne rootlets. Once the stem has pushed itself up beyond a certain point, they simply fall over, and now hanging down, will start to grow with their tip upward for as long as they can until their own weight pulls them down again. In its natural habitat, along cliffs by the ocean, we can see how it can keep itself up in case the airborne rootlets find a place to hold on to. *Cactus grandiflorus* is a wonderful remedy for a heart in which the blood is too heavy, pulling the heart down too much as it were: this is the case in valvular insufficiency, where the heart has to continuously pump against the back flow of the blood: it is an uphill battle with no chance of winning. While it is not clear that *Cactus* will correct the valvular defect, it fortifies the heart against the burden, giving it the extra strength it needs. Another example of a plant with rhythmically arranged leaves is Tiger Lily, employed in Chinese medicine to clear heat and fevers from heart and lungs. Solomon's Seal is used in a similar manner to cool and moisten the lungs.

Hairiness

Roughness can mean adhesion or, as in the case of Cleavers, which was once used to put into the funnel for milking to filter the milk, point to filtering qualities. Cleavers support the kidneys in their filtering action.

Hairs can take several meanings—the soft down found on some leaves means that they have to do with tenderness and sense of touch. In Edelweiss, they also protect the plant from ultraviolet radiation. In Mullein, they are a signature for the ciliae in the bronchi—Mullein is a specific for cough so harsh you feel you might vomit. The bronchi feel raw, and we can imagine the ciliae being in need of regeneration. Coltsfoot is another velvety cough remedy, as is Windflower. In Brooklime (*Veronica* off.), Clary Sage and Sage these hairs represent the tickling sensation of temporary throat irritation, and the prickles of Prickly Lettuce also point to it as a bronchial remedy (Harris 1985, p. 72 and 119). In Speedwell, it points to tickling sensations, inner or outer, while the hairy down of Staghorn Sumac points to it stopping the vexing irritation of bronchial ailments, as well as cuts and sores (ibid., pp. 171 and 177f). These downy hairs are made out of organic silica, and silica is strengthening of the nerves and mucosa, as well as to fragile people. In downy Windflower, it is also the psyche that is fragile. These hairs can also be a cloud signature (see the below chapter on *Animal Signatures*). A number of plants, such as Borage, Comfrey or Pumpkins, form spiny hairs of silica on their surface, to varying degrees of prickliness. In Borage, they point to the overall fortifying properties to the skin, and in several other plants from the same family, such as Lungwort and Hound's Tongue, to bronchial ciliae and lung ailments.

Harris states that Native Americans took the fact that the dried leaves of Coltsfoot, Sage, Hoarhound, Everlasting, Marshmallow, Clary Sage, Mullein and other hairy, velvety leaves stick together once pressed together to mean that they adhere and thus transport toxins out of the body (toxins here meaning useless intermediary metabolites, mucus or cell debris rather than poisons) (Harris 1985, p. 84f). He says about the stems thickly coated by a hairy down: "The signature informs us that the herb will stop the hoarseness or tickling in the throat and soothe and subdue the pain of pulmonary catarrhs and general bronchial disorders" (ibid., p. 126f). The ciliae of the respiratory tract are "downy hairs," indeed!

Thistle

Velvety leaves such as of the Australian Flannel Flowers (Australian Bush Flower Essences), Edelweiss, and even the soft down of Pussypaws (Flower Essence Society), all relate to touch, and softness of touch. Touch is the sense associated with the heart chakra, so soft, velvety leaves and flowers have a heart-softening, heart-opening quality. They also relate to fear of being touched, fear of the intimacy of being touched, and the trauma from inappropriate touch, such as of sexual abuse.

The ***stinging hairs*** of Nettles are a signature for the treatment of "pins and needles," pleuritic and other stitching pains, especially those of arthritis (Harris 1985, p. 131). They treat the kind of itching pustular rash they can cause (nettle juice). Wood uses it as a plant for numbness—it heals what it can cause, getting stung severely can make the part numb. This hairy plant is one of ancient Europe's chief hair tonics. The glassy poisonous hairs on Nttles stand for meanness—Anne McIntyre calls Nettle "the flower of spite" (1996, p. 229). Nettle flower essence is indeed for people who are so hostile that getting in touch with them gives us the same impression as being burnt by Nettles.

Spines and Thorns

Spines mean that the plant is bristly. It takes a well-defended stance against anticipated hostility. A lot of spiny plants make excellent flower essences for hostile people, who put their bristles up like a hedgehog or porcupine at the slightest sign of real or imagined hostility. As Dr. Rudolph Ballentine once said, "Imagine trying to hug a Holly bush." Well, if that's the impression you are getting from someone you are trying to approach, they need Holly essence for hostile behavior. In Oregon-Grape, the imagined hostility has grown into a sense of paranoia. Echinacea, a flower with a spiny core is what I call "the flower who has the best defended core of self." It is for people whose sense of self has been shattered by trauma. Another spiny and very well defended flower is Thistle. It gives children the courage to stand up to a bully: "Hey! Don't mess with me!" Gorse is very spiny. I once treated an extremely prickly teenage girl. She was so bristly that she even noticed it herself, but was unable to stop her behavior. I made her a combination of Holly, Oregon-Grape, Echinacea, and Thistle essences, giving the image of the hedgehog and the spiny plants with it. This almost made her laugh in her misery. Her prickliness was much less after finishing the course. I was therefore intrigued when I found the following account about a German woman testing Teasel tincture on herself: "The tincture had a definite effect. I felt more relaxed, happier, and energetic. The nasty sharp 'pins and needles' inside of me, which were directed against me, seemed to dissolve. The thistly plant seems to have something to do with auto-aggression. My husband confirmed this; he noticed that I was a lot less snappish and irritable" (Storl 2010, p. 158). It is important to understand in this context that auto-aggression in psychological terms is aggression turned against oneself, because it cannot be expressed to the outer source of the anger.

In anthroposophic, or Goethean, botany, spines and thorns are regarded as a plant part in which the etheric force that should become a leaf or other plant part is held back. They are, on the level of formative forces, contracted hardened leaves or sprouts. "...the strong vitality is not visible, it is held back, dammed up, and this gives the key to understanding this plant [Blackthorn]" (Grohmann 1989, vol. 2, p. 46f). They therefore bear special healing forces. Anthroposophic medicine makes a preparation from the spines of Blackthorn (Sloe), which are botanically speaking withheld, morphologically metamorphosed shoots. Sloe preparations are administered for exhaustion. "This plant does not possess healing powers by virtue of being stunted, untidy, and densely twigged, but it has a superfluity of forces because it does not dissipate them in rapid growth" (ibid.). Pelikan describes the vital Dog Rose as follows: "In its branches, however, it contracts its life [force] into thorns, thus saving much etheric force, which it thereby does not expend. Every thorn is a withheld branch, every spine a withheld leaf" (Pelikan 1980, p. 236ff). This process gives all the thorny plants in the *Rosaceae* family their strong etheric forces. Spines and thorns are thus thought to have an especially stimulating and energizing effect on the body. Pelikan continues to describe the Hawthorne as a *Rosaceae,* in which the etheric forces fight the strong hardening tendencies in its wood and thorns (ibid.). This makes it one of our best remedies for arteriosclerosis, hardening of the arteries.

I did not know that some take spininess to be a signature for enhancing immunity when I discovered that Gorse flower essence, taken at short

Echinacea, showing the pickly, self-defending center (photo by Sandra Lory)

intervals, can abort a cold or fever in the beginning stages. I used it as such because it blooms year round, even in frost and snow, but also wondered about its spiny defense. Echinacea, used to enhance immunity, does not just share the spines, but also the intimate love-relationship to frost: it needs frost to germinate. Another example of an adaptogen and immunity enhancing plant that is spiny is Eleuthero, and the thorny *Smilax* species are lesser-known adaptogens.

Spines are mostly made out of organic silica, and hence bear much resemblance in healing qualities with homeopathic Silica, or *Silicea*, as it is sometimes called. The same is true for hairs or prickles. Refer to the above section on *hairiness* and silica as a healing substance for more details.

Hildegard of Bingen wrote that Teasel drives poison from the body (Storl 2010, p. 172). Since this is true of all the thistles, such as Milk Thistle and Blessed Thistle, I am wondering whether the outward gesture of the spines is not a signature for driving poisons out of the body. After all, there is no more thistle-like plant that is not a thistle than Teasel.

Here is a case history of a plant: my front-yard Rose in Brooklyn had happily produced a flower that grew toward the garden fence. The next morning, someone had ripped it off in a very crude way. The plant stopped growing toward the fence where the light came from. The next sprout it put out was in the opposite direction, away from the fence, and more densely covered in thorns than I have ever seen a rose branch. For the rest of the summer, it grew and bloomed as far from of the point of assault as it could, with unusually dense thorns on the branches.

Last but not least, spines and thorns are a signature for the intense pain they can inflict. Examples are Prickly Ash (torturous pains), Blackberry (gripping diarrhea), Hawthorn (angina pectoris pains, especially under the left scapula and clavicle), Barberry (liver and gallbladder pain), Holly (pains of pleurisy, bronchitis, and rheumatism), Raspberry (labor and period pain, pains of diarrhea), Motherwort (headache and menstrual pain), Rose (sharp pain of heat and irritation in the tissue), *Aralia spinosa* (pain throughout the body, of rheumatism) and Gooseberry (pains of catarrhs and fevers) (Harris 1985, under herbs). Spines and thorns are also a *yang* signature and denote a sense of strength, or tension in a negative sense. Herbalist David Winston calls Prickly Ash "phenomenal for nerve pain." He says that in Cherokee medicine, spines and thorns are not so much seen as a signature for pain, but rather for protection. Red Cedar would be considered the most powerful among those remedies. Prickly plants are, of course, among the best defended; most animals cannot graze on thistles. Cat's Claw (*Uncaria tomentosa*) has nasty recurving thorns and is used for arthritis pains. The Chinese relative *Gou teng* is used to treat headaches. The signature is seen as the hook on the vine indicating that it can go into the head and grasp the pain to pull it out. It is also said to represent the plant's strength to penetrate and puncture a lump, such as a tumor (understood as lumps of thickened mucus). Wood quotes the advice of a Native American medicine woman, "There's something in the thorn [of Hawthorn] that causes the skin not to heal when it is pricked. But if you pick that thorn and prick a boil it will empty out and heal up" (2008, p. 214). He recommends Hawthorn tincture for irritation and redness of the skin, describing how it increases the skin's ability to form a healthy scab (it heals what it can cause; ibid., p. 213). Incidentally, William Coles wrote in 1657: "The said distilled water of the Flowers [of Hawthorn] is not onely *cooling* but *drawing* also, for it is found by good experience, that if Cloathes and Spunges be wet in the said water, and applied to any place whereinto *thornes,*

Splinters, &c. have entered and be there abiding, it will notably draw them forth, so that the *Thorne* gives medicine for its own pricking" (p. 367). The birdlime made of Holly bark also serves to draw forth thorns, pricks, and splinters (p. 386). Blessed Thistle and other thistles have been used for stitching aches and pains, such as stitches of the side or of arthritis. Native American medicine men and women use thistles for pains and spasms of the stomach and dysmenorrhea (Harris 1985, p. 180). A thorn for a thorn, and a stitch for a stitch!

The Shapes of the Stem

In general, a **straight** stem is imbued with *yang*, a **bending** one with *yin* forces (see the section on yin and yang below). Wood takes a bending stem as that of Solomon's Seal as a signature for debility and lack of nutrition (1997, p. 401f), which are *yin* deficiency symptoms.

The **sprout**, when rising from the ground, can look like a **snake** lifting its head. Native Americans saw that as a signature for snake remedies and used those plants against snakebites. Rattlesnake Master and Black Cohosh, also called "Black Snakeroot," are good examples. In the case of the latter, the sprouts appear in groups and have pendular motions, thus, really looking like a den of snakes waking. **Phallic** shapes as in Shatavari, Yucca and Maltese Mushroom *Cynomorium coccineum* (called *suo yang* in Chinese, *tarthuth* in Arabic, a parasite from the Broomrape family) are used for infertility and impotence. See also under *Buds and Shoots* (pages 153–155).

A **hollow stem** points to the hollow, tubular organs (Harris 1985, p. 47). We can think of excellent bronchial remedies such as Garlic and Onion, in fact all *Allium* species, Angelica and the other *Umbelliferae*, Comfrey, and Elder. Traditional Chinese medical texts still state of Lilies, *Allium*s, and Green Scallions, for instance, that they "unblock because they are hollow inside." They also all help digestion, aid in moving the food through the alimentary canal, as well as are diuretic, moving the urine through the ureters, opening the pores and helping blood circulation. The Onion clan also serves as an antibiotic in the intestinal tract, and Garlic expels worms. They aid any passage: Wood teaches that hollow stems point to a plant's ability to increase the imagination and aid in shamanic astral traveling, "because the tube represents a passage to another world" (1997, p. 27). Elder branches are not hollow as much as filled with a soft pith that pits under the slightest pressure. Crollius considered that to be the signature for

Yucca

dropsy—and pitting edema (Coles 1657, p. 296). The hollow Bamboo culms can contain a silicious secretion that is called *bamboo manna* in Asia. It is used in Ayurvedic medicine as a tonic in respiratory disease.

Square stems are taught to be a nerve signature by the Europeans and Native Americans. The best example is the entire *Labiatae* family, so rich in nerve-calming remedies like Lemonbalm, Wood Betony, and Lavender, to name a few (Wood 1997, throughout), but also Passion Flower, members of the Vervain family, and Cleavers.

The **bunch of fine stems** of Maidenhair Fern are thin and shiny and resemble a vigorous crop of hair. They have been used for hair and scalp, as well as alopecia areata (Harris 1985, p. 125f).

Swollen knots at the leaf/stem insertion point are considered a signature for swollen joints and joint problems. Some herbalists use the Knotweeds in this way. Native Americans use Knotweed to break up hard, arthritic nodular deposits around the joints (Wood 2008, p. 394). Chinese Cornbind, *Ho Shou Wu,* is useful for "weak 'rubbery' feeling in knees and lower back" (Reid 1995 p. 77). Jewelweed is very watery and has swollen joints. It serves in dropsical conditions (Harris 1985, p. 116). The **knotted stem** of the Knotweed is the "knot signature" which "has also inspired the use of Knotweed as an antidote to magical curses made by tying knots in strings. Thus, William Salmon (1710) notes in passing, "Some use it in the transplantation of diseases, and removing of incantations" (Wood 2008, p. 394).

The leaf stems of trailing Ground Ivy grow **hairy tumors** caused by insects as the season grows old. It has of old been used for boils, tumors, and abscesses (Harris 1985, p. 78). Wood reconfirms its usefulness in cancerous growths (2008, p. 281f).

Straight, rhythmically structured stems reminiscent of the spine can be a spine signature—Horsetail Grass springs to mind. Please refer to the *Organ Signature* section for more details.

S-curved stems can stand for the naturally S-curved spine. Black Cohosh sprouts and spikes make undulating S-curves while growing. They dry into a painfully contracted, stiff S-curve when going to seed: a prime remedy for whiplash and spinal issues. The otherwise straight stem of Blue Flag Iris dries into an S-curve under the proportionally big and heavy skull-shaped seed pod. The flower essence is excellent for neck problems.

Curled-up stems like that of unfurling Ferns has been taken as a signature for a worm-expelling remedy since the ancient Greeks. The Cherokee Indians recognized the same signature (ibid, p. 95). Many ferns are known to contain vermifuge substances. Maidenhair Fern was used "to help unbend and straighten the constricted muscles of the rheumatic patient" by the Native North Americans, who used it for initial rheumatic pains (ibid., p. 125). Royal Fern is used for lower back pain with great success.

The ***stems*** of Scarlet Pimpernel ***that bend or curve backward*** have been regarded as a signature for epilepsy, for which it has an old curative reputation (ibid., p. 143).

Creepers, Climbers and Winding Plants

Since the stem is usually what gives a plant uprightness, these "spineless" plants cannot hold themselves upright. It is an overall *yin* signature. In all flower essences that I am aware of that are made of creeping or winding plants, the person needing them **lacks healthy strength of ego**, or sense of self. This can take on several flavours: in Clematis, the person is not present, but fleeing the challenge of life by daydreaming. The Vine personality is a bully, not based on true inner strength, but out of an inner weakness that needs to overgrow, engulf, and suffocate others in the same way that a wild

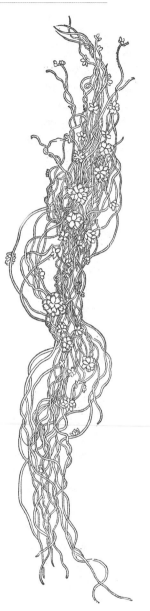

Dodder

vine kills big trees. Morning Glory people are prone to all kinds of addictive behavior out of a lack of healthy ego strength. Mullein, on the other hand, grows very straight and tall, thus being an excellent spine remedy, giving inner integrity and honesty—when it is blown over, the upper part of the plant will reassume the upright position.

Creepers in herbalism are also used for magic as **binding** remedies: Periwinkle is a prime example (Gould, 2008). It was thought to bind a couple together for life. Similarly, Haitian Morning Glory is used for binding spells (Derivière). Not only does it bind in this way, but physiologically it stops diarrhea, bleeding, etc. Culpeper called it "the great binder." Binding here refers to their action of stopping a flux, such as Periwinkle for blood, or Chinese Cornbind (*Polygonum multiflorum, ho shou wu*) stops spermatorrhea. If one ponders the chaotic tangle Periwinkle forms on the ground, one can appreciate that as a flower essence, it "helps to clear the mind and engender a sense of inner clarity" (McIntyre 1996, p. 236). Tangles help to disentangle. The uprightness of the stem is *yang* and connected with a sense of individuation. The absence of this in creepers like Periwinkle make clearer why they would bind a couple in love—in order to stay true to one another for a whole lifetime, one would certainly have to abdicate some sense of individualism.... Bittersweet Vine (*Celastus*) as a Native American remedy is a climber which hangs over hedge rows and borderlines. It has to do with entanglements and unclear boundary issues (Matthew Wood). Some climbers have tendrils, others, such as Ivy, can attach themselves to trees and walls by way of their roots. These plants (Ivy, Periwinkle, Passion Flower, Wild Yam, or the European cousin, *Tamus cummunis*), which can hold other plants in their grips of clasping tendrils or otherwise, have anti-spasmodic qualities. Ivy has also been understood to remedy pain as if from pressure around the body part, since it strangles whatever it grows on. It is useful for intracranial pressure, for instance (Harris 1985, p. 114f). The most archetypal of the plants to discuss here would be Dodder (*Cuscuta* sp.). Reduced to a mere stem with flowers, this leafless parasite without root chokes whatever plant it ensnares, and can over-run vast areas. Fittingly, the Afro-Haitian herbalist Oliama Derivière uses it as his prime asthma remedy, a disease that causes the bronchial to muscles strangle the sufferer. The local name is *Lamitié,* a Creole word for friendship. In addition to its use for asthma, it has been employed as a love charm in the following way: one throws some Dooder into the yard of the person one loves. If it takes root, the person will be received favorably. Fuchs remarks that it opens the bile flow of the liver when congested, and thus helps in jaundice and relaxes spasms of the ducts (1543, chap. 131).

Fine, ***thread-like stems***, especially between creeping plants such as in Cinquefoil, Septfoil (*Potentilla*), Cleavers and Goldthread roots (*Coptis*) are taken as a "needle-and-thread" signature, which means it's a wound herb which stitches back together the open wound and are thus also useful for bleeding and ulcers.

Dodder; showing the orange thread-like growth (photo by Cynthia Thomas)

The ***trailing stems*** of creeping Ground Ivy have been given the same meaning. In Strawberry, they seem to also be a blood circulation signature. Similarly, the ***creeping stems*** of Woodbine, Strawberry, Yarrow, and other herbs have been taken as a signature for a blood vessel signature (ibid., under the mentioned plants).

Goldthread (Coptis genus) rootlets (photo by Sandra Lory)

Harris names vines as a ***signature for nerves and the bloodstream***, for instance Virginia Creeper is a blood cleansing alterative. Other traditions also speak of vines as magic herbs used for binding: Passion Flower and Honeysuckle vines were used in rituals as an image for the two lovers clinging together. The lore of the Maya explains the origin of the Vanilla by saying that it sprung from the blood of two inseparable lovers. The above-mentioned Chinese Cornbind is said to have been discovered as an herb that works against infertility when it was observed that the vines would embrace and cling to one another, then part again, only to embrace anew.

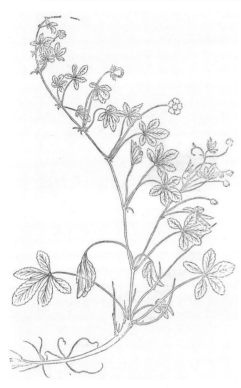

Cinquefoil

The vine of the Maya species of Wild Yam is seen as a signature for the **blood vessels** by the local women (Kimberly Hart). This is also true of Periwinkle, which is a prime herb to enhance circulation, especially in the brain. Arvigo names it as a plant for high blood pressure in her *Rainforest Remedies* (1998, p. 159). Grapevine leaves is the most used herb to increase circulation in France. The French herbalists use specifically the red variety, again adding to the blood signature.

Native Americans not only saw climbers as a signature for blood vessels, but also for the **nerves**. We can appreciate this if we imagine a native society preparing the kill of the hunt for eating, and pulling blood vessels and nerves out of the flesh—they look like a tangled vine. And what are stems but the plants' organs to transport fluids, nutrients, minerals and salts, hormones, and even electrical impulses. In France, leaves from red grape vines are a well-known circulatory remedy. Passion Flower vine bears other nerve sedating signatures, too, and is a good example. *Rauwolfia serpentaria* is a tranquilizing climber (Harris 1985, p. 154f).

We have seen the theme of climbers and winding plants as love charms and to cast binding spells. Vanilla is another wonderful example: it is a long, climbing orchid whose aerial roots fasten themselves to the host tree. Mexican mythology tells us that when one of the princesses, forbidden to marry a mortal, fled to the forest and was beheaded with her lover, and Vanilla Orchids grew where their blood touched the ground. In the light of this discussion, we will not be surprised to find that it is a nerve remedy that acts not only on the brain, but also has an effect on the spinal column (ibid., p. 186). It stimulates the nerves, brain, and is an aphrodisiac (an effect shared by other orchids, which are nerve tonics and tone the sexual powers via strengthening the nerves), as well as having an effect on the circulation (Murphy 2000, p. 1821). The origination myth fittingly talks of two inseparable lovers, clinging to one another like the vine to the tree. The image of the symbiotic couple fits the symbiosis the orchid has with one specific kind of pollinating bee, and its being a sexual tonic. Other vines used in love magic to bind lovers together are Periwinkle, Passion Flower, and Honeysuckle.

Tendrils have to do with the plant reaching out and holding on. They correspond to those abilities in us. The way tendrils reach out and hold on for life once they touch speaks of clinginess. I have noticed that severely codependent women, some of them inescapably so because of being tied to handicapped children, tend to draw flowers with tendrils. It is via those tendrils that plants cling to other plants to pull themselves up. So they are a signature for codependence. This becomes especially clear when pondering the tendril that has not found anything to pull itself up on, and, clasping around nothing, tightens its grip onto thin air. They can also indicate a spasmolytic plant.

Canes that arch and re-root at the tip where they touch the ground as in Blackberries and Wild Roses stand for a very strong, uncontainable life force, but also of their abilities as pioneering plants: they invade, form tangles in which young trees can grow up undisturbed by wildlife, until they finally shade out the ***brambles*** and a new forest is born. The pioneering abilities of the brambles stand for strong willpower and ability for manual work, or carrying out manual tasks, for much life force in the limbs. Wild Rose and Blackberry flower essence help to break through apathy and stop procrastination. They make the energy descend into the limbs (this is partially due to their fivefold nature, but they do this much more so than the other *Rosaceae*).

Buds and Shoots

A Cabbage is really a ***gigantic swelled-up bud.*** When cut horizontally, the pattern looks like a spinal chord or diaphragm. Red Cabbage (which is the preferred color) is healing to chest ailments, as well as for stomach ulcers—the two organs between which the diaphragm is sandwiched. Harris takes the spinal pattern to refer to the spinal nerves, and quotes Cabbage as a nerve calming remedy and good for insomnia (Harris 1985, p. 75f). The famous French herbalist Maurice Messegue, however, became famous for his treatment of rheumatism and arthritis, putting large, round Cabbage leaves on to the large, round joints. A French *truc de grandmère* (grandmother's trick, or home remedy) is to put a warmed, slightly bruised Cabbage leaf over one's head to chase a headache. Don't we call it a head of Cabbage? A friend had learned this from her grandmother in Normandy and would go to bed with a Cabbage leaf over her head like a hood, swearing it was useful. A different example is the large, edible flower bud of Artichoke, excellent for curing gallbladder headaches. The head-like flower bud here points to the head.

Horse Chestnut makes seven layers of **very sticky scales** to protect its embryonic leaves and flowers throughout the winter. For more on the meaning, look under *Stickiness* in chapter 9, on *The Feel When Touched.*

The dried flower buds of Clove are **tooth-shaped** and such a good remedy for toothache and gum infections that the cloves and Clove oil still sell as such in places like India, and are even used in modern-day dentistry.

The Zulu and Xhosa like many other nations around the world saw the sprouting flowers of *Agapathus* and *Asclepias spp.* as **phallic or snake-like**, and used these as aphrodisiacs, for barrenness, or as snakebite remedies. Their name for *Agapanthus* was "a snake in the grass." Similar associations and uses apply to phallic shoots worldwide. The *Allium* species such as kitchen Onion, similar to *Agapanthus,* have flower buds that are covered by sheets, from which the flowers emerge once the phallic stem has reached its full height. These have been seen as a signature for both the sheath of the glans penis and the womb in birthing (Wright 2007, p. 3ff). Well-known for their aphrodisiac qualities, Garlic and Onion and their kin were also employed to "provoke urine and mensis," expel worms, and to treat the bites of venomous animals (Culpeper 1653, p. 206). Culpeper also names Onions as a drawing agent, fitting for a snakebite remedy, and says they increase sperm, "especially the seed of them." While I do not know what he meant by the latter, it sounds very much as if it increased its quality, especially the success in fathering children (ibid.). Coles says of Garlic: "the decoction thereof used for a Bath, or Fume to sit over, brings down the Flowers [menstruation] and afterbirth [placenta]." He remarks that it "dryeth the Seed of Generation," thus being too hot to increase the quality of semen like Onion or Solomon's Seal, rather decreasing its quality (Coles 1657, p. 136f). Snake-looking signatures were often seen as worm-like, and thus Garlic is also a time-honoured vermifuge (Gerard 1633, p. 178).

The nascent sprouts of Stone Root emerge as ***livid purple loops*** from the ground. It is a prime remedy for hemorrhoids with passive venous congestion, which look like livid purple loops.

Twigs and Branches

The ***wart-like excrescences*** on Thuja twigs honour the doctrine of signature with the finest anti-wart remedy.

The ***heavy, drooping*** branches of Horse Chestnut that curve back up at the tips illustrate the venous blood giving in to gravity for which it is a remedy.

The branch of Elder, filled by a soft pith that can be pushed out, is a signature for its diaphoretic action and of pushing out mucus from the bronchial tubes (Harris 1985, p. 91) and nasal cavities.

Sap and Latex

The rise and fall of the ***sap*** in plants and especially trees has of old been seen as related to the blood. This is especially clear in the old folk ideas about blood, as for instance in the states of Southern US American folk medicine. As the sap thins and rises in the trees in spring, so does the blood thin and rise with spring and summer heat. As the sap falls and thickens in the fall, so does the blood thicken and become heavier in the winter season of the year. Thus, Sassafras bark to thin the blood is picked in spring, and in the fall to thicken the blood. Its medicinal properties change according to the seasons.

The leaves of Celandine, reminiscent of liver lobes, ooze yellow latex when injured. They show the signature of a jaundiced liver.

Large amounts of ***watery liquid*** flowing from a cut plant obviously indicate a high water content. This points to an action on the water economy of the body, and the urinary system. Examples are Squashes, Pumpkins and Melons, Cucumbers, but also Celery.

Latex or milk sap has already been discussed in the chapter on color and we may be reminded of its consciousness-diminishing properties, Opium being the prime example. As we saw, latex is often rich in protein-digesting enzymes and thus the latexes of Celandine, Dandelion, Staghorn, Sumac, Fig, Milkweed and so on have all been topically applied digest warts and other excrescences. Harris takes the fact that Celandine latex exudes slowly (thus forming excrescences as it dries) as a signature for it removing them, hence it is used for warts, corns, eczema and ringworm (Harris 1985, p. 78f).

It is also a milk-signature, and some plants rich in milk sap have been named *Polygala* in Latin, meaning "much milk," or "rich in milk." Milkweed (*Asclepias syriaca* and other species) and Milkwort (*Polygala spp.*) were used by the Native North Americans as what Harris calls "symbolic therapy" to prevent faulty lactation (Harris 1985, p. 31 and 128). This is the only signature he does not seem to trust. I myself could not relate much to latex standing for increased lactation, and asked the Haitian herbalist of African tradition Oliama Derivière his opinion on this. He said "Not all plants with latex improve lactation, but some of them do. I know of two, for example *Coton rouge* (Red Cotton)." David Winston confirmed that the Cherokee hold the belief that milk sap increases the flow of milk. He named Dandelion and Wild Lettuce as examples. In Belize, Wild Poinsettia of the *Euphorbiacea* family is used (Arvigo and Balick 1998, p. 221). I only fully understood white latex as a galactagogue signature after reading Culpeper: he explains that Lettuce "increases milk in nurses," because "the Moon ownes them, and that's the reason they cool and moisten what heat and dryness causes, because Mars has his fall in Cancer" (Culpeper 2007, p. 170). In other words, if lactation is lacking due to dryness and heat in the tissue, Wild Lettuce, Dandelion and similar plants will be the remedy. This is confirmed by Wild Poinsettia's use "to relieve swollen breasts," indicating mastitis (Arvigo and Balick 1998, p. 221). Steiner relates latex to a long bygone phase of cosmic development called "the old Moon," thus latex is a Moon signature. Fitting for a lunar substance, many of them are related to sleep and dreams such as the narcotic and hallucinogenic Poppy and Wild Lettuce latexes (Pelikan 1980, p. 111ff). The Moon, in turn, is the planet which also rules the first seven years of life, especially infancy, and watery events such as lactation.

Some of the milk sap containing plants have been used for leucorrhea and other catarrhal or oozing conditions, such as Queen's Root (Harris 1985, p. 152). Lion's Foot is another example of which the white sap would be the signature for leucorrhea. Seneca Snakeroot was used for catarrh. He states that Native Americans took the oozing juice as the signature of pus flowing from a wound or canker sore (ibid., p. 123).

Latex is also a sticky exudate which closes up the plant's wound. Harris says of the abundant milk sap of Milkwort, "Its true intent is antiseptic, to heal broken skin and infected sores. The milky exudation was also thought to quicken the removal of deposits from the bowels and kidneys" (ibid., p. 128). Thus, latex also takes a similar meaning as a signature as the gums and resins discussed below.

I am not aware of a meaning of the **sugar-rich sap** yielded by several plants, such as Sugar Maple or Agave, beyond its obvious significance for nurturing. Pelikan (1984, p. 44f) describes Sugar Maple as a tree that has kept its internal chemistry in a liquid phase rather than making its carbohydrates into hardwood, keeping them as a sugary liquid. He relates this to the liver, an organ that deals with hydrating sugars to put them back into the blood stream. This is all in keeping with the Jupiter signature of Maple (see under *Planetary Signature*), since the liver is ruled by Jupiter. I have always been impressed how much young Sugar Maple flowers look like drooping threads of sugar syrup. Herbalist Kate Gildae found that Sugar Maple flower essence helps access a sense of nurturing and sweetness of life.

Gums and Resins

Gums and resins are the result of the plant's sap leaking out, for the most part due to an injury to the plant tissue, although in some cases, the resinous exudation is spontaneous. As it leaks out, it turns hard and sticky, thus sealing the plant's wound. This is the perfect signature of the blood coagulating to close off a wound, the sap indeed being the plant's blood as it were. The same image could be taken to mean a wound that has become pussy. We are not surprised to find gums and resins utilized as wound healers the world over, from Fir Balsam (*Abies balsamea*) used by the Native Americans, to the Myrrh and Frankincense of the Near East, to "Dragonblood" resin in China. Many of them stem from Conifers, and many of them

Resins exude when the plant is injured, as the pine in this photo. They are a signature for coagulated blood and mucus, which they resemble and treat.

are highly aromatic. While one could argue that it is the antiseptic value of those essential oils that make them so valuable for wound healing, there are also gums that do not contain any, such as Gum Arabic from Acacia trees. They serve the same healing purpose, however. The more aromatic and warming, the more the action will penetrate the tissue and break up what is called *congealed blood* in Traditional Chinese Medicine. This is considered "reducing *kapha*" in Ayurveda (their prime example of an aromatic resin is *guggulu*), or, in Western terms, a stimulating action to depressed tissue. Gum Arabic is a non-aromatic gum that becomes viscid and soothes the mucus membranes of throat and bronchi, as well as in the intestinal tract, aiding expectoration. The list of examples here is so long and impressive, that it is hard to say this signature is "all in the mind"; we can name Acacia, Balm of Gilead, Balsam Fir, exudation of Wild Cherry, Dragonblood, Frankincense, Guggulu, Myrrh, Pine resin, Sumac (the milk), Storax, Spruce, Spurge, Tamarack, Tolu, Turpentine, Tragacanth, White Pine, Grindelia, and Rosin Weed (Harris 1985, 1985, under the plants concerned). Another example is Yerba Santa, the leaves of which are covered in resin. It most effectively brings up cold, wet mucus from the lungs, since it is warming and drying. The resinous leaves collect dust as the year grows old, looking increasingly like tar-stained lung tissue. The coming together of the resin and lung signature make the healing effect gravitate toward this organ. The resinous scales of Horse Chestnut buds stand for being held back by the past, as the flower essence has shown. Propolis also belongs in this section, since it is made mainly out of the resin the bees collect off of poplar bud scales.

Resins from resinous trees make their wood immune against fungal attacks, which explains why they take so much longer to rot. Tamarack, for instance, and Larch wood in Europe have this property, and it is a signature for the antiseptic properties of resins.

Gums and resins are sticky like mucus, thus *kapha*. They treat *kapha* conditions, such as catarrhs, bruises, as well as what would be called "congealed blood" in Chinese medicine. Apart from being wound healers and moving congealed blood, the stickiness of gums and resins has been recognized as a signature for sticky or stuck mucus, which these substances promptly dissolve. This is again in part due to the present essential oils, or for the gums the mucilaginous substances. The latter are also demulcent, in their own way softening the tissues, which the resins do by way of their essential oil content breaking down the congealed blood.

The Bark

Gums and resins are often exudates of the bark, and the bark is the outer skin of woody plants, its outer barrier, thus reinforcing our outer barrier. They are two parts of the same signature—the bark being the skin, and the sap being blood oozing from the wound. We will again encounter an endless list of barks being used for skin healing purposes. Some of them have simply been employed to heal up wounds, other have been recognized to have special signatures. Slippery Elm is called thus, because the inner bark is mucilaginous, in fact one of the most valuable agents to lubricate the passage of whatever it might be; in constipation, passage of stones or the baby, or to cough up phlegm. Most barks are rich in tannins and minerals and are thus rather astringent and drying, thus toughening to the skin and mucosa. Tannins literally make the mucosal surface proteins lie flat to make a stronger surface protection. They are thus used to transform animal hides into leather. They are the dead substance pushed out by the growing tree in the case of thick outer barks such as Oak, or the thin living layer, utilized in Witchhazel (both are prime astingents). Witchhazel's medicinal effect goes more to the blood; it is no wonder that the tea or tincture turns red. The smooth, white bark of Birch has been taken as a signature for clean skin, and the tree, happy resident of swamps, cleans out our lymphatic system and toxins from the blood in a very effective way of clearing the skin from the inside out.

The **thick, rough bark** of Oak is a signature for it having and bestowing strong outer boundaries, in this case tanning leather and toughening skin and mucosa, our "bark."

The slightly *scaly and rough bark* of Dogwood has been taken as a signature for ulcers and erylsipela (Harris 1985, p. 90).

Excrescences on the bark of Birch were made into moxa for warts by the Native Americans (ibid., p. 68).

Peeling bark as of Plantain Trees or European Birch have been taken as a signature for skin regeneration. In Hydrangea (Sevenbarks), it has been taken to signify the kidney or gallstones flaking off in layers under its action (ibid, p. 113).

Lenticles, as in Elder or Witchhazel, are fissures in the stem's epidermis that serve as breathing pores. Harris names them as a signature for itching and inflammation of the skin, pimples, acne, and other skin eruptions. Native Americans used Witchhazel in their sweat baths, and for skin irritations, burns and insect bites . "The lenticles [of Wild Cherry bark] indicate the astringent and healing properties of the bark, a decoction of which may be allied directly to external sores and cuts" (ibid., under the plants discussed). Elder's oval lenticles are a prime signature pointing to the skin and pores, and Elder is the best diaphoretic among all European remedies.

The Shape of Fruits, Seeds and Seed Pods

Fruits and seeds come in al kinds of shapes: as burrs, with prickles, blown up pods, winged, fuzzy, or plump and juicy. Apart from their shapes being tied in with the predominant element (see in the chapter on the elements) or the healing properties being determined by their color, we can outline a few basic considerations.

The **large, round, and heavy pods** of Cocoa spring directly from the branch and mature in the shade of the tropical rainforest. Attributed to the Aztec Goddess of the Earth, the entire signature of this tree is of a predominance of the earth element. When cut open, the mature seed pod sports a five-pointed star with five bean-shaped seeds arranged around what is called *la placenta*. Thus it is not surprising that Cocoa has of old been called "food of the gods," since it is a plant that nurtures all of the human being. A tonic for

The white substance inside the cocoa pod is seen as a signature for sperm in its native Mexico. It is called "la placenta," a name we can appreciate from seeing it wrapped around the embryo-like cocoa beans. Cocoa is therefore used as a fertility tonic (photo by Sandra Lory)

the weak and sick, the seeds of this pod that looks like a pregnant belly or round abdomen filled with organs, it was used in the West since the discovery of the Americas. William Coles writes:

> The *Confection* made of *Cocoa* called *Chocolate* which may be had in divers places in *London* at reasonable rates, being taken in substance, or, as is more usual, relented in Milke, is of wonderful efficacy for the *procreation of Children*; for it not only vehemently incites *Venus*, but causeth Conception in Women, and hastens and facilitates their delivery, and besides that, it preserves health, it makes such as drinke it often to become fat and corpulent. (Coles 1657, p. 44f)

The hulled seeds look like guts, and accordingly Coles lauds Cocoa for digestion and the plague of the guts, which seems to be dysentery. He lists Cocoa and Chocolate under aphrodisiacs, and they are also used in this way in the African cultures where Cocoa is cultivated. Vermont herbalist Sandra Lory gives the following account:

> Sturdy and voluptuous, her trunk and branches bear huge and heavy cavernous fruits of gold, maroon and copper. Her delicate blossoms are tiny spider-like florescent clusters that face downward toward the rich, moist soil. She is an under story tree and thrives in the bio-diverse, dim jungle. A sacred plant, Cocoa is called *Yollotl Eztli,* or "Heart Blood," in one ancient Mexican language. From her plant signature, one can see that a single fresh bean resembles a vital organ rich with blood. An opened pod is uterine in form, and the cord that links the seeds together inside is called *la placenta* in Spanish. This gives great insight into her medicinal capability. Cocoa's plant spirit leads us to our own hearts, to bittersweet experience, to teachings of the Earth Mother, divine nourishment, gravity, and power. Many creation stories involve the Cocoa tree, and Maya Cocoa growers consume chocolate drinks prior to planting corn to celebrate the birth of a child and on feast days. Maya Healer Ms. Beatrice Waight taught me to use the leaves as a poultice to cure fevers and headaches. Ecuadorian healer Rocio Alarcon uses a warm paste of ground chocolate in a traditional breast massage technique that drains the lymph. (from her presentation "Global Golds: Cacao, Sugar Cane, and Coffee, Three Sacred Plants of the Global South")

While we could call Cocoa pods pregnant uterus-shaped, other large, round, heavy tropical fruits such as Papaya are empty. Known for digesting protein, the enzyme papain also breaks down progesterone. Papaya is eaten in Sri Lanka as a contraceptive (Wood 2008, p. 164). The

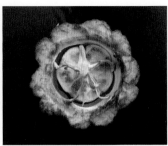

Raw, shelled Cocoa bean (left); cross section (center); and Cocoa star
(courtesy of herbalist Sandra Lory)

An unususal view of Black Walnut sporting a heart signature. Before overly rich food became a threat to public health, the rich unsaturated oil of Black Walnut was a valuable healing food for brain and cardiovascular health. Black Walnut leaves were used to treat enlarged heart and blood vessels, as well as ballooned intestines. This photo captures the image of Black Walnut's power to hold in the flabby tissue of a dilapidated heart. Walnut flower essence will open an emotionally armored heart.
(photo by herbalist Sandra Lory)

empty fruit is the non-pregnant belly. The full and heavy Avocado is very nutritious, thus good to eat for pregnant women. The tea made from the seeds is a natural contraceptive used in Belize.

Nuts with nut meat, with their hardness around a soft core, pertain to the skull and brain. The Walnut is nature's precise imitation of the scull and brain in two hemispheres, with the skin of the walnut looking like the pia mater. However, a cracked-open Walnut also looks like the intestinal cavity filled with intestines (Walnut is an excellent remedy to restore intestinal health), as well as a vessel filled with of squirming worms (it is a famous anthelmitic). Nutmeg nut is another example of a skull-like nerve remedy. Haitian herbalist Derivière uses Nutmeg to close open fontanelles in children (externally). He employs ripe Coconut to heal headaches, fevers, and kidney ailments—the latter two correspond to the water content of the Coconut.

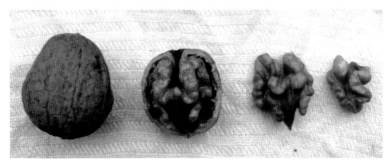

Walnuts show several signatures. To the left, the most famous nut, looking like a skull with the brain. Walnut oil was an important nerve and brain nutrient in the ancient times, before people were generally overfed. The second image from the left could also be seen as a brain, as well as an abdominal cavity, with the intestines curled inside. Black Walnut is an important remedy for ballooned intestines (leaves), as well as intestinal parasites (hulls). The third walnut shows how they have two lobes, like a thyroid. Black walnut hulls are one of the best thyroid remedies. The walnut piece to the right shows the worm-like shape, marking it as an anthelmintic.

Stone-like hard seeds, whether occurring by themselves or in a pod or fruit, have traditionally been regarded as a signature for stone-breaking remedies that break up kidney or gallbladder stones. Examples are Burdock and Gromwell (*Lithospermum*) seeds. This includes the stones of Plums and so on (Harris 1985, p. 59f). The same is true of the tiny hard seeds on Strawberries. They have been taken as a signature for gravel and stones, and employed as such with good success. Some of these remedies have also been useful for tartar and rheumatism, all diseases of precipitation of mineral-like matter within the body. Strawberries as a whole also look like skin erupting in allergic hives, and it is one of the worst hive-causing allergens.

Watery fruits such as a Cucumber and Watermelon consist mostly of water and are excellent diuretics and serve to increase the water content of the skin, thus promoting skin healing. In Haiti, Watermelon rinds were rubbed over one's face and neck to cool the head in the summer heat. This is very effective, and rejuvenates the facial skin at the same time.

Watery fruits with hard seeds such as Watermelon and Grapes act not only on the kidneys, but also help dissolve kidney stones (Harris 1985, p. 105f; Wood 2008, p. 221).

Soft fruit such as Peaches and Strawberries make me wonder whether they have a "touchy" and "softness" signature. According to Matthew Wood, Peaches were traditionally used by

Native Americans as medicine to "soften the blow" of bad news. They are the fruit that can "suffer a blow" more easily and bruise most upon falling than any other fruit I can think of, except of course for Strawberries, infamous for becoming mushy when handled. Wild Strawberry flower essence touches on the principle of inner child-like softness and sweetness, healing overly sensitive "touchiness." Coles recommends them for the treatment of leprosy. He also sees the fruits as heart-shaped and uses them in the treatment of heart palpitations (Coles 1657, p. 178).

The **peachy skin** of Peach is a signature for it being a fine skin healer for irritated skin, as well as its downiness pointing to it as a hair tonic (the boiled kernels in vinegar; Harris 1985, p. 138). We can appreciate the image in Chinese poems of women being of outstanding beauty when their cheeks are like peaches: this is the baby skin fruit! Peach kernel oil is also invaluable as a cosmetic oil. See under *soft fruit* above for more.

Round, sun-colored fruits such as Oranges and Grapefruits look like sun-lanterns hanging in the tree in sunny climates, where they sOak up tremendous amounts of sunshine while ripening. Like sunshine itself, the essential oils in their peels are anti-depressant, especially in the depression of winter in the dark Northern winters. They also stimulate bile flow and support the liver, as they should according to their color.

Orange peel skin is another name for cellulitis. Nothing in nature resembles cellulitis so much as citrus fruit peel. The cause is internal toxicity and lymphatic congestion, often combined with a toxic colon. Grapefruit and Orange stimulate peristalsis, and the essential oils of the peels detoxify. They are useful in the treatment of cellulitis (Davis 2004, in the relevant sections).

The **soft, boil-shaped fruits** of the Fig tree have been used to treat boils: "Cut into two and steeped for two to three minutes in hot water, the soft interior forms an excellent poultice for an abcess or inflammatory, maturing boils, or as an application to a gum boil. It is interesting to note that this food was used as a remedy for boils by Hezekiah over 2,400 years ago" (Harris 1985, p. 96). Figs are very soft fruit and have a softening effect throughout—softening boils, stool, and having a demulcent action on catarrhal conditions. What looks more like an abscess than a livid purple fig, red and yellow on the inside once it bursts open when overly ripe?

What is the thing that looks most like an **egg** in the plant world? An Avocado. What are eggs famous for nutritionally? Their high content of proteins and saturated fats. Avocados are equally high in protein and tropical saturated fats. They even have an egg-like taste. An Avocado is a huge tropical "tree egg," so to speak. Very nutritious, it is a good food for pregnant women. The tea of the seeds, however, is abortifacient. Certain mushrooms in the *Gasteroid* family look like brown eggs, and they are high in protein like an egg.

The rows of swollen **berries** of Poke Root, a chief lymphatic herb, remind me of strings of swollen lymph knots for which they are therapeutic. Raspberries, once plucked, resemble the uterus. Raspberry leaves are one of the best partum preparators, alleviating labor pain, as well as menstrual pain.

The **large stone** of Hawthorn berries is the signature of it being a stone remedy; Holly were used in the same manner (Coles 1657, pp. 367 and 386.)

The **bright red, flame-shaped fruits** of Cayenne pepper, heating, burning to the taste and upon touch, possibly causing blisters as if from a burn, are a clear fire signature. They combat cold diseases. Diarrhea being primarily a cold disease, they help prevent diarrhea from tropical diets.

The **star-shaped pods** of Star Anise look like the sinuses radiating from the root of the nose. It is excellent to clear sinus congestion, especially of the maxillaries (Wood 1997, p. 27).

Long, hanging seedpods of beans are taken to be a signature of skinniness, and the slimming effect of a rice and beans diet is well known (now said to be caused by the low glycemic count). Beans are also diuretic, and slimming in that sense. The long, brown, hanging seed pods of Senna and *Cassia fistulosa* and *grandis* resemble human stool and yield effective laxatives. Tamarind would be another example. In the case of Vanilla pods, they could be seen as a phallic shape, fitting for an aphrodisiac. For more on the Vanilla signature, see under *Climbers*.

The **straight, erect seeding spikes** of Plantain, with their snake-like look, mark it as a snakebite remedy, hence its folk name Snakeweed (Harris 1985, p. 146f). It is indeed one of the best remedies for bites of poisonous animals. Wood gives an account of how the leaves saved the life of a woman who was bitten by a black widow spider (1997, p. 391f).

Burrs or hairy seeds have been classified as remedies for the hypothalamus by Matthew Wood (unpublished material on the Endocrine System). He names the furry, brown seed pods of Burdock and Licorice, examples for Bear medicine (see under *Animal Signature*), suitable for a depleted adrenal cortex. *Pulsatilla* or Windflower seeds look like whiffs of clouds, hence they

Burdock burrs (photo by Sandra Lory)

are Cloud medicines. Wood describes the relationship of Cloud medicine to the hypothalamus, and homeopathic *Pulsatilla* covers about the same symptoms as potentized hypothalamus (the organ prepared to a homeopathic potency). The silvery hairy fuzz on Clematis seeds make the vine look dream-like as it sways on the hedge rows in autumn—a flower essence for daydreaming. "The hair of the head was represented by the hair of the globular, head-shaped fruits of castor and burdock." The receptacle of Burdock full of the downy seeds resembles a head full of hair: seeds and root have been famous for increasing the thickness of hair. Castor seed pods are covered with soft, hair-like spikes. The oil has been recommended as a hair tonic by Egyptians as early as 1552 BC (Harris 1985, p. 47 and 77), a function for which it is used still today in Haiti, as well as to stop hair loss and the hair to stay black. Horse Chestnuts have also been made into hair tonics. See also *burrs* below.

"***Thorny nuts and pods*** represent mental tension, obsessive thought, and mental illness (Thornapple, Horse Chestnut, Wild Cucumber)" (Wood 1997, p. 26) If we think of the round fruit as the head, then the thorns would represent spikes of mental tension protruding, like lightning rods or hairs standing on end. On another occasion, he mentioned prickly pods as a signature for an overactive brain. In the case of Sweet Chestnut, they stand for the profound anguish of the heart: Dr. Bach pioneered it as a flower essence for the "dark night of the soul." The ***spiky pod*** of Sweetgum is a wonderful example for the doctrine of signature—when green, it tangles with the other pods to form impenetrable barriers. This can be taken as a signature for its action of dissolving coagulated blood. When mature and drying, the round pod pops open all over and ejects seeds in all directions. For this reason, the Chinese call it "all roads open." Hence its medicinal action is that of opening all orifices—facilitating the movement of blood, chi, unblocking the meridians, promoting menses and lactation, as well as urination, flushing out edema. The dry seed pod with all "orifices" open does indeed look like the body with "all roads open."

Hollow seedpods stand for the hollow organs or blown up lungs, such as the dried seed pod of *Lobelia inflata* standing for a stomach (it relaxes *all* hollow organs, however, not just the stomach), and for the alveoli inflated in acute asthma.

The **heart-shaped seed pod** of Shepherd's Purse denotes a remedy that strengthens the heart and uterus. Filled with countless tiny seeds, it is also a gravel remedy that removes even the finest of gravel (Wood 2008, p. 159ff). It's two sides can also been seen as the two kidneys on either side of the spine, filled with gravel.

Lobelia inflata (*Indian Tobacco*), *showing the blown-up seed pods like an alveoli in asthma*

The **claw-shaped seed pods** of the rare South African Devil's Claw is an excellent herb for rheumatoid arthritis and other painful conditions—with pains as if claws were in the flesh. In fact, it is dreaded to step onto one of those seed pods on the ground lest one of the many spines beset with hooks get into one's flesh. It also looks like a hand gnarled by arthritis. Devil's Claw is a present-day pop herb with a very clear signature. Our ordinary Figwort, with its knotty and knobby roots, contains the same medicinally active compounds as Devil's Claw does and has been used traditionally for swollen, arthritic joints.

The recurved spines of the nut burrs of Beech nuts were taken by Native Americans as a signature for lower back pain. The nuts and leaves are also kidney remedies, and who ever had a kidney ailment knows how much that distorts the lower back in pain (Harris 1985, p. 66f). It is interesting to note that burrs developed when mammals occurred, to which fur they could stick. Strangely, Burdock yielding burrs is one of the best fur-enhancing plants (e.g. increases hair growth—the oil applied externally), and Agrimony with its burrs treats "a bad hair day," that is unmanageable and tangling hair (Wood). Another example of a burr-like seed is Castor plant, and castor oil stimulates hair growth, too.

Phallic seedpods or glands may stand for male prowess; examples are acorns and *Impatiens* seed pods, the latter even ejecting the seeds far upon the slightest touch, image of premature ejection. The flower essence of Pale Corydalis, also called Harlequin Flower, can evoke dreams about sexual abuse by a male perpetrator in sexual abuse victims as they work through the issue. Vanilla beans, on the other hand, are aphrodisiacal.

Watery plants with many small seeds are seen as signature for kidneys and gravel, such as in Purslane (ibid., p. 150).

Winged seeds denote a strong relationship with the air, a lightness. A lovely example is that of the Australian Dagger Hakea, a flower essence from a nastily thorny bush, hence "dagger." The flowers transform into white winged seeds that fly off like little angels: it is the flower essence for resentment and bitterness toward those close to us, and teaches us forgiveness. What nicer illustration for the release of forgiveness than angel-winged seeds sailing away.... (White 1996, p. 69). **Parachute-like seeds** of Dandelion and the thistles that travel far and wide in the wind give those flowers a sense of boundless freedom. This ability to ascend is a *yang* signature (ascending, light), and, as herbalist Jacquelin Guiteau says, "Once high up in the air, the parachute has to come back down—dandelion and its relatives like burdock and thistle are all making toxins come down and out." The crystalline parachute part is made of organic silica, imbuer of light. All these plants "brighten the *chi*" as flower essences, and give a sense of boundless freedom and fearlessness. See above under *hairy seeds* for the seeds of Burdock.

The seeds of Viper's Bugloss resemble the **head of a snake**, and the plant has a long reputation of a snakebite remedy (Harris 1985, p. 74).

Our common Linden tree does not only have **heart-shaped** leaves, but the seed once freed from its pod is reddish brown and looks like the anatomical heart. Shepherd's Purse is easiest recognized by its heart-shaped seed pods. Both have cardiovascular properties. The latter can also be taken to be uterus-shaped, since it stems uterine bleeding and heal prolapse of the organ.

There are countless **organ signatures** among the fruits and seeds. Some famous examples include Walnuts and other tree nuts looking like the skull with the brain, Sweet Chestnuts being heart-shaped, Horse Chestnuts looking like the liver, and *Lobelia inflata* seed pods looking like inflated alveoli or a stomach. Beans resemble kidneys. Of course they all heal those organs. Nutmeg seeds look like a skull, and are a wonderful narcotic for a hyperactive brain. Gooseberry (*Physalis peruviana*) fruit in their paper lantern mark it with a bladder signature as a diuretic.

The Shapes of Roots

Grohmann points out that roots in general are much less differentiated in form and colors than the rest of the plant. "The root grows in the opposite direction from the shoot, thus showing affinity to the earth. It is averse to light and seeks darkness and damp; only rarely does it appear above the ground. Through its root, the plant becomes united with Mother Earth. Though each species has its characteristic root system, the differences between plants are far greater in their upper parts. Living in the soil gives roots a certain similarity of appearance" (1989, vol. 1, p. 18). It should not be too surprising that roots tend to be rich in minerals and harden quickly, thus being the "earth-element pole" of the plant, nurturing our earth element in return. Little differentiation none withstanding, there are several root forms that stick out and take meaning. The most basic consideration is whether the roots are strong or weak.

Strong roots indicate a strong stance, grounding, and a strong relationship with the earth. This may be one reason why the Native Americans, so dedicated to Mother Earth, preferred the roots as the part used in herbalism. We can also consider the size of the roots in relationship to the entire plant: by looking at the herbaceous part of Stone Root, one could never predict the size and shape of the big, round roots. This relative imbalance speaks of a predominance of *Apana vayu*, of too much energy below. Hence it is a prime remedy for hemorrhoids, where the venous blood is bunched up below as it where. Hellebore is a Lily that grows in the stones near cold brooks, and its long, thread-like roots are strong like iron ties.

It is a prime homeopathic remedy for strong diarrhea with icy coldness all over the body. As a flower essence, it gives a strong stance and empowers.

Vertical roots such as tap roots are *yang,* **horizontally** creeping ones *yin* (for more on *yin* and *yang,* see the section below).

Taproots, going straight down, form one straight line. They reach down deep and therefore are often mineral-rich. They render the plant practically impossible to rip out or eradicate—the slightest bit left in the soil can regrow into an entire plant. This shows how much life force these plants have below. It is a signature for groundedness and the ability to take a stand.

Horizontal roots give rise to **perpendicular intersections with the stem**, a Native American Indian signature for transformation or "need of a new direction in life." Wood gives a lucid description of this for *Apocynum androsaemifolium,* which he calls Werewolf Root. Even more unusually so, it forms "T"s, with one part of the root running off in the opposite direction of the other (1997, p. 125ff). Right angles are a wolf medicine signature. Solomon's Seal rhizome does not only form a right angle with the stem, but is also fleshy, sweet and nutritious. It is a remedy for needing a new direction in life, as well as lack of tissue nutrition—see also the paragraph below.

Pilewort (Ficaria ranunculoides)

The **banded rhizome** of Calamus is ribbed and strongly resembles a trachea. It is one of the best remedies for hoarse voice, laryngitis, and other respiratory problems. It's Sanskrit name, *vacha,* means voice.

Many roots are the plant's **storage organ** for starch or sugars, and thus nutritious. This is a signature (a very obvious one) for tissue nutrition, and on a more subtle level for our ability to give and receive nurturance. This does not only apply to plants used as food stuffs such as Tobinamburs, Potatoes, or Yams, but also to medicinals such as Kudzu and Arrowroot, which yield Kudzu and Arrowroot starches. These nutritious roots, being storage organs, are usually round and "fat"; we could see them *kapha* caricatures (the typical *kapha* type being a "couch potato"). Being *kapha,* they naturally reduce *vata* where tissue nutrition is always less than optimal. The Maya variety of Wild Yam root is said to look like a heart above ground, and like a uterus below ground. It is healing to heart and uterus (Kimberly Hart).

Large, downward bearing roots, such as in Turkey Rhubarb or Poke Root, can point to badger remedies and speak of moving things down and out. Turkey Rhubarb is a powerful laxative. Wood names Poke Root as a remedy for "pushing through obstacles." This would also be true of the very powerful Asparagus sprout, only in the latter case, the pushing is upward, not downward. Poke was used by Native Americans for dysentery (Foster and Duke 1977, p. 56).

Hard roots that cannot be cut with a knife such as of Gravelroot, Wild Yam, or Stone Root point to hard, mineral rich parts of the body—the bones, or stone formation for the latter.

Another signature is ***entangled roots;*** Black Cohosh grows from a tangle and is one of the best flower essences to break from unhealthy entanglements in relationships. They can be a signature of intertwining snakes, pointing to a ***snake***bite remedy, or as in Pinkroot, also called Indian Pink (*Spigelia marilandica*), the rootlets look like small snakes or ***worms***, and is an effective anthelmintic (expeller of intestinal parasitic worms) and vermifuge (expeller of round worms) (ibid., p. 145). The roots of Black Cohosh creep across the soil surface like a bunch of dark snakes.

Snake-shaped roots are an important Native American signature for a snakebite remedy. Rattlesnake Root, also called Seneca Snakeroot (*Polygala senega*), was used by the Seneca Indians as a snakebite remedy. The root is twisted into a spiral like a snake. Rauwolfia has a long, snake-like root. It has been used in India for over three millennia as a snake and insect bite remedy (ibid., p. 154). While we might not believe in such things, snakebite remedies have been known to every culture, and there are enough case histories from the time of the eclectic doctors to prove that they work. The twice distorted (bi-stort) root of Bistort (Snakeweed) also marks it as a snakebite remedy, as well as one for hemorrhoids. William Coles breaks down the signature as follows: the root being reddish points to blood, thus it stems bleeding; it is snake-shaped, thus it is good for both snakebite, those of other venomous creatures, and polyps. It also looks like the sigmoid, making it a fine diarrhea remedy (Coles 1657, p. 75). Bistort is of use in the plague of dysentery type and a dilapidated colon.

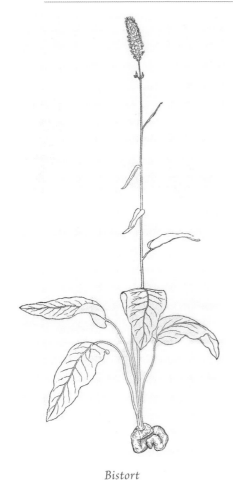

Bistort

The same is true for the Red Root: "Huron Smith interviewed a Meskwaki medicine man who valued *Ceanothus* highly for intestinal problems, because the **S-shaped roots** looked like an intestine. It is, indeed, a tonic astringent for failure to thrive due to diarrhea and lack of absorption in the gut.... Furthermore, the S-shaped root is surrounded by nodules that fix nitrogen; they look like lymphatic glands surrounding the intestines. Shortly after picking they shrivel up and disappear. It is an important remedy for swollen glands and water-filled cysts" (Wood 2009, p. 104).

The **penetrating roots** of Couch Grass, sporting a thorn-like tip at the ends of their long rootlets, can thus poke through much larger and sturdier roots of other plants. "A decoction of the roots is considered a most worthy penetrant of clogged urinary apparatus, to help eliminate stone and gravel from the kidneys and the bladder. It is a thorough demulcent-diuretic and is especially useful in the treatment of cystitis and other catarrhal diseases of the genitourinary tract" (Harris 1985, p. 90). Anyone who has ever gotten stung by the sharp tips of the roots will appreciate this "thorn" signature of the roots standing for pain, and cystitis can be very painful, indeed, passing kidney stones being considered about the most painful condition of all. Coles says it cures worms by signature—the roots here being the worms that penetrate the gut walls, I imagine.... He explains that the tangles of the roots look like a bed of worms (Coles 1657, p. 360).

Plantain has prominent "nerves" not only in the leaves, but the same *fine, linear* structure is also in the fine roots, a very nerve-like signature. Lady's Slipper was also called Nerve Root, and sports thin, fine roots resembling nerves. It is one of the best nervines available, especially for trigeminal neuralgia. Those same roots are taken by Harris to be a "needle-and-thread" signature of a wound herb that stitches a wound back together, as those of Gold Thread (*Coptis*) (ibid., p. 104f). The fine-meshed roots of Valerian, a prime nervine, are said to resemble the brain structure (ibid., p. 185).

The **swollen roots** of the aptly named Pilewort (*Ficaria ranunculoides*) look like slender Figs hanging from the plant and actually look like hemorrhoids, which they are employed to heal.

Bulbs are like drop-shaped, underground water-storage organs, helping especially the desert Monocots through periods of drought. Crocus or Snowdrop bulbs, for instance, truly are drop-shaped (see Grohmann 1989, vol. 2, on bulbous plants). They stand for water, moisture, and lubrication, and nourish *yin* and heal diseases cause by dried out tissues. Onions are special bulbs not made up out of scales like some of the others, but of **concentric layers** that are, in fact, spherical, and mirror the spherical inflorescences. Both speak of the concentric layers of the planet and the universe. The ancient Egyptians saw Onions as such sacred cosmic images that they included them in their religious rituals. They noted that the concentric layers all adhere to one another at one point, and saw that as the signature for contagion not to adhere to the patient, but to the bulb. It was thus hung up in sick rooms to absorb the poison (Harris 1985, p. 134). Onions are now known to be very antiseptic. Red Onion flower essence restores in us a sense of wholeness and connectedness with the entire cosmos. Matthew Wood sees the layered bulb as a signature for it being a shock remedy, restoring the energetic bodies to wholeness after being torn in a state of shock. The layers of the bulb here are the signature for the layers of the aura. William Coles thought of Onion bulbs having the shape of a head, and therefore being the remedy for head colds, as well as head lice (Coles 1657, chap. 226). They are, indeed, one of the best sneeze and snuffle remedy. Garlic bulbs have been likened to an abscess, for which a poultice thereof is very effective. The same logic and traditional use applies to Onions and Lily bulbs of various species (roasted bulb externally). Looking at the life of bulbs throughout the year, we see that they have a very rhythmic life—swelling from summer to fall, rooting in winter, breathing out as it were in spring and becoming very thin, only to swell again in an in-breath, as it where. While this is a signature pointing to respiratory healing, it is also analogous to the heart beat and menstruation. The bulbous lilies, which share such a life cycle, are healing in all three departments.

The **round tubers** of various Orchids, occurring mostly in pairs, have been seen traditionally as a testicles signature for a sexual tonic. However, they were equally famous as poultices on boils, themselves being boil-shaped (Fuchs 1543, chap. 210ff). The tubers of Cyclamen, called "Sow's Bread" in medieval Germany, are unusual for a member of the *Primula* family. It is big for the size of the plant, and stimulates all downward movements, such as stool and menses, as well as childbirth. It also heals hard swellings and tumors (ibid., chap. 171).

Herbalist Libby Rupp from Minnesota considers the **air pockets** in Peony roots a signature of the brain's ventricle (it being an epilepsy remedy), while in general air pockets such as those of Angelica root illustrate its relationship with the air element, as well as its aerating qualities to the tissue.

Brown, fuzzy, furry, oily nutritive roots such as of several *Umbelliferae* (Angelica, Lovage, *Lomaticum*, and Bear Root, also known as Balsamroot, or Osha—*Balsamorhiza*) and Spikenard are Bear medicines. They nourish and build up a depleted adrenal cortex and are a general tonic for the bear type (Wood, unpublished materials on the endocrine system).

Knobby roots have been taken as a signature for rheumatic joints, and used in this way. Wild Yam is a good example. Wood uses it also for osteoporosis, pointing to its **chalky** look as the signature (2009, p. 132). Hence its nickname Devil's Bones. The knobby roots of Sweetflag, Galanga (Harris 1985, p. 100) and Solomon's Seal are also used for rheumatic complaints. Based on the same signature, Stone Root was used by Native Americans for swollen joints and sprains (which makes sense given that it contains similar essential oils as Rosemary, and blood stasis-removing properties based on the other signatures) (ibid., p. 175). Wood adds Leatherwood (*Dirca palustre*) (1997, p. 27).

The **knotty, tuberous roots** of Figwort (*Scrofularia*) are a signature of it healing swollen lymph knots (scrofula), since they look like a string of swollen lymph knots and the swollen arthritic joints that they treat. "Knobby swellings indicate glands—see especially the incredible nodules on the roots of Red Root or the nodular roots of Figwort" (Wood 1997, p. 27). We might add Red Clover and the very glandular looking roots of Day Lily.

Human-shaped roots (divided tap roots) have of old been revered as especially potent in treating man, the oriental example being Ginseng (meaning "man root"), the occidental Mandrake. Legend has it that Mandrake will give off such a piercing scream when pulled out (which would be equal to killing the little root man), that it harms those who hear it. It was prized as an aphrodisiac and for magic. The Native Americans saw a person in the huge Poke root, often the diameter of a leg. The main root represented the torso, the roots branching off the limbs. They used it when all other herbs failed (ibid., p. 147f). In China, *Ho Shou Wu* is said to sometimes yield roots the size of a baby. Like Ginseng, a rejuvenator and general tonic, it bestows fertility in particular. These roots were also seen as **groin-shaped**. "Plants like mandragora, poke, ginseng, and bryony, whose root formations resemble the forked structure of the human groin, led the ancients to employ them as aphrodisiacs or as a means to overcome sterility" (Harris 1985, p. 47). "A

Ginseng root (photo by Sandra Lory)

class of plants highly valued as medicines are those having a divided tap root supposed to resemble the legs of a man. An example of this is spikenard. The medicine woman already quoted brought the writer a plant which she said she had hesitated a long time before showing. Her affection and admiration for the plant itself were evident as she caressed its straight stalk, delicate leaves, and fine white roots, reluctant at last to part with it" (Densmore 1974, p. 325). This story being from a Chippewa medicine woman, Spikenard is another example of a powerful tonic for the entire person.

Some roots have **organ signatures**. Some are human-shaped, such as Ginseng, and speak of being a tonic for people in general. Day Lily roots look like a cluster of lymph knots being pulled out of the earth. They heal breast afflictions, and help the lymph. Some are penis-shaped for infertility; and Rudolf Steiner saw a goiter signature in potatoes. Pilewort (*Ficaria ranunculoides*) roots look like hemorrhoids. Orchid roots (*orchis* = testicle) have testicle-shaped ovoid tubers, and are a fine sexual tonic, as do some of the tropical Wild Yams.

LOWER PLANTS AND ODDITIES OF THE PLANT KINGDOM

Algae, Mushrooms, Lichen, Mosses, Horsetail Grasses, Ferns, Grasses, Parasites, and Carnivorous Plants

Most of the discussion up to this point pertains to higher plants—the monocots and dicots. The doctrine of signature, however, applies also to the lower plant life. In a brief overview, **Algae** are the most primitive and oldest plant form, living in the primordial ocean. Irish Moss is an algae, and like most sea water algae high in iodine (hence for obesity) and trace minerals, but also softening, as we would expect from a watery salty plant. They regulate the water content of the tissue, thus can be useful in dry coughs. Bladder Wrack (Kelp) has iodine-rich water filled bubbles at the "neck" of its thallus. Its German name means "bladder algae." These swollen bladders filled with iodine-rich water could been see as a signature for goiter, for which it is a prime remedy. Phyllis Light says that it is specifically indicated in hypothyroidism with nodules in the thyroid, due to lack of iodine (Wood, unpublished materials on the endocrine system). Bladder Wrack is also used to treat water retention, the gallbladder, uterus and prostate, all indications that go well with the water, swollen signature. Corsican Algae (*Alsidium*) looks like a bunch of thin worms and has been used to expel them. Some kinds of algae like Irish Moss (*Chondros crispus*) are called *chondros,* Greek for "cartilage." It is used for rickets, when the bones lose their hardness and become soft like cartilage (Delaveau et al. 1980, pp. 158, 301).

Mushrooms, whether growing on the ground or on trees, grow in a rotting environment and make big tumor-like lumps. Preferring dark, damp habitats, they are really made up out of mycele threads that are composed of a substance close to chitin, which is what the external skeletons of insects are made of. Rich in protein, this again places them somewhat close to animal life. It is their task in nature to break down organic substances that have been abandoned by their life

Reishi mushrooms (left); Regrowing Reishi mushrooms (right); note the stumps of an old mushroom near the tree trunk. These mushrooms illustrate the tissue regenerating power reishi bestows, as well as the power with which tumors and metastases grow, or regrow if not cut out completely in surgery. Reishi is an important cancer healing plant. (Photos by Sandra Lory)

force. It's no surprise that they have been used worldwide for cancer treatment and have been shown to contain tumor-inhibiting factors. We can think of Chaga, Reishi, or Mesima.

Another tumor-like growth is Tuckahoe. When I first snacked on a dried Tuckahoe piece, I could not understand why I was tasting pine; they are the result of an underground fungus, causing Conifer roots to make hard, starchy tubers. It has been shown to contain cancer-inhibiting properties (Reid 1995, p. 188f). Psychological research has shown that cancers take over the body when someone no longer fully inhabits one's life; cancer is the ticket out of an unbearable situation, breaking down the body abandoned by life force. This is akin to life forms that start to grow on hosts with feeble life force—mushrooms move in to break them down, take them to death. Mistletoe is a parasite that grows like a cancer on the host tree and will finally kill it. The extract can kill cancer cells. We can see that the ***parasite*** or symbiotic state is closely

Island Moss (in reality, a lichen)

Usnea is a lichen that looks like yeast threads. It is anti-fungal and kills yeasts (photo by Sandra Lory).

related to cancer, in which the tumor takes on a life of its own with a parasitic relationship to the host's body. Another example would be Beech Drops (*Epifagus virginiana*), also called Cancer Root. This parasitical growth on Beech roots has a folk use in cancerous ulcers (Harris 1985, p. 67). "Parasitical growths have a "sticking-to" property. This herb was much used in a variety of skin disorders, thus earning its common synonym, cancer root" (ibid., p. 44). Several of those tree funguses such as Chaga look black like a necrotic tumor—they are indeed invaluable in clamping down the blood supply to cancerous tumors and thus making them become necrotic. Giant Puffball has also been shown to stop cancer (ibid., p. 150).

Lichens are a symbiosis of mushrooms and algae. Thanks to acids they excrete from their roots, they are able to live on dead surfaces: on rocks, barks, walls and roofs. They are able to "extract life from a dead rock" so to speak. Lichen thrive in moist, foggy areas (in weather that moistens the lungs) and need clean air to grow. In the same way, the lungs need moist, clean air to do well. Some lichen look like lung tissue—Island Moss is one of the most reliable remedies for dry coughs. A lichen with alveoli-like air bubbles is called *Pulmonaria* and used to heal the lungs. Pelikan points out (1982, p. 15ff) that as they are pioneers that settle the dead Earth, the organ first confronted with life on Earth (as opposed to the ocean) were the lungs, hence lichens are lung healing plants. Since a plant has to be extremely tough to grow on a rock, he considers them healing for states of general weakness of life force. The lichen Liverwort, on the other hand, looks like liver tissue and is a liver remedy. Many lichen are antibiotic. The Usneas are some of the most used. Also called Old Man's Beard, the signature of it looking like fibres was taken as pointing to its use as a wound dressing. Being anti-bacterial and anti-fungal, it serves well as such. The long, thin fibres also look like candida and similar fungi, and Usnea is a good treatment for those. While not a parasite (see discussion below), lichen that grow in symbiosis on tree bark are somewhat similar, and Usnea has been used to treat thyroid cancer in Asia. Other lichens and ***molds*** look like psoriasis, eczema, and other skin disorders, which is what they treat. They contain antibiotic substances that inhibit *staphylococcus* bacteria (Harris 1985, p. 120). ***Mosses*** were much used in ancient times as wound dressings that speed wound healing and prevent infections. Mosses scab over the barren earth, and come off like scabs when pulled, leaving a naked spot of earth that looks like a wound in the mossy area. Club Moss became

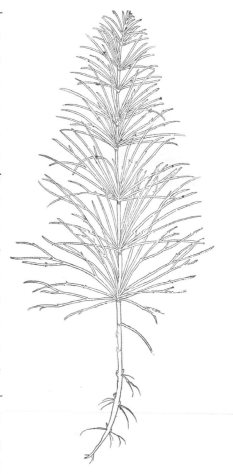

Horsetail Grass

famous as a polychrest in homeopathy under its Latin name *Lycopodium*. The spore-bearing capsules look like kidneys, and Club Moss serves as a healing agent for various kidney complaints. Harris takes the long, trailing stems to be a nerve signature. It was used for various nerve disorders down to epilepsy (Harris 1985, p. 84).

Horsetail Grasses are primitive plants that are, as Pelikan puts it, all stem. Being conduct or tube only, they pertain to the kidneys and the urinary conducts. They grow in moist soils and are filled with air throughout. Steiner considered Horsetail Grass the archetypal kidney remedy, and points out the kidney's specific need for, and relationship to, oxygen. Pelikan describes other kidney-healing plants to follow the Horsetail Grass type in growth and relationship to air, such as the whorly structures of Cleavers, Madder, and such being reduced to a stem, like the Brooms or Asparagus, and being hollow-stemmed like the *Umbelliferae*. (For more, see the *Kidney Signature*, pages 276–278.) Its strict rhythmic structure marks it as a musculoskeletal remedy.

Ferns are the first complete plants with roots, stems, leaves, and "flowers." Not bearing flowers like the higher plants, their spore-producing organs are still more mushroom-like. Worm Fern unfurls like a worm and expels them. So do other ferns. They produce poisons in their roots that are toxic to lower life forms, such as intestinal worms. Their unfoldment has also been likened to the graceful movements of the spine, and thus used for rheumatism. The *Polypodium filicula* fern was used for sprains (Fuchs 1543, chap. 223f). In the Middle Ages, many ferns were considered spleen remedies. A good number of them have the serrated leaves mentioned above as a spleen signature. Hart's Tongue fern, *Asplenium scolopendrium,* can be named here (ibid., chap. 111). Wood uses Royal Fern as the infallible lumbago remedy.

Pelikan describes **grasses** as the plant family that covers the earth with a living layer of plant material. They are carpet-forming plants, and Kaminski considers them to help group conciousness. The flower essence of Quaking Grass aids to develop a "harmonious social consciousness" and to find a higher identity in group work (Kaminski and Katz 1996, p. 360). The roots of Couch Grass are extremely penetrating. They grow horizontally, and are equipped with a thorny tip: "The long, smooth roots have been found to penetrate the fleshy roots of other much larger and sturdier plants." He calls it "most worthy penetrant of clogged urinary apparatus" (Harris 1985, p. 90). **Cereals** are within the grass clan, adding a nutritive note to the grass itself. While all grains are nutritive, and in their roasted form stimulate digestion, the dried silk of Corn has been used as a diuretic.

Carnivorous plants are higher plants that make roots, stems, leaves, and flowers. Sundew can "digest" warts if the juice is put on them. The flower essence of California Pitcher Plant, another carnivorous plant, helps with digestion. Pelikan (1958, p. 125) points out that the carnivorous organ is always the leaf. In the "normal" plant, it is the flower that interacts with the animal world. He sees the carnivorous leaves with their various organ shapes as an astrality too far descended into the plant. The astral forces in humans are responsible for emotions according to anthroposophic thought, but if entering too strongly into the physical will cause cramping. The leaves are analogous to the rhythmical organs, so Pelikan deems it obvious that therefore a plant with a carnivorous leaf would help with cramps in the rhythmic organs, such as for whooping cough. He elucidates how these plants flee a real embrace of the earth, but prefer to send weak roots into soggy soils that are poor in minerals,

Mullein rosette

such as moors. Equally soggy tissues we find in the bronchi of a child with whooping cough.

Coles mentions Sundew as a cancer remedy "by signature." The fact that Sundew can digest insects suggests its signature would be to dissolve a fleshy growth (Coles 1657, p. 153).

THE DANCE OF PLANTS AS THEY UNFOLD IN TIME

Plants do not just pop up ready-made. They are in constant flux, undergoing metamorphoses as they flow from one shape into the next. To hurried passers-by, they might appear static, but most plants move a lot more than meets the eye. They might not move from where they are rooted, but stems, leaves and flowers are in constant motion. The stems turn and rock, flowers open and close with the light, tendrils circle in search of something to hold on to, buds unfold, wilting structures collapse. Observing the dance of the plant is one of the most beautiful and profound ways in which to get to know it on its turf. Let me give an example: Oregon-Grape buds unfold as soon as the air turns mild in spring. Clusters of grape-like small round yellow flowers appear between light green, glossy folded leaves. Just as the flowers open, the divided leaves released from the bud look like the sharp claws of a medieval monster clawing at them. Put yourself in the position of the flower opening to life; it is a monstrous outlook. Soon, the leaves swing up and around, making nice and round surfaces, with soft spines at the edges. The paranoid image is only present for a few days in

Left: Black Cohosh racemes and stem in snaking motion (photo by Sandra Lory). Right: in this image of Black Cohosh, showing its snaking motion and movement that changes by the minute, we see why this plant is also called Black Snakeroot.

the life of this plant. However, Oregon-Grape is the prime herb for paranoia—the feeling that the whole world is out to get you. As if in a play, the plant acts this out before our eyes.

A true *movement signature,* the **uncurling** of Fern was at once seen as a signature of snakes or worm, hence they were found to be vermicides, and for the straightening out of contracted limbs, hence a rheumatism remedy (Harris 1985, p. 31f). The movement reminds us of the movements in yoga, curling the spine forward and backward to keep it healthy and flexible, the best prevention for rheumatism.

> Jonathan Carver (1766), a British officer traveling in the interior of North America, recorded a signature which suggests that the Indians also used time as a signature. He mentions the widespread use of Rattle Snake Plantain by the Indians as an antidote for snakebite. "It is to be remarked that during those months in which the bite of these creatures is the most venomous, that this remedy for it is in its greatest perfection, and most luxuriant in its growth." (Wood 1997, p. 28f)

Black Cohosh comes up from a mass of densely entangled black snake-like roots and rootlets. This might be seen as the signature of the "feeling as if of a black cloud hovering over one" (which it cures), or for it being one of the great snakebite remedies. In early spring, several sprouts come up in pendulous motions truly resembling a waking den of snakes rearing their heads. Blackish purple, they also resemble demon's claws. As these stretch upward, unfolding leaves in sets of three, each long stem divides into three spikes. These con-

Black Cohosh

tinue to make snake-like motions, sometimes intertwining in the way that the two side channels or *nadis* are said to cross the central channel at the chakra levels. Once the small, round buds open to become crème white flower puffs, the stem straightens out, making a long, upright spike along which the flowers are arranged rhythmically. As soon as the flowers fade, the spike seems to contract sharply into an S-shape, which is how it dries and releases the seeds from its dried pods with a rattling sound. If we did not take time to ponder the entire dance of Black Cohosh, we could never appreciate all aspects of the signature: the process of its growth points to it being a very important spinal remedy, increasing spinal flexibility and the flow of cerebrospinal fluid along the nerves (Wood 2009, p. 118ff). As a flower essence, it clears energetic blocks in the energetic channels along the spine. The puffy flowers look like the spinal nerves protruding from the vertebrae, and, indeed, Black Cohosh acts on the spinal nerves. The contracting into the stiff S-shape of these long spikes that were whipped by

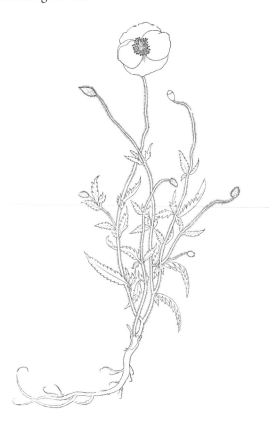

Corn Poppy

the wind is the signature for Black Cohosh being one of the greatest remedies for whiplash and rheumatism, by which the body turns stiff. The leaves in sets of three point to it as one of the greatest female remedies, which together with the spinal nerve signature becomes a remedy for menstrual cramping and labor pains. The rattling sound of the dried seed pods reminds us yet again of it being a remedy for rattlesnake bites, as did the snaking motions throughout, and its cadaverous smell speaks of it being a flower essence for having "skeletons in the closet"—for dark secrets. This is also echoed by the monster-claw-like nascent leaves, pointing to the paranoid experiences the person needing Black Cohosh went through, or might be projecting out.

Another beautiful example is Mullein. During the first year of its life, it forms a basal rosette from which the stem shoots up as high as two meters in the second year. If we did not have the patience to look at Mullein at the end of its life, we would miss how much it becomes a spine remedy by growing one, shooting up like lanky teenagers; indeed, it is one of the best remedies for the spinal weakness in tall people who grew too fast as teenagers and are now prone to muscular back spasms that pinch the intercostal nerves because of a weak back. (For a discussion on **biennials**, see *Rhythmically Arranged Leaves,* pages 140–142.)

Understanding the Plant in the Context of Its Botanical Family

In order to really grasp the healing properties of a plant, we need to understand it in the context of its own botanical family, and ideally within the context of all botanical families. This requires a thorough familiarity with botany. Since the doctrine of signature is an applied herbal science, we do not get away without thorough knowledge of the matter at hand if we want to master the subject. In order to understand the flexibility of color and form within a botanical family, and the sometimes blurred lines between them, it is most helpful to spend time looking through plant guides in which the plants are organized by botanical families, and within those families by similarity of shape. A classical example is *The Wild Flowers of Britain and Northern Europe* by Fitter and Fitter, illustrated by Blamey. By going over the pages, we start to get an idea of the underlying archetype or building blueprint as it were, although the archetypal Primrose or Buttercup in and of itself does not exist. However, there is a plant that comes closest to expressing or embodying it, and others that are straying far from the statistical middle. This is the deviation from the middle ground mentioned in Part One that gives rise to the abnormality or special healing power the herbalist is searching for. The well-balanced type yields a well balancing medicine; the distorted cousin heals stronger distortions of health in us.

The idea of the archetypal blueprint sounds very Platonic. However, when we think about it carefully, the fact that we do not find the pure archetype, plus that there are more deviations from this fair ideal than expressions of it, validates Rupert Sheldrake's morphic field theory, which states that the morphogenetic fields that give rise to shape act as a *probability structure,* from which many similar forms can arise. This blurred "mold" that allows for plasticity and the ever evolving metamorphosis of colors and shapes does more justice to nature than Plato's rigidly eternal "ideas" (Sheldrake 2009, p. 115ff).

Failing to see the plant in the context of its botanical family can give rise to misinterpretation of the signature. I was asked at one time about the significance of Celandine as a flower essence. The observation was that it looks like a satellite dish and the essence should therefore serve in communication. The first point is that it is difficult to compare an ancient organic thing such as a flower to a modern technological creation such as a satellite dish. Let's say the flower is an open cup shape, standing for reception, a shape satellite dishes have to take to imitate nature and operate within her laws. The second

Cowslip, or Primrose (Primula veris)

point is that there are many, many flowers that have this less-than-perfect open-cup shape, so it cannot be very significant as a signature. The reverse conclusion would say that there are countless flower essences to facilitate communication specifically and directly. This is not the case, however. It also goes against what seems obvious, which is that trumpet shapes should be much more significant for communication. Last and most important, Celandine, if seen in the context of its botanical Poppy family, has the least showy, cup-shaped flowers of all (so it makes little sense to pin the overriding healing effect on that), but is well-known for its unique distortion within not only the Poppy clan, but the entire plant world: its abundant yellow latex.

So, let's start again the right way round. If we had studied Celandine flowers in the context of its plant family, what conclusion would we arrive at? The Poppy family is a botanical clan in which the plants have few leaves, mostly in a basal rosette, and they exhaust themselves in profuse and showy bloom in vivid colors. The Corn Poppy is probably closest to the archetype as we think of "poppy." All true poppies, *Papaverceae*, have abundant latex, while the subfamily of *Fumarioideae* to which Smoke-of-the-Earth and Bleeding Heart belong, do not produce it. Poppies grow in barren, dry soil in the bright light, mostly as annuals. In the hotter zones, such as California or India, they form thistle-like leaves. Otherwise, the leaves are silvery and adorned with soft hairs. The *Fumarioideae* prefer barren and moist soil, not able to compete against other herbaceous plants, and some of them grow in rocky walls (Larkspur) or in the shade (wild Bleeding Heart). Among the true poppies are only two plants that flee the intense light and heat of summer that calls forth the intense show of color of the petals: Celandine and Bloodroot. Bloodroot prefers to stay small and send up inconspicuous small white flowers with the first rays of sunlight in spring. A woodland plant, it is done flowering as soon as the deciduous trees among which it grows don leaves. In Bloodroot, the leaves and flowers are small but balanced in proportion to one another.

Celandine, like Bloodroot, is perennial, while most other poppies are annuals. In temperate climates, it blooms from spring through late fall. It is the only *Papaverceae* in which the leaves are the most prominent plant part, almost drowning out the small non-showy yellow flowers. They blend in with the yellowish-green foliage of the herb in the moist half-shade or shade in which it

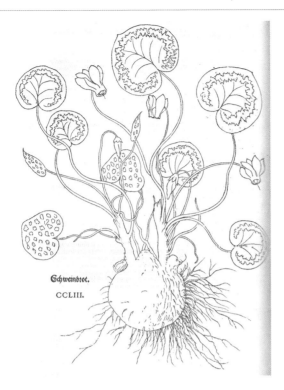

Schweinbrot.
CCLIII.

*Cyclamen (left); Cyclamen flower drawing by Wilhelm Pelikan showing
the signature of seeds burrowing into the ground (from* Heilpflanzenkunde, vol. 2)

grows. Celandine is the poppy with the smallest, most suppressed process of flowering. Where did it go? According to Goethe's idea of metamorphosis in nature, if one thing shrinks, another characteristic becomes more prominent. Whatever is lacking in color and abundance in bloom in Celandine, we find it in the latex: it is bright yellow-orange and abundant, oozing out of the plant wherever injured. It's closest relative-in-shape, Bloodroot with its pale white flowers, shows the poppy red in its bright red latex. It is as if those two have taken the flowering process into their latex formation process. Since Celandine's is the only yellow latex in the plant world (as far as I am aware), it is the most unique feature this plant has to offer. I would therefore be mistaken to put an emphasis onto the color and shape of its flower, which is the result of the main formative force having moved away from the flower into another plant part. Celandine is one of the most often quoted examples for the doctrine of signature: the abundant green leaves, lush even in the frost and under snow, in their swelling lobular appearance with a yellow bile-like exudate, have of old been recognized as an example of a liver and jaundice signature. Celandine is one of the best herbs for increasing bile flow or regulating it in case a disturbed bile flow causing migraines. Bloodroot regulates the blood flow, however being such a close cousin to Celandine, is also a reliable cholagogue, as are Smoke-of-the-Earth and some of the other *Fumarioideae* such as Turkey Corn. Even when prepared as a flower essence, Celandine acts chiefly on the solar plexus chakra and the liver/gallbladder energy. This chakra is connected to the principal of personal power and social interactions. Celandine flower essence empowers us by giving us courage to be who we need to be, and do what we believe in. In that context, as a secondary effect, it helps to communicate in the sense of courageously and powerfully speaking up, or exerting positive personal power through speech. It does not, however, act on the throat chakra.

Looking at the flower essences of the Poppy family, preparations which bring out the emotional-mental healing aspects of the plant, we find that Opium Poppy and California Poppy, the two great sleep remedies, have to do with escaping into dreamworlds (they can cause hallucinations) and into sleep. Corn Poppy, with its flamboyant colors, addresses the display of our true colors and the expression of strong emotions. Celandine holds middle ground, helping us to empower ourselves. The *Fumarioideae* have neither the showy flowers, nor the latex. While all poppies are radially symmetric, they orient themselves horizontally and become side-symmetric. We cannot fully appreciate the healing power of Bleeding Heart unless we understand that it is made of two fused flowers, each making one half of the heart. While Larkspur addresses deep emotional pain, Bleeding Heart is for the pain and depression of codependence, or losing one's other half. The fusion of two flowers into one is the signature of not being able to live without the other. Pale Corydalis, also called Harlequin Flower, looks like a jester and heals the pain hidden behind the mask of the compulsive joker—the sad clown. In the addicted family system, it is the healing plant for the joker child.

Let's look at Primroses. First of all, we should remember that the deep red and blue horticultural versions are human fabrications and not what nature intended for this plant family. Naturally, these spring flowers (*Prim-rose* means "spring," *primavera*, "Rose") come in light pastel colors reminiscent of the pale light sky in cool early spring when they bloom in profusion.

Primroses are naturally yellow, pink, pale violet and white. They grow in wet places flooded by the light of spring. Pelikan calls them "flowers of etheric spring rhythms" (1984, p. 210).

The typical Primrose makes a basal rosette of leaves, sending up a cluster of tubular five-petalled flowers to the light. The higher the stem, the more they form a round cluster, an image of the stars in the cosmos. Preferring the hues between golden and light yellow, light violet and pink, they have a spiritual note for opening the heart. The only exception to the color scheme is Scarlet Pimpernel, and it is poisonous (for further explanation, see *The Signature of Poisons*, pages 285–289), addressing rage (Wood 2008, p. 89). Other Primrose cousins crawl away and creep over the ground, Water Violet grows in water, and the Shooting Stars and Cyclamens turn upside down and flex their petals back. The well-balanced Primrose with five heart-shaped petals fused into one at the center yields one of the finest heart remedies.

As a flower essence, the Primrose stands for love and peace (the rare pink versions preferred). Water Violet, swimming and unreachable in the water, addresses a haughty royal feeling of superiority, of not wishing to mix with "commoners" and a desire to be distinct. It maintains the pink flower with five heart-shaped fused petals, so we would expect an injured heart behind such a need to set oneself apart. While "normal" primroses look upward or sideward, to reach for the sky in their gesture of flowering, Shooting Star, as the name evokes, seems to be aimed earthward. It is the flower essence for the kind of hurt heart that caused the person to choose being a space cadet as a coping mechanism. They do not put distance between themselves and the rest of humanity by way of water as Water Violet, but retract into space.

Spaced-out people who do not feel that they belong on this planet and are not part of humanity are more common than one would think. Shooting Star flower essence helps them to descend to Earth, as Water Violet helps people off their high horse. Cyclamen likes the high Alps. With retroflexed petals like Shooting Star, it is more plump overall and earthbound. This becomes especially clear in its way of going to seed: Cyclamen's seed pods spiral to the ground, where they open pressed against the earth. With soft red heart-shaped leaves, it stays true to the original heart theme of the family, yet as a flower essence we can see that it represents a higher octave of the Shooting Star—the earthbound quality is even stronger. It also grows a huge (uterine shape) underground tuber. So, we will not be surprised to find that to not only works on the heart, but also on its lower metamorphosis, the uterus, where it activates held back menstrual flow.

These examples will suffice to illustrated how enriching it is for the understanding of the signature in a holistic way to contemplate the plant in the context of its botanical family.

CHAPTER NINE

SMELL, TASTE, SOUND, TOUCH, AND UNDERSTANDING

"Through the study of the natural history, environmental patterns, chemical properties, taste, smell, appearance, etc., a person can learn to see similarities between plants and people. Through experience, the interior eye is trained and certainty in knowledge and practice increased. Although we start in a place of weakness and vulnerability to delusion, we are enabled through experience to arrive at a place of wisdom." —WOOD (1997, p. 22f)

SMELL SIGNATURES

The sense of smell is linked to the sense of taste. Sweet is a taste as well as a smell. We smell aroma, and taste it as well. Strictly speaking, there are no taste receptors for aroma, rather while eating, the aromatic substances rise into the back of the nasal cavities, where the smell receptors detect them. Smell communicates via the air element, but also belongs to the ether element, since smell has such a strong effect on the mind. Mindy Green, an aromatherapist from Minnesota, teaches that smell is vapor and as such exists in the realm between spirit and matter. So it is through fragrance that we connect to spirit. This vapor emitted via the air element that we breathe in enters our system via the nose, from where it goes into the blood which brings it to the limbic system in the brain. This is an ancient part of our brain that rules survival reflexes and hormonal responses. Through their action on the limbic system, smells—very primal in human life—trigger physiological changes via neurotransmitters which change hormonal responses. Smells also immediately change our emotions, a fact that is very important in aromatherapy. It is of interest to note that essential oils are typically manufactured by oil glands on the skin of the plant. We, too, have oil glands on our skin, and they are ruled by hormones. And it is those hormones that give rise to our body odor.

In considering the meaning of smells in medicines, we can divide them into some broad categories:

Some plants and flowers have **dull or heavy** smells. They dull our senses and make us feel sleepy. A dull smell points to sense-dulling qualities. Sometimes this smell can be sweet and dull or heavy at the same time. The oriental lilies are a good example. They can have an almost narcotic effect on some people.

Other plants and flowers have a *fresh* smell. It quickens and sharpens the senses, waking us up. Lemon and Peppermint are good examples. All **lemony** smells fall in this category. They are also famous for driving away insects, especially mosquitoes. Lemongrass is chief among the natural smell-based mosquito repellents. The signature in the latter case is the fact that it grows in swamps where mosquitoes breed (Harris 1985, p. 83).

Sweet smells are highly prized for perfumery. Kaminski points out that the sweet smell of a flower is a heart signature. The most divine of refined, sweet smells in the plant realm might be attributed to either Lily of the Valley or *Angelica archangelica*. Both are remarkable heart remedies. The refined nature of the smell points to the spiritual dimension of their healing qualities. A simple sweet, honey-like smell such as of Linden yields a good heart-calming remedy. Holly flower literally drip with nectar when in bloom, and the flower essence is a prime essence for opening the heart.

Nectar-rich flowers do not always smell strongly or sweet, but it seems that a rich flow of nectar is also a signature for a heart-opening plant. It is a generous gesture of the plant toward the insect world, and generosity is flowing from an open heart. Harris relates nectar-rich plants to the bees that visit them, pointing to it as a signature for plants that cure bee stings and insect bites. This is certainly true of Lemon Balm; *Melissa* means "bee" in Greek. He gives Bee Balm as an example (Harris 1985, p. 66)

Aromatic smells betray the presence of essential oils. Many of them are antiseptic and warming and move blood and stagnation (reduce *Kapha* in Ayurvedic terms). They are highly volatile, hence kill airborne germs: the signature here is that of the "airborne" substance that remedies the airborne disease. Aromatics are often used in smudging and in incense as "air purifiers." This use comes down to us through many systems of traditional medicine and predates any knowledge of germs. It was observable, however, that aromatic fumes could cure and prevent the spread of contagious diseases. True to the principal of correspondence, aromatic smells help to dispel unpleasant odor from the body, whether halitosis, foul smelling wounds, or indigestion. This is in part because of their antiseptic actions, as well as their ability to detoxify the body. I noticed that all the Haitian herbs for colds and coughs shown to me by the Afro-Haitian herbalist Oliama Derivière are aromatic. The main domain of aromatics are their actions as antiseptics, for coughs and colds, and for the digestion.

Pungent smells are warming, and pungent essential oils make excellent rubefacients (bringing blood to the skin) for cold diseases such as rheumatism. They are also stimulating, thus quickening consciousness. Pungent substances activate tissue activity. To illustrate the stimulating action: Rosemary grows in hot, dry climates. It is warming and increases the blood circulation to the periphery as well as the brain. It hence has a mild coffee-like effect. Its distant cousin Stone Root grows in the shade of deciduous forests. It contains small amounts of the same essential oil, as our nose will tell us. Stone Root being an overall more watery and earthy plant with huge tuberous roots thus stimulates the circulation in the lower half of the body—heavy, watery venous blood in varicose veins and hemorrhoids to circulate better and heal.

Sulfurous smells occur in plants such as Onions, Garlic, and Elder. They are heating in property. Sulfur naturally occurs in volcanic rock and hot springs—the fire of the earth. It is related to fire, digestive fire, and inflammations. Sulfurous plants stimulate digestion and elimination. They represent *Pitta* in Ayurveda.

Elder is one of the plants with a *stinky*, sulfur smell. It is an excellent detoxifying herb, removing all kinds of stink from the body via the intestines or skin. I find that halitosis (bad breath) is a telltale sign that someone needs a cure of Elder juice, which will remedy the condition.

For *sour* and *acrid* smells, see the following section on tastes.

There are of course also smells related to the *elements*—some plants smell earthy, especially the roots; others remind us of water or the ocean (not just the seaweed); yet others have a fiery scent, even burning our nose like Cayenne pepper, or fill the air with their scent. Smells pertaining to ether (space or mind) are fine and fresh smells that seem to expand and sharpen our mind, making it calm and lucid at the same time. Angelica is a good example, and the angel-imagery of the name points to the realm of space. We can call scents heavy (earth), fresh or light (air), or warm and pungent (fire). Patricia Davis gives a beautiful example for an earthy smell, describing the essential oil Vetivert grass roots as having depth and a "dark" aroma. "However, perhaps the most important actions of Vetivert are on the psyche. Its Indian name 'Oil of Tranquility' expresses its character beautifully.

Vetivert is deeply relaxing, valuable in massage and baths for anybody experiencing anxiety, insomnia, or depression. To sOak in a Vetivert bath is one of the most relaxing experiences I know. Because of its earthy quality, being extracted from the roots, it is a very grounding, stabilizing oil, useful for people who "live in the clouds" a bit too much (2000, p. 307).

Another earthy smell from a root is Valerian, and it, too, remedies insomnia and anxiety— both of them reducing *vata* as it were.

Some **other smell signatures** are in the nature of like cures like—the Ayurvedic tonic *Ashwagandha* smells of horses, and is said to impart the stamina of horses. Nettles smell of urine and are an effective diuretic. Figwort is very stinky, and it is a deep acting cleanser of blood and lymph—waste-laden body fluids giving rise to bad smells, as do the lymphatic infectious conditions it is curative for. Black Cohosh has an unpleasant cadaverous stink, so much so it is nicknamed Bugbane for its ability to chase away bugs. It deals with dark emotional states (especially "skeletons in the closet") and stagnation of fluids—and stagnant fluids stink. Several plants from the Nightshade family have an animal-like stink, which in this case with the rest of the signature points to them being poisonous. Celandine leaves smell like raw liver (Storl 2010, p. 139).

TASTE PHARMACOLOGY

Taste pharmacology, exquisitely elaborated in Ayurveda, Tibetan and Traditional Chinese Medicine, is the art of knowing what the healing properties of a plant are based on its taste. It is what we could call the *taste signature*. Since the taste induces the medicinal effect, we should remember that **the taste *is* the signature**. In some cases, the taste signature became the plant's name, as in Bittersweet, Licorice (from the Greek *Glycyrrhiza* for "sweet root"), and all kinds of pungent plants that go by the name "pepper," such as Waterpepper. Wood states that perhaps no other attribute of the plant leads as directly to knowledge of the energetics of a plant as its taste. He acknowledges having initially learned this from herbalist David Winston. It is beyond the scope of this book to go into the details of taste pharmacology, so therefore the following will remain a brief sketch. Next to smell and some aspects of physical sensation, it is the part of the doctrine of signature closest related to organic chemistry, and therefore quite scientific even in reductionist terms. For instance, it is quite easy to detect oxalic acid by way of tasting the typical somewhat lemony acidic taste and feel the strange coating sensation it causes on the teeth. In plants, oxalic acid (occurring in *Oxalis,* Wood Sorrel) endows them with the ability to relax the smooth muscles in the organs, hence it eases or causes cramping of internal organs, depending on the dose. The Cherokee culture also acknowledges taste as a signature. While there is some overlap with the Chinese concepts, herbalist David Winston explains that Chinese medicine became standardized and things were forced to fit the theoretical outline even if they did not quite. However, Cherokee medicine was never systematized, and "things are what they are." If they do not fit, they are not made to. For instance, the Wild Yam used in Traditional Chinese Medicine really tastes chalky, but was forced to fit the scheme and classified as "sweet." In Chinese thought, bitter is the taste that affects the Heart and Small Intestine energies. The concept "Heart" here includes *shen,* or spirit, and actions on the nervous system. In Cherokee medicine, bitter affects the liver and gallbladder, and thus digestion and absorption. Herbs such as Hops and California Poppy are bitter and would be seen as acting on the heart and *shen* for the Chinese practitioner, however on digestion, absorption and elimination for the Cherokee. In the European tradition, bitters act primarily on liver and digestion, however in small doses are used to strengthen the nerves and nervous constitution. Some of these differences might be explained by the difference between the two Wild Yam species employed by these two different cultures.

My acupuncturist friend Peter Schell gives another explanation of the traditional Chinese taste pharmacology: not merely remaining a first sensation of the taste buds, there is an underlying or "inherent" taste of the herb. This means that the person tasting it is also feeling the energetics of the herb—the taste has developed sufficiently and impacts the body, provoking a physiological reaction. For example, the first impression of Ginseng in its prepared form tastes bitter, but underlying that is a deep sweetness indicating that it is toning, harmonizing and moistening.

In addition, how you can get a sense of that from its complex taste. To give you an idea of the subtlety and complexity of real taste pharmacology: Ginseng is generally thought of as warming. However, its bitterness does drain some deficiency heat (as in insomnia from heart and kidney deficiency) while its sweetness supports the primal *chi* so its draining ability does not weaken the patient. This is to illustrate Ginseng's many-layered—adaptogenic—properties. Shan Yao (*Dioscorea oppositae*, which is a little different from the Western Wild Yam *Dioscorea villosa*) may have a bit of a chalky taste initially, but underlying is a sweetness with a bit of sour. It also has somewhat of a blandness which helps it not to cloy and create dampness like a more obvious sweet taste (sweet in Chinese is thought to clog the tissue if over-consumed and to create dampness in the tissue). That bland taste is similar to Fu Ling (Tuckahoe). Tasting these subtle flavors beneath the initial impression is something one has to learn.

We should bear in mind that the classification of taste or other energetic properties of an herb are always subject to much contradiction between herbalists and esteemed herbals: generally, no two of them agree entirely with one another. In my experience, the taste of an herb also changes quite a bit, especially in the more subtle shades, according to climate, soil, recent weather, whether the herb grew wild or was cultivated, the time of day, which star sign the Moon is in, the moment of harvest, and so on, not to mention my own constitution or momentary energetic state; many of us might have the experience that the same thing tastes more or less bitter, sweet or sour to us on different days. Ayurveda even distinguishes between the taste in the mouth and the post-digestive taste, which we could define as the physiological effect the food or herb unfolds in the body. It seems to me that the traditional Chinese taste classification echoes some of that.

Another thing worth considering is that most people's tastes are corrupted because of diets filled with artificial flavors and taste enhancers and loaded with refined sugars and salt. In my experience, one cannot taste the flavors of an herb unless one has been off those ingredients for a while, at least a week or two. This is equally true of the large amounts of chili pepper in some indigenous foods. After two weeks off of all refined sugars and concentrated sweets such as honey, maple, or agave syrup or dried fruits such as dates, we will be surprised at how very sweet cooked beans or raw fennel tastes. There are also are huge cultural differences in taste preferences—Western culture has almost completely eliminated all tastes but sweet, sour and salty, whereas other cultures, such as the Indian, include huge amounts of pungent as well as some very bitter tastes, while the Tibetans dislike concentrated sweets, but adore their very salty butter tea.

Trained herbalists will want to rub, sniff, and chew on any new plant they encounter in order to discern its taste and smell. As a word of caution, however, it is always wise to know your botany very well and to be accomplished in identifying plants in the field, recognizing which one is poisonous before nibbling on them. I have not found the poison signature to be a sufficiently reliable tool to know for certain which plants, or which part of a plant, may be poisonous. It is always better to respect the "skull and crossbones" in your plant guide.

In Traditional Chinese Medicine, the medicinal actions of the tastes are outlined as follows: acrid enters the Lung, salty enters the Kidney, sour enters the Liver, bitter enters the Heart, sweet enters the Spleen. This indicates only a general tendency and is not always clinically relevant. In addition to taste, the organ affinity of the herb and the state of the disease, and so on also play important roles in choosing the medicine.

While the taste does tell of an herb's physiological action, this does by no means make it an easy tool to use. For instance in Chinese terms, acrid or pungent herbs enter the lungs and can be used to disperse Lung *chi,* but one would need to add bitter herbs for their draining and drying action to really remove phlegm. If the lungs are already dry, these herbs would only aggravate the dry cough, for instance, and one would need to use sweet herbs to moisten them. Salty food might help protect the kidney during winter, but too much will injure it. This reminds us of the traditional wisdom that it is not the substance that is harmful or nontoxic, but the dose that determines which path it will take in the body; small amounts of sour foods help generate the liver, but if the disease is in the tendon layer, which is controlled by the liver, one should abstain from sour foods. Peter suggests putting this to the test by sucking a lemon when experiencing a stiff neck or shoulder, which will make it much worse. Bitter herbs are used to clear liver/gallbladder heat and might be used for Blazing Heart Fire. However, one needs to be extremely cautious not to injure the Heart Yin because of their drying properties. Sweet is used to tone the spleen, but it creates dampness. The spleen does not thrive on dampness, so only a little is needed—the kind of sweet hidden to our taste buds while we are eating concentrated sweeteners. This gives us the impression that taste pharmacology is quite complex and requires many years of study and experience to be understood.

Peter Schell points out that a more useful way of looking at the medicinal tastes in Traditional Chinese Medicine is to consider their actions:

Sweet/pleasant taste: tones, harmonizes, moistens
Bitter: drains and dries
Sour: astringent, preserves *chi* and fluids
Salty: purges and softens
Acrid/spicy/pungent: disperses and moves
Bland: leaches damp, promotes urine
Aromatic: penetrates turbidity

Strictly speaking, the latter is not a taste, since it is not perceived by the tongue but by the smell receptors in the back of the nasal cavities.

Bitter: The most bitter of meats of the body is the liver due to the bile. Thus bitters are liver remedies and cholagogues, that is they increase the flow of bile. An intensely bitter taste sends a shudder through the system. Thus strong bitters are remedies for intermitted fevers with chills. Wood explains the connection as follows: "The chills run through the autonomic nervous system, which regulates the gallbladder and the digestive tract. The management of the bile is upset, so the chills coincide with symptoms of biliousness, indigestion, bitter taste (in the mouth), gallstone concretion, and jaundice. *Cnicus* (Blessed Thistle, a strong bitter) settles chills and biliousness, increases biliary secretion, and can remove gallstones" (2008, p. 201). Ayurveda uses bitter taste to reduce *kapha*. Cardiac glycosides are bitter, which gives some kinds of bitter a connection to the heart" (David Winston).

Sweet: Chinese medicine is fond of the sweet taste, which is not just the sweetness of pure sugar, but the natural sweetness of grains and beans, for example. According to Chinese medicine, sweetness increases "dampness," which is the moisture content of the tissue and strengthens the Spleen and Stomach energies. These substances are often very nutritious. Sweet and nurturing herbs include American Ginseng and Solomon's Seal. Very sweet though not nurturing herbs would be Licorice or Stevia. I find that they tease the body; the sweetness of taste is not followed by the post-digestive increase of tissue nutrition. Ayurveda uses sweet taste to reduce *vata* (fattening up the skinny type), which should be avoided to reduce *kapha* (mucus, cloying, and overweight). According to Chinese medicine, the sweet taste is related to the stomach and spleen energies, which include the pancreas. This makes a lot of sense in biomedical terms, too, as well as the recommendation that a little sweet tones, and large quantities harm these energies.

Astringent: This is the taste that makes the mouth contract and dry like a persimmon that is not fully ripe. Often found in barks, astringents toughen the body's outer surfaces and hold in moisture. One class of astringents, tannins, are used in making leather and often develop in plants to protect themselves from moist environments. Examples of astringent herbs that contract tissues are Horse Chestnut, Oak bark, and Trillium. Owing to its contracting action, the astringent taste trims tissues and is not indicated in lack of (tissue) nutrition, but, for example, for slimming plump people. One of the tastes of the famous Ayurvedic *triphala*, it tones the intestinal surface when too flabby after prolonged diarrhea. While in the West, astringent remedies were traditionally used to tone the tissues, the Chinese tradition vary that use lest the astringency block the proper circulation of fluids in and out of the tissue. They prefer the sweet taste to tone tissue (build *yin*).

Pungent: These tastes are warming, like fire. The classical example is cayenne pepper. Pungent tastes are more common in plants from hot climates, and they stimulate and deeply penetrate and warm the tissue. Ayurveda uses pungent taste to warm up *vata* and *kapha* constitutions. The world over, they have been used to ease digestion by toning the digestive fire.

Sour: The most sour part of the body is the stomach with the stomach acid. In Ayurvedic medicine, stomach acid is considered the chemical manifestation of digestive heat, thus fire. Sour is classified as heating, and we call the rising of stomach acid "heart*burn*." In Wood's observation, small doses of sour such as in fruit can also be refreshing and cooling. While Ayurveda classifies acids as heating, they use sour fruits as cooling. Lemon juice is known to cool one off, as are other "refreshing" sour fruits, and other foods such as yogurt, whey, and vinegar.

Salty: Water follows salt, and salts dissolve in water. Salty tastes relate to the kidneys and the bodily fluids. I had a friend who craved eating celery throughout her pregnancy, and her body swelled up tremendously in that period. Tibetan Ayurveda works salt into the herbal pills for the kidneys to guide the medicinal effect to that organ system.

Acrid: Acrid is the taste of bile in the back of your throat after vomiting. Acrid plants are antispasmodics, as Blue Cohosh for example. In this case, it even is the remedy for dyspepsia from a spasmodic stomach or vomiting, where spasms cause the acrid taste in the back of the throat.

Samuel Thompson named the **diffusive** taste, which is a sensation of almost electrical tingling going from the tongue through the nervous system. Examples include *Lobelia inflata* and Echinacea. Wood widens the list of tastes to include **oily** and **mucilaginous** tastes. Oily plants lubricate and oil the body and fatten the tissue, while mucilaginous ones make internal passageways more slippery: they aid the mucosa. I personally consider mucilaginous a sensation rather than a taste. Other tastes that do not fit the classic categories include the moldy taste of Yellow Dock root, a very valuable Candida remedy.

SIGNIFICANT SOUNDS

The only sound signature that I am aware of is that of the dried seedpods of Black Cohosh rattling like the rattlesnake whose bites it cures. Wood notes, "Not many plants have distinctive sounds. However, the sound of wind blowing through the tall White Pine has a peculiar relaxing effect, which this plant carries into its medical action. Pine is soothing and strengthening to the nerves, at the same time it is an expectorant and antiseptic (it brings up viscid, green, sap-like mucus), and a powerful drawing agent (consider the power it takes to draw up that sap into the tall trunk)" (1997, p. 28). My friend Peter Schell points out that different woods make very different sounds, and that which ones are ideal for which musical instrument is part of the sound signature of a plant.

THE FEEL WHEN TOUCHED

Some flowers are **sticky** because of resins or sticky sap. This is a signature for sticky mucus as in Grindelia, a big asthma and cough herb, where it helps liquefy the tough mucus. In plants such as Sticky Monkeyflower it talks of the stickiness of the situation, in this case sticky sexual relationships. In Chestnut Bud flower essence, it illustrates getting stuck in a situation that no longer serves us, and being glued to the family mind-set of our family of origin and not being able to

move beyond that. Chestnut buds are composed of seven layers of scales that are covered in an extremely sticky resinous exudate. Once the bud has broken through such resistance, it emerges looking as if entirely covered in cobwebs—what an image of having to struggle one's way out of the past!

Slippery plants that contain mucus such as Jewelweed, Mallow, or sOaked Linseeds are healing to the mucosa, easing the passage through the body's internal pathways.

Not quite knowing where to place this, plants that retain moisture for a long time once picked and are hard to dry for herbal teas such as the leaves of Sage, Artichoke, and Aloe are moisturizing. They retain their own moisture, refusing to dry out, and Artichoke even rehydrates upon contact with the air.

Chestnut bud

Please refer to the chapter on shape for the explanations of prickly, hairy, or velvety leaves or other plant parts. Ayurveda considers smooth plants to be *kapha*, whereas rough plants are considered *vata*.

WARM AND COOL: THE TEMPERATURE OF THE PLANT ITSELF

The relative temperature of a plant permits it to interact with the weather. The two big plant families with sulfurous inner fire, the Onion and Mustard clans, are also the two that will furnish the winter vegetables that survive in snow and ice in the garden. While Garlic and the Onions start their growing season in the fall, Leeks come on in fall and throughout the winter, as do various cabbages. The other winter vegetable, Corn Salad, belongs to the Valerian family and unlike

Lettuce but like Valerian is warming. Echinacea, which needs to have frost go over it for germination, is also a warm and warming, stimulating plant. Plants keep cool by way of being very watery. Lush, juicy plants are often surprisingly cool in a hot summer environment. Warm plants would be classified as *pitta,* while cool, watery plants would be *kapha.* Plants capable of creating their own heat to melt the snow are called *thermogenic*; warming Skunk Cabbage is a classic example.

See the chapter on color for the section on warm and cool colors.

THE SIXTH SENSE: UNDERSTANDING

In the Tibetan Buddhist tradition of cognitional theory, mind is a sense called *yid wang,* or "mind sense." In the same way that the eye apprehends form, mind apprehends meaning. In contemplating plants, it is our mind with its understanding that synthesizes the entirety of details and characteristics into a meaningful message. It is the mind that analyzes (left brain) and comprehends holistically or intuitively (right brain). It is with our minds that we apprehend the beingness of the plant, its personality, its essence. Mind is also considered the fifth element, the most refined one, *in lieu* of space (or equal to space, owing to its spacious nature) in some of the Asian traditions. While not a characteristic of the plant, mind has to be there for a signature to arise in the perception of someone's mind. And we should remember Heisenberg's uncertainty principle from quantum physics that states it is due only to the mind apprehending that the measured events take place the way they do; we do not, however, know how they would have taken place had we not apprehended them in order to measure.

In the context of mind, we can again remember that all the above categories of color, shape, taste, and smell are man-made—they are a result of the kind of senses we have. If we were certain insects, we could smell things right now undetectable to us. If we were dogs, we would get excited about smelling excrements. If we were bees, we would see a world broken down in facets, and in infrared. Each being can only perceive of the totality of Nature what our mind and senses permit.

PLANT CHEMISTRY AND ALCHEMY

Alchemy is not concerned with isolating chemicals, but with understanding archetypal processes that govern the relationship between substance and essence. As such, alchemy describes principles of process or functioning, named after archetypal substances that illustrate the principle in its purest form in the material world. Alchemy, as it were, looks for the signature of those three principles in all of nature. Thus, it does not concern itself with chemical substances in the sense of present day chemistry much, but rather stays in the realm of imagination and holistic thinking.

Nonetheless, plant chemicals can be isolated. While chemicals as such are not signatures, since not apprehensible with the senses, their color, shape, taste and energetic properties are. Without needing to know their chemical nature—what the molecule looks like or is named—their color, taste and so on nicely represents the doctrine of signature. For instance, the bit-

terest and yellow body part is the liver, due to the presence of bile. **Berberine** plants, such as Oregon-Grape, Goldenseal, Goldthread, and Barberry roots, yield yellow and bitter medicines that heal the liver and bile flow. The mucosa is the body part that needs to produce mucus to function properly, protect and heal itself—from the respiratory mucosa to the colon. **Mucilaginous** plants are healing for those organs.

The hairs and hard prickles on plants, which are semi-translucent, are made of plant

*Pulsatilla, illustrating plant silica
(photo by Sandra Lory)*

silica. They indicate healing plants for hair, nails and skin—organs rich in silica that depend on organic silica for their health, and are hairy, hard (nails), and semi-translucent (hair, nails and skin). Barks are the outer skin of the tree. They are rich in **tannins**, which toughen up skin and mucosa, helping to create a stronger outer boundary. They are used to make leather, giving toughness to the animal skin. **Calcium** rich plant parts are strong and hard, and do not easily decompose in the winter. The dead stalks remain upright, dry and stiff into the spring. They can survive months of being inside a compost heap unchanged. In the same way, once the tissues little rich in calcium have decomposed, all that is left of a corpse are the bones. The body's **salt**

balance is determined by the kidneys. Salts and salty plants gravitate to the kidneys in their heal-ing effect. The kidneys and skin are the two organs that balance the **water** content of the body. Watery plants and fruits are often diuretic, and restore moisture to the skin—we may think of Watermelon and Cucumber. *Gums* and *resins*, coagulated plant liquids, are very effective to treat coagulated blood or hardened mucus. The *oils* in plant material restore the oils in the body. Most strongly *aromatic* herbs that we smell heal our respiratory system, often decongesting the nose when we cannot smell any more. They also have pronounced *tastes* and increase the diges-tive juices and power. On the chemical level, the molecular structure of hemoglobin and chlo-rophyll, the main coloring agents of plant and animal, is identical except that where animals and humans have the iron atom, plants have magnesium. Plants need iron to produce chlorophyll, and eating deep green vegetables with lots of chlorophyll is an old folk remedy against anemia. When we contemplate in this way, the profound correspondence between plants and mammals based on groups of substances becomes obvious.

These analogies can also be looked at in the context of the three alchemical principles of alchemical processes. The art of alchemy, which predated chemistry, understood signatures and correspondences. Alchemy is the path of transformation, taking the outer transformation of substances as a model, guide, and inspiration for inner and spiritual transformation and refine-ment. As such, it had the outer appearance of a chemical lab or plant-medicine-making factory, as well as the inner dimensions of physiological and spiritual practice and evolution. Due to this, we can see how the alchemists of old such as Paracelsus could be reduced to pre-modern chemists on the one hand, or to quacks on the other. In truth, alchemy is a holistic approach to life as a whole, and it has been practiced all over Europe, Asia, and Northern Africa for at least two millennia. Different sub-forms developed in different cultural context, such as Taoist alchemy in China or the hermetic alchemy of medieval Europe. All of alchemy is based on an understanding of the elemental energies, grading them as more or less refined or material. Alchemy looks very different when explained from the point of view of someone melting metal ores in the alchemical chemical lab, or someone practicing alchemy for psychological or spiri-tual growth. On the physical level, there are metal alchemy and plant alchemy. While the first is related to transforming base metals into alchemical "gold," the latter aims at creating refined plant medicines that enhance inner healing and development. Maybe alchemy could be called "holistic, process-oriented chemistry."

In the European tradition that developed from the hermetic tradition, the outer aim was to set the essence or soul or energy of a substance free from its material encumbrance, reduce the latter to ashes and recombine the two. European alchemy, is based on the three princi-pals, *Salt, Sulfur,* and *Mercury. Salt* means that which is crystalline, solid, pertaining to the earth, and slow to react. It was defined as that which is left after combustion: the salts found in potash. The elements assigned are earth and water. Fire is *Sulfur,* or what becomes gas-eous or airy through combustion. It is the process of burning. *Mercury,* representing water and air, is the liquid metal that becomes a gas, or what goes between the liquid and gaseous state and alco-hol in making tinctures. The three principles of alchemy thus are:

Dandelion flower gone to seed, illustrating silica in the plant realm

Mercury—the primal essence of the thing, that which is most spiritually refined, the life force. Since quicksilver is the only metal that evaporates, *Mercury* stands for vapors and what can be distilled. In this sense, it represents the true air element. It is spirit in the sense of the higher self or who you were born to be in this incarna-tion. Paracelsus considers it restorative to that which has been consumed.

Sulfur—the fire of transformation, energy, the heat of the process. Fire stands for the energy that gets used up in the process of combustion, thus it is the life force that gets used up during life. *Sulfur* also stands for the soul. According to Paracelsus, it modifies the excess of the two other principles.

Salt—the impurities or ashes left behind when the essence is separated out from matter. *Salt* stands for the earth, the physical body, the self, one's character, and the person that goes through an incarnation and learns lessons. The idea of salt standing for character comes out in expressions such as "he is a salty dog" or "they are the salt of the earth." Paracelsus explains that *Salt* purges (saline laxatives), softens, and preserves flesh from putrefaction.

Together, these three primal essences, or *tria prima,* form a body with one single essence. That is, within the human body we have these three principles at work, however as humans or individuals, we are one and not three. Paracelsus sums it up as follows (Rivière 2000, p. 52):

> *Sulfur* is what burns.
> *Mercury* is what evaporates or rises as fume or steam.
> *Salt* is what remains in the ashes.

He diagnoses disease as being in the nature of one or the other of these principles, and chooses to treat accordingly: all disease of too great a tissue relaxation comes from *Salt,* those of the tendons, musculoskeletal system, nerves, and so on from *Mercury,* and *Sulfur* diseases of the inner organs, where only *Sulfur* could penetrate (ibid., p. 53). A mercurial remedy is chosen to treat a mercurial disease, and so on.

All of these three have two aspects, *essentia* and *substantia,* for the alchemy of plant medicine. The essence is that which is more refined, and which can be separated out from the substance. Thus, for *Sulfur* the substance aspect is fixed fats and wax, while the essence aspect is the volatile essential oils. For *Salt,* the carbons in the *caput mortuum,* the reject or leftovers of plant matter, represent the mortal parts of the body and are the substance aspect, while the salts in the ashes of the leftovers represent the intelligence of the body, and the essence aspect. For *Mercury,* what can be distilled is the essence, not the substance.

We find these three assigned differently in different places, since alchemy was not a highly standardized tradition. In the Chinese tradition, these three principles would be akin to *jing, chi,* and *shen*; and they are somewhat similar to *vata, pitta* and *kapha* in Indian alchemy. These three principles are also the basis of the threefold man in anthroposophic medicine. It is interesting that quicksilver or mercury featured prominently in the Chinese quest for the elixir of immortality, while Ayurveda states that any disease can be healed with quicksilver in the right (alchemical) preparation. It is one of the most profound and versatile homeopathic remedies.

Paracelsus says, "Realize that Alchemy is none other than the art to purify the impure by way of fire....It can separate the useless from the useful and transform it into its final substantiality, which is its essence" (Jakobi 1991, p. 192). This sounds like the descriptions of the digestive fire, transforming food into the pure and impure in Traditional Chinese Medicine and Ayurveda, which Paracelsus also recognizes as such.

In alchemical preparations of plants, called *spagyrics*, the plant is processed on the day of the week ruled by its ruling planet, and the hour of the day that is ruled by that same planet. Paracelsus explains that spagyric really means to separate the pure from the impure. The extracting medium of alcohol, sometimes water, is the mercurial principle, the plant refuse that is filtered off and reduced to ashes is *Salt*, and the fire over which it is burned to ashes is the Sulfurous principle. The ashes are then mixed back into the alcoholic "essence." A medicine prepared in this way is considered far superior and to have a more profound effect on the astral energies of the person, as well as able to not only mediate physical health, but personal and spiritual advancement. The spagyric alchemical process of dissolving and coagulating mimics the archetypal chemical process.

> Plant constituents are assigned as follows:
> Plant body, plant ash, alkalis (such as potash)—*Salt*
> Essential oils, waxes, oils, fats—*Sulfur*
> Alcohol (sometimes water)—*Mercury*

Plant alchemy is simpler than metal alchemy, because when using alcohol, one can extract the mercurial and Sulfurous elements in one go, while in metal alchemy this would require several different procedures. Since *Mercury* always refers to the water- and alcohol-soluble part of a plant substance, and since water-soluble substances dissolve in alcohol, as do essential oils, one alcohol extraction is sufficient to extract both *Mercury* and *Sulfur*.

In all three volumes of *Healing Plants,* Pelikan calls the mercurial process the one that brings the air in relationship and solution with the watery, liquid phase. It is of interest to note that salt, mercury, and Sulfur are three of the greatest homeopathic polycrests: *Natrium muraticum, Mercurius vivius,* and *Sulfurus.* If we take *Salt* to stand for minerals and crystals, we find inorganic silica, *Silica* in the homeopathic *materia medica,* as well as many other salts. These three alchemical processes that are images of primordial processes within nature are also found in plant alchemy. Plants themselves can contain salts, silica, or Sulfur in organic forms. While they might not contain mercury, they do contain mercurial substances, such as saphonines, or stimulate or carry out mercurial processes. Because of their presence in living plant material, I would like to quickly point to the main medical virtues of those substances when used in medicine.

> *Silica* strengthens anything within the body that is rich in silica, namely all skin, mucosa, hair, nails, tendons, connective tissues, and the nerves. Thus, all silica-rich plants easily distinguishable by their crystalline structures, such as spines, prickles, hairs, etc. if they look as if made out of glass, share similar medical virtues. We may think of Borage for the skin, Horsetail Grass for the connective tissue and tendons, and the spines of *Cactus grandiflorus* that dissolve with the plant body into the tincture, and calm the nerves, most specifically the nerves of the heart.
>
> > Crystals are made of silica; hence, silica-rich plants like Horsetail Grass form crystal-like rays.
>
> *Salt*, or common table salt in the case of *Natrium muraticum,* governs the water content or balance of soluble versus liquid. It corrects too much or too little of moisture in the tissue. In fact, Stavish, in *The Path of Alchemy,* considers all homeopathic salts falling into this category. They have, of course, widely different actions.
>
> *Sulfur* in malodorous, pungent compounds as found in Garlic, Onions, and Elder do what Sulfur does in homeopathy or as a powder: they ignite the digestive fire and are great skin healers for red, itchy rash conditions. The *Cruciferae,* or Mustard family, is the second big Sulfur-rich botanical clan, and we can think of Horseradish and Mustard as illustrating the Sulfurous digestive fire.

Examples for **mercurial substances** are **saponins** (Pelikan 1958, p. 200ff). Soap-like, they produce leather. The mercurial action here is the bringing into interaction of water and air. Poke root has been called "vegetable mercury" due to the fact that a good number of its healing effects are identical to those of mercury.

The most important link between alchemy and healing is the concept of the essence, of being similar, and that one could bring about healing by way of manipulating the *chi* or energy based on those principles. Thinking alchemically helps develop one's intuition, because it renders one's thoughts more sensitive to detecting similars.

CHAPTER TEN

THE ELEMENTS AND THE ENVIRONMENT

YIN AND YANG

The terms *Yin* and *yang* refer to the archetypal "female" and "male" categories so vitally important to Asian thought and medicine, and of course, there is a *yin* and *yang* signature. They are important in the context of the elemental signature, since they represent water (*yin*) and fire (*yang*), the primary elemental dyad. *Yin* and *yang* are the first polarization that evolves from the all-one, and the precursor to the five element theory in Traditional Chinese Medicine. As the primordial elemental diagnostic structure, we can consider all polar opposites as having a *yin* and a *yang* part. We can see from the following examples that they also extend into other categories of signature, such as the environmental and planetary. To give some examples pertinent here (modified after Blum 1995, p. 36f):

YIN:	YANG:
female	male
water	fire
Moon	Sun
new moon	full moon
dark	light
cold, cool	hot, warm
wet	dry
matter	energy
pastel colors	bright colors
blue, green, purple	red, orange, yellow
cool colors	warm, radiant colors
sweet, sour, bland	salty, bitter, spicy

descending, falling	ascending, rising
fall, winter	spring, summer
low	high
introverted	extroverted
soft, flaccid	strong, rigid
profound	superficial
fruit, vegetable	grains, animals

Solomon's Seal

All organs are also classified as either *yin* or yang, such as the kidneys being the receiving *yin* and the bladder the expelling *yang* aspect of one organ system.

Thus, *yin* plants have horizontal roots, hanging structures with soft leaves and flowers, grow in moist and shady places, and have pastel and subdued colors. Their tastes are subdued or bland, maybe sweet, and they may contain mucilage and be nutritive. They do not grow tall, and have cascading or hanging forms. Solomon's Seal has a horizontally creeping root-stock, over which the stems arch with numerous drooping cream white and light green flowers. The heavy, blackish-blue berries drop to the ground. It thrives in damp soil in the half shade. The root-stock is mucilaginous, sweet, and very nurturing. Solomon's Seal is useful in treating nutritional deficiencies as found in *yin* deficiency, infertility, ovarian pain and repetitive strain injuries.

Yang plants can have straight taproots, upright strong stems, bloom in bright radiant colors, love sunny, dry exposure and possibly rocky soil. They have strong flavors and may be pungent or bitter, and may act on the gallbladder. Thistles grow with deep strong taproots, straight and upright like soldiers. They are a pioneering plant as well as ones so well defended that most animals do not—or cannot—graze them because of their spines. Thistle seeds fly high into the sky. They bloom bright red or yellow and are valuable bitter tonics of the liver and gallbladder, and useful in treating androgen excess. While we would expect it more to increase androgens, there are few plants that act on the androgen balance at all—so the fact that it does at all relate to male sexual hormones is remarkable. If we think of plants as teachers, we could say that it teaches us to be in perfect androgen balance.

Clockwise has been thought of as *yang*, outgoing, male, and counterclockwise as yin, receptive or introverted, and female. It is remarkable how the leaves of Madonna Lily form a perfect counterclockwise swirl, and Madonna Lily is a wonderful *yin* tonic and medicinal plant for female reproductive disorders.

Madonna Lily leaves

On a side note, the category of healing plants called *yang tonics* in Traditional Chinese Medicine are plants that strengthen the yang aspect of the kidneys, and are as such kidney remedies (a *yin* organ)—remedies to strengthen *yang* within *yin*, fire held in water. Those plants therefore have a mix of *yin* and *yang* characteristics. Thus, a plant being a yang tonic is different from a plant having a *yang* signature. Many of the plant and animal substances used as *yang* tonics live in cold climates, such as *Yar Tsa Gun Bu* (*Cordyceps sinesis*), a phallus-shaped parasitic mushroom that grows only above 3,300 meters in the high Himalayas and invades a caterpillar to for its nutrients. Their ability to maintain their own warmth or inner fire (*yang*) in the cold, watery environment (*yin*) was probably a signature to those who compiled the Chinese *materia medica* more than a thousand years ago. Many *yang* tonics also have phallic shapes (we have seen that erect, upright shapes are *yang*, which is male), such as *Cynomorium coccineum* (Maltese Mushroom, a parasitic plant which is not a mushroom—*suo yang* in Chinese, *Tarthuth* in Arabic). It was used in Asia, Arabia across the Sahara into central Africa, and the Mediterranean basin in a similar fashion. Yang tonics include animal substances such as seal penis. Many of these substances not only boost *yang*, but also nourish (*yin*). *Suo yang* is botanically related to the Northern American Broomrape, or Squaw Root (*Onobanche*). Both plants have been used as aphrodisiacs on all continents. *Suo yang* is classified as tonifying kidney *yin* and *yang*. It is a reddish-brown, fleshy stem covered densely with tiny flowers that strongly resembles a phallus. Legend has it that it sprouted from the ground where wild stallions (a very *yang* image) dropped semen onto the ground. "Due to these virile associations, the root has long been regarded as an aphrodisiac for women and a stimulator of semen production in men" (Reid 1995, p. 99). He continues "The obvious phallic imagery and sexual lore associated with this herb might incline skeptics to discount its reputation as an aphrodisiac as a typical example of the Doctrine of Signatures, rather than herbal science. In fact, however, the herb's sexually fortifying properties have been long established by clinical experience in China" (ibid., p. 100). The point is to understand that the elders did not attribute these stories and weave associations around an herb if it did not live up to the expectations... but rather, that the doctrine of signature *is* herbal clinical experience.

Sedum male (left) and Sedum female

When I acquired a reprint of the 1543 German herbal with full botanical illustrations by Leonhart Fuchs, flipping through the pages I was bewildered that many of them were labeled as "male" or "female." For instance, there would be "little Mullein man" (*Wullkraut mennle*) and "little Mullein woman" (*Wullkraut weible*, *wull* for wool and *kraut* for herb, the suffix *-le* being the diminutive). When I investigated, I found that this classification goes back to Dioscurides. Fuchs follows Dioscurides' *materia medica* in both the energetic qualifications given to the herb, as well as in listing whether or not it has "gender" (*Geschlecht*). Under gender he lists plants which have a wild and cultivated gender or form (e.g., Teasel and Angelica), those that have a big and small gender or form (Sage), those which have a male and female form, and those which have many forms. These are not growth forms of the same, but different, closely related botanical species. It seems to me that Fuchs calls *Angelica sylvatica* the wild form, and *Angelica archangelica* the cultivated, which is the case in Germany: *Angelica archangelica* is not native. When comparing the male and female forms, I was intrigued to find that the characteristics of the "female" herb would be *yin,* and that of the "male" herb *yang.* Could it be that Western energetic herbal medicine

had its own form of *yin* and *yang*? For instance, Pimpernel is classified as "this herb is of double gender / woman and man. The man has a scarlet-red-colored flower. The woman however has a beautiful sky blue flower/is otherwise of same shape as the man" (chap. 6, trans. by the author). The male is *Anagallis arvensis;* the female is *Anagallis coerula* in modern terms. They look alike, except for the color of their flowers.

By looking over the entire old herbal, I found that in general, the male form is red, magenta or another bright color, while the

Colubrina (left) and Bistort

female form white, brown or more subdued in color—for instance, yellow *sedum* is male, the white flowering kind female (chap. 10), *Sedum purpurascens* is the male, and the white flowering counterpart is the female (chap. 312). The male growth form is bigger, higher, more upright and with more pointed leaves. The female is smaller, more bushy or creeping and hanging, with rounder, softer leaves and horizontal roots. Of *Veronica,* the upright form we would call Speedwell is the male, while the female "creeps with its thin and hairy stems on the ground" (chap. 54). He lists *Verbena* man and woman: "The male is called Recta (upright) by Dioscurides / and Crista gallinacea / that is / Cock's Comb / due to its cut leaves / that are like a cock's comb" (chap. 226). In the *Polygonum* family, what is now *Polygonum bistorta* (see Bistort drawing, page 213), tall and erect, is the male, while to me unidentifiable *Colubrina,* with much broader, rounder leaves and growth, is the female (see drawing below). The male has a root shape like a contorted snake, while the root of the female looks surprisingly uterine (chap. 298). The white female form of *Sedum purpurascens* is depicted with roots branching out horizontally in a way not representative of the male. Fuchs describes a male and female Martagon Lily, though he admits to having never seen the male, since it is not native to Germany, but relies on Dioscorides for its descrip-

Mandrake roots anthropomorphized

tion. *Lilium martagon,* found wild in Germany, is the female form. Its bulbs are said to be less pungent than that of the male form. While the bulbs of both are classified as warm and dry, "the female / not as much as the male" (chap. 40). For Mandrake, he lists the female as having smaller leaves and a bigger, blackish root, whereas the male has a larger, whitish root and larger leaves and berries that are "of a strong unpleasant smell" (chap. 201). Here the *yin* and *yang* analogy would be that of dark and light, the blackish versus the whitish root.

The gender of plants are echoed in old English herbals such as in Culpeper (masculine and feminine Peony in the *Herbal*), Coles, and Gerard (the authors were well acquainted with the ancient writers). However, the only echo we might still find of those old Dioscruidan classifications is among the orchids. To this day, one form is called *Orchis mascula* (male Orchid). However, this is not the one classified as male by Fuchs. He writes, "The orchids are of fivefold gender. The first is very big in leaves and flowers called *Orchis mas latifolis* in Latin, in German Broader Male Orchid." He goes on to name a big and small male, and big, middle, and small female genders. He describes and classifies several other orchids in his book, but they are not part of this gender group. The gender seems to include only very close botanical relatives.

Fuchs also tells us about the differences in healing effect: if men eat the big tuber, they will conceive a son; if women eat the small tuber, they will bear a girl. It remains unclear whether he means the big and small parts of the double tuber of the same, or of the bigger and smaller varieties respectively. He continues, "This is the reason why in many places such as Thessalia [or Thessaly, in central Greece] there was the custom to take the small one in goat milk so that they were enticed to unchaste deeds" (chap. 210). Orchids live up to their reputation as an aphrodisiac.

While looking through the online translation of Dioscurides' complete *materia medica* in German, I was able to verify that he lists plants as male and female, assigning gender, but have to date not been able to find any text that explains the theory behind this ancient custom.

If we consider Fuchs' classification, it is surprising how much his male and female categories are in keeping with the ancient Chinese categories of *yin* and *yang*. Paracelsus explains the phenomenon thus: "Why is the world made in such a way that one herb is female and another male? The reason for this is that the diseases too are different. If they were all identical, why should nature have divided the remedies into these two species? But because there exist two worlds, the world of woman and the world of man, there are also two kinds of remedies. And just as man and woman are different in their infirmities, so their remedies differ" (Jakobi 1991, p. 86). These are not the only cultures I am aware of which assign gender to plants. Native Americans thought of the *Trillium*s as the part of the Lily family, in which the male and female had separated out to form the red and/or erect male, and the white and/or hanging female form. In this case also evocative of sexual symbolism, this would again be in keeping with the categories of *yin* and *yang*. All three continents have assigned red to the male, and white to the female gender: we are feeling the pulse of planetary herbalism.

THE ELEMENTAL SIGNATURE

When we talk about the elements in this section, we are not so much talking about chemistry, nor chemical elements. What we are talking about is more akin to the four states of aggregates. What we really mean is the energy or phenomenology that is akin to the element in question; thus the earth element, or earth energy is what performs an earth-like function: the earth is dense, heavy, solid, hard, and stable. Thus, that in a plant or body that bears those characteristics is its earth element. These parts might also be rich in minerals, as the earth itself, such as the bones or the bark of a tree. Similarly, the water element is like water—liquid, moist, with adhesive powers, viscosity and surface tension coherent in form like a drop of water but taking the shape of that which surrounds it, and tending toward a flat surface, ripples and wave-like motions and forms. The fire element is that which is hot or warm, or burning—in the form of a flame, or else in the form of a metabolism "burning" of calories. The air element is that which is light (as a feather), hollow, and instable, and always in motion. We may think of flying, feathery seeds such as those of Dandelion or Willow tree. There is a fifth element, called ether or space according to different traditions. In the alchemical tradition, ether is the spiritual dimension of a thing or substance, and can be the mind of a being. In the tantric alchemical tradition of ancient India and Tibet, space is the all-pervasive, underlying element that allows all other elements to exist, thanks to the fact that it allows them space in which to manifest; it is also consciousness, or naked awareness. While we do not think of plants as having a soul, mind, or spirit, the mere fact that we study the plant means that the five elements come together magically into wholeness—our mind being the fifth and most refined of the elements.

One of the most basic considerations of Goethean and anthroposophic plant study is to contemplate the plant's morphology in terms of its elemental resemblances. Thus, Grohmann points to the stem as straight, upright and linear—like light rays (1989, vol. 1, p. 18). It is thus akin to the light/air element. It is of interest to note in this context that creepers do not have the true stem part developed, hence they creep. Leaves stretch our as if following a spherical surface, like water spilled out over the ground. Leaves are closest to the water element. Roots tend to form hard, dense masses. Rich in minerals, they represent the earth element.

Anthroposophy assigns the elements to the plant parts as follows:

fire	seed and fruit	ripened by heat
air/light ether	flower	pollinated by the wind or flying insects
water	leaf	evaporates and assimilates water
earth	root	rich in minerals

Yin and *yang*, water and fire as medicinal categories become the four elements—*yin* excess becomes damp, or water; *yin* deficiency dry or air; *yang* excess heat or fire and *yang* deficiency cold or earth. They are even more closely related to the four basic tissue states of dampness, dryness, heat or cold (Wood 2004, p. 17ff).

In the alchemical tradition (especially that of India), the elements are arranged from dense to refined as if along a spectrum. The densest is earth, followed by water, fire, air, and space/consciousness. We can see that as a plant sprouts from the dense and earthy seed, sinking down the rootlet first, through the emerging leaves and the flowering and fruiting process, it follows this alchemical spectrum of refinement, in which the seed would at once represent its refined essence, as well as the bridge back to the earth (element).

Earth is represented in tough structures in the plant such as Oak bark, which has an almost mineral-like appearance and is very rich in minerals, and the very tough stems of Rue or Solomon's Seal. It is also represented in stems of Mullein, which are left behind in winter, chalky white and hollow like hollow bones and contain a lot of calcium. Before I became acquainted with Stone Root, I received a shipment of medicinal plants. I went through the parcel with excitement, pulling out one dormant root after the other. At the end,

Pulsatilla plant and seeds

only some coarse fiber and a rock were left. "Why did they send me a rock?" I wondered. I fished it out, only to find to my amazement that it was too light to be a stone—that it was, in fact, a dormant root. It was only then that I remembered also having ordered some Stone Root. Eyeing it curiously, I could find neither rootlets nor an eye on it, and I was impressed by the degree to which it lived up to its name. It was not until a year later, when I harvested some to make it into a tincture, that I discovered that it is impossible to cut: rock hard! Clearly, such "rock mimicry" stands for a strong presence of the earth element.

Water is represented by all soft, watery structures, for instance juicy fruits and the gel contained inside of Aloe leaves or Cacti, or very watery plants such as Chickweed, as well as plants growing in or by water or needing lots thereof.

Fire is represented by the plant's ability to endure fire, heat or frost, and flame-like shapes, as well as pungency, warm scents or warming properties and red-orange color. We might think of bright red hot burning Cayenne pepper fruits. I would like to add that I have noticed that in my garden, the same species in different colors will always bloom in red or orange before the "colder" colors, as if the red color gave the flower increased innate warmth. In Chinese medicine, for instance, Red Peony is classified as distinctly warmer than the white one.

The *air* element is present in hairy, downy structures, hollow stems, roots, flower heads, air pockets of any kind and finely cut leaves that have a feathery look such as of Chamomile or Cosmos. It is also related to content of etheric oils and wind pollination and flying seeds. Considered identical with light, or *light ether,* as Rudolf Steiner called it, the air element is represented by all silica-rich structures, especially down and hairs on leaves and petals such as on *Pulsatilla* flowers.

The *ether* element is also akin to the mind, and here we would think of plants that enhance the mental capacities of the beings around it, such as the scent of a conifer forest that open the nasal passages and ears, as well as clears the mind and thoughts. It is, of course, also the space in which all other elements exist, and as such present in plants that form empty spaces like an Iris flower.

Of course, plants are made up of all elements, the signature being a predominance of one over the others. Different plant parts may also be akin to different elements, such as roots being generally earthy, leaves watery, stems often hollow (air) and straight like beacons of light, and flowers fragrant, shining forth in radiant colors and (scientifically proven) warmer than the rest of the plant due to their increased metabolic rate, thus fiery. Grohmann elaborated this point wonderfully in the first volume of *The Plant.*

Not only can plants have the signature of one or more elements overall throughout their bodies, but the predominant element can as well, or the element being expressed, change within the life cycle: Witch hazel is a shrub with a string root system and strong, large, earthy leaves. Once they are shed, it blooms with tiny, fine and airy flowers. A plant might also change its association with the elements through its life cycle; Fireweed pioneers the ground that has been devastated by fire; as a flower essence it stimulates the will's "fire," loves to grow by water, and is very watery (its second name being Willowherb). Thus, it cures "camp fire diarrhea" from dirty water, a damp-tissue condition, only to release downy-white, very light seeds into the air, which fly far and wide before landing and germinating on barren, burned land.

In Ayurveda, the five elements are grouped to make three groups — earth and water are called *kapha,* fire *pitta,* and air and ether *vata.* In this way, much easier to handle in applied medical practice than a system of five, the two coarsest and the two most refined elements are grouped together, leaving fire, the element of transformation from one state to the other in the middle position. Frawley and Lad write in *The Yoga of Herbs:*

> The three *doshas* [*vata, pitta* and *kapha*] exist in plants as they do in all nature. *Kapha* plants are characterized by luxuriant growth, abundant leaves and sap; they are dense, heavy, succulent, and contain much water. *Vata* plants have sparse leaves, rough, cracked bark, crooked, gnarled branches, spindly growth habits, and contain little sap. *Pitta* plants are bright colored with bright colors; they are moderate in strength and sap, and they may be poisonous and burning in its effect.
>
> Soils, climates, geographical zones, and countries can similarly be classified by *dosha.* Through this we can understand the life forms produced by them and how to adapt to them.
>
> The root and bark of plants (representing the elements of earth and water) tend to work on *kapha* conditions. The flowers (as fire) tend to work on *pitta.* The leaves and fruits (as air and ether) tend to work on *vata.* (Frawley and Lad 1986, p.15)

Ayurveda likewise assigns elements to plant parts: "The roots correspond to the densest and lowest part, connected to the earth. The stem and branches correspond to water, as they convey the water or sap of the plant. The flowers correspond to fire, which manifests light and colors. The leaves correspond to air, since through them the wind moves the plant. The fruit correspond to ether, the subtle essence of the plant. The seed contains all five elements, containing the entire potential of the plant within itself" (ibid., p.10).

It is interesting to note that research into plant physiology has found that flowers are indeed the hottest part of a plant—explained as due to the highest metabolic rate—and then *pitta,* or fire, in the human body is also the heat of the metabolic rate.

Maria Thun has found by way of scientific testing that the roots of a plant are stimulated by predominance of earth elemental forces in the planetary constellations, stem and leaves by water, flowers by air/light, and fruits by fire/warmth. If we reread the above Ayurvedic associations carefully, we can sense that the one of air with the leaves feels somewhat less compelling and as if it was just necessary to somehow fit the scheme. In anthroposophic botany, stem and leaf elements have the reversed assignment: the stem is associated with air/light, and the leaves with water (Grohmann 1989, vol. 1, p. 17ff). This makes sense if we consider that it is the stem that causes a flower to follow or not to follow the Sun (thus, the stem is the part of the plant that is sensitive to light in that way), and the leaves that evaporate and absorb the majority of water. The association of leaves with the water element is further clarified if we think that pure water plants such as algae do not fruit and flower in the ordinary sense, and many of them do not root themselves; they are "pure leaf." It is furthermore relatively easy to observe how wet climates result in an abundance of greenery, and how much rain or watering lets the leaves multiply but will not draw forth flowers, and fruit will tend to rot. Conversely, if water is sparse, leafy plants such as Lettuce will abandon their leafy nature and quickly bolt into flower.

THE SHAPES OF THE ELEMENTS

The elements, of course, give rise to specific forms and colors. Traditionally, the four, five or six elements have always been put into order according to decreasing density or increasing refinement, which makes alchemical sense. It follows that their colors, shapes, and texture become increasingly refined and immaterial. One begins to see that they are a seamless spectrum of phenomena spanning from the material to the non-material. Pelikan points out : "No wonder, the earthy and fluid elements are tending much more toward form…., the air element however, and even more so the fiery…toward dissolution, even destruction of form" (1984, p. 14).

We can easily see how fire destroys materials with their forms, and how air dissolves clouds and makes water evaporate, as a gale shredding forms to pieces. In the realm of plants, the earth element gives rise to heavy, solid forms. Water makes lush, juicy greenery with large leaves. The fire element does not express itself chiefly through form, but more through other characteristics: while flame-shapes and shapes that rise (heat and fire rise) pertain to the fire element, its main domains are flamboyant colors, pungent or malodorous sulfur smells and tastes and heating properties. The air element breaks up form, making leaves finely cut and "feathery" (pertaining to air creatures!), as well as air pockets or hollow parts in the plant. The air element also expresses itself in the aroma: essential oils being highly volatile, in intimate love-relationship with the air element, so to speak, or one might call them flighty. The air element is often found where there is nothing—in a finely feathered leaf such as those of Chamomile; where the body of the leaf should be, there is a void filled with air, and just the ribs of the leaf are left to form a "feather."

Chamomile

When teaching a plant shape class one time, one of my students angrily and accusingly said "but all our different leaf examples here show only the water and air element!" She had missed the point: naturally, earthy structures tend to be found in the roots, the greenery is the area where water and air elements interact and shape the leaves, and the flowers, seeds and fruits are begotten from the interaction of the air and fire element. To find an earth or fire signature in the leaves is therefore rare and significant.

The Environmental Signature

The *environmental signature*, how the place where the plant naturally grows is a signature, is tied closely to the elements. This is because the environment of a plant consists of the outer elements: earth, water, rain, air, wind, and fire, with the latter present either as bush or forest fire or as heat or sunshine. These are closely linked to and mediated by the weather, the weather itself being interplay of elemental forces mediated by planetary constellations. Thus, a sunny day in a hot climate brings a lot of fire element to a plant; Rosemary growing by a hot Mediterranean beach is a pungent, heating plant with a predominant fire element. Grohmann (1989, vol. 1) gave a masterful planetary overview over the plants in different latitudes and climate zones that I will not repeat here.

Environmental associations can be by way of being similar or opposite to the predominant element of the plant. For instance, Oaks with their strong astringency do not mind their roots growing in underground water; in fact, they thrive on it—they are so water-resistant (hence, ancient sailing boats and barrels made of Oak), because they lack the water element so that even an abundance of it does not throw them off balance. Or it can be by way of sympathy—algae are so watery that they do not mind growing in water; it feels like home. Watercress strikes a balance—a watery water plant, it is also intensely pungent, thus embodying fire contained in water. By virtue of holding its "inner embers," as it were, it can thrive in water. Therefore, we see that the relationship can be either by way of being so opposite, there is no harm; or so similar, it feels like home; or having found within itself the perfect balance, so it can balance itself. It is by way of the plant being a teacher that whatever it has mastered to live in without getting sick, it can energetically teach its organism to survive in, or heal from.

Plants in Water, Riverbed and Swamps

Plants that grow near or in water have mastered dampness; they are therefore healing to bodily systems that involve water management, such as the kidneys, the bladder, and lymphatics, as well as healing edema. The French herbalist Dominique Lepage told me the following story: An elderly neighbor woman had swollen, water-logged legs. He gave her Birch leaf tea to drink, based on the signature that Birch trees thrive in swampy soil and are known to pump tremendous amounts of water. Within three days, the Birch tea had pumped the water up and out of her legs, and being a good diuretic, eliminated it from her body. He points out that Meadowsweet and Willow thrive in wet, cold soil—thus becoming a remedy for diseases cause by damp cold, such as colds, fevers, etc. (2007, p. 7f). Damp soils here relate to dampness in the sense of Traditional Chinese Medicine, *kapha* in Ayurveda, and the damp tissue state of the Western tradition.

William Coles explains that Willow leaves, bark, and catkins "stop bleeding and other fluxes," and they grow by a stream (Coles 1657, p. 165).

> Plants growing in turgid brooks, wet lowlands, and swamps are associated with diseases of wetness: rheumatic disorders, feverish colds, and coughs. These plants include the Willow, Water Pepper, Mints, Verbena, Sweet Flag, Elder, Boneset, Jack-in-the-Pulpit, and Skunk Cabbage. (Harris 1985, p. 42)

> Plants growing in damp or wet places correspond to diseases produced by an excess of dampness—respiratory problems, mucus, lymphatic stagnation, swollen glands, kidney and bladder problems, intermittent fever and rheumatic complaints (*rheuma* = "dampness" in Greek). Here we think of Horsetail (low, wet sands/kidneys), Eryngo (salty, sandy seashore/kidneys), Gravelroot (swamp/kidneys), Swamp Milkweed (swamps/kidneys), Hydrangea (sides of streams/kidneys), Boneset (wet soils/joints and fever), Willow (low grounds/joints and fever), Meadowsweet (low ground/rheumatic pains, intermittent fever), Northern White Cedar (cedar swamps and margins of lakes/lymphatic), Labrador Tea (cedar swamps and margins of lakes/ lymphatic), various Knotweeds (low ground/kidneys), Sweet Flag (swamps/mucus, lungs, and joints), Angelica (damp, shady, cool valleys/damp, cold, rheumatic and respiratory conditions). (Wood 1997, p. 25)

"Mucky soil signifies mucus excretions" (Harris 1985, p. 42). He lists Eucalyptus and Sunflower as plants that sanitize those swampy areas "and are similarly employed to cleanse out the 'swampy' areas of the body" (ibid.)—conditions of inflammations of the respiratory or urogenital tract.

"Herbs and shrubs found growing on the banks of clear ponds and fast-moving brooks are mostly indicated as diuretics, such as Horsetail, Bedstraw, assorted aromatic mints, Smartweed, Black Alder, Water Agrimony, and Hydrangea. These plants can help cleanse the urinary system of its waste and stone-forming deposits" (ibid.). These plants that grow in ***wet places*** and treat wet tissue states are diuretic, treating urinary troubles or dropsy, sweats or fevers, diaphoresis, etc. Here are some: Birch, Bidens, Black Alder, Asparagus, Arrowhead, Topinambur, or Jerusalem Artichoke (malaria), Boneset, American and European Brooklime, Buckbean, Buggleweed, Ground Ivy, Cleavers, Cranberry, Erica, Elder, Rattlesnake Master, Eucalyptus, Figwort, Irises, Sweetflag, Forget-Me-Not, Wild Ginger, Grindelia, Swamp Honeysuckle, Jack-in-the-Pulpit, Willow, Queen of the Meadow, knotweeds, Lily of the Valley, Maidenhair Fern and other ferns, Pond Lily, Marsh Marigold, Masterwort, Peppermint and other mints, Pitcher Plant, Plane Tree, Reed, Spring Beauty, Stone Root, Turtlehead, False Unicorn, Blue Vervain, Cramp Bark, Black Haw, Valerian, Watercress, Water Soldier, Whortleberry, Willow and Willowherb (Fireweed), to name a few. Some of them are also stone or gravel remedies, readjusting the balance between solid and liquid.

Sandy, Gravelly Soil

Once plants grow in **wet, rocky, or gravelly soil**, the stone and gravel signature becomes more pronounced. We may list *Parietaria,* Trailing Arbutus, Broom, Wild Columbine, Horsetail, Cochlearia, Speedwell, and the Stonecrops (*Crassulaceae*). Plants that grow in **gravelly or sandy soil** can also help to adjust the solid–liquid balance in the body, healing the hard deposits of stone formations or arthritis, for instance. Examples are Viper's Bugloss, Cowberry, Butter and Eggs, Juniper, Horsemint, Parsley, Pipsissewa, and Thyme.

> Herbs inhabiting gravelly places may also be found growing over large rock formations or completely covering, sandy, barren areas. Such plants can help cleanse and remove from the mucus linings and from their associated areas—i.e. the alimentary and bronchial systems—the harmful stone-forming and catarrhal accumulations. An inflammation may be reduced and disease be prevented by the use of the following: bearberry, horsetail, peppergrass, parsley piert, shepherd's purse, juniper, may flower, gromwell, and the two "Stonebreakers," sassafras and saxifrage. (ibid.)

Stonebreakers

There are many plants that have healing powers to break up stone formations. Many of them grow in rock crevices, as if breaking the stone in order to thrive. Hence, some of them are named

Stonebreaker, or *saxifrage* in Latin after *saxum,* "stone," and *frangere,* "to break." This gave rise to the name Sassafras, and the aromatic tree grows in rock crevices, as if breaking through the rock (ibid., p. 161f). The *Saxifragacae* family is found mostly in high, rocky mountain areas. Called *Steinbrech* in German ("Stonebreaker"), *Saxifraga granulata* has many small tubers at the root that look like a cluster of gravel. According to Wood, Gravelroot "actually precipitates gravel around its roots" (1997, p. 25). This was seen traditionally as a stone signature. Botanical cousins were used in the same way (Delaveau et al. 1980, p. 156). Fuchs says that it has the power and virtue to "break stones of both, kidney and bladder." He says about the white-flowering variety (*Saxifraga alba*) that it "grinds up and breaks the groin and bladder stone" (1543, chap. 286). He calls *Capillum veneris* "wall herb" and counts it among the "stonebreakers" (*Saxifraga* = "Stonebreaker") (ibid., chap. 280). The Northern American *Saxifragae* have been used in a similar way, under the name of Stonebreak or Rockfoil (Harris 1985, p. 162). The flower essence of Canyon Dudleya, of the same plant family, grows on rocks in a canyon. It is useful for people who are addicted to drama, who "try to press life out of a rock" (Patricia Kaminski). Stonecrop flower essence is for people who feel isolated from others, as if cut off by a glass wall. The breaking through this social projection is akin to breaking through the rock on which the plant grows.

Parietaria officinalis (Pellitory-of-the-wall), from the Nettle family, is also called "stonebreaker" in French folklore. It cascades down from old stone walls, preferring moist places. French lore says that it "breaks the stones" in order to thrive. The tea is used to break up kidney stones and calm kidney colic (Lepage 2007, p. 8). Foxglove, naturally occurring in rocky areas and outcroppings in rainy climates, was originally used as a diuretic and to break up stones. Its heart toning properties were only discovered later (Harris 1985, p. 89). It seems to prefer growing in granite soils. Houseleek, Kidney Wort (also called Wall Pennywort, *Cotyledon umbilicus*) and some other succulents grow among rocks. They have been used for urinary troubles (ibid., p. 112).

Swamp Drying or Growing Plants

Plants that can be planted to dry up wetlands such as Eucalyptus, Sunflower (damp soils), or Tamarack will help dry up damp tissue states—both treat soggy colds and coughs. Lemongrass dispels mosquitoes, growing in mosquito-ridden swamps (ibid., under the plants).

Plants Growing in Warm, Sunny Places

Plants that grow in a lot of sun and warmth seem to store the sunshine in their bodies only to impart it onto us. A friend of mine insisted that oranges are pure sunshine, and the anti-depressant properties of the various citrus is remarkable and as effective as sunshine therapy. Chamomile equally thrives in a warm, sunny environment, being at its therapeutic best when grown in a Mediterranean environment. The flower essence restores a sunny disposition and inner joyfulness especially in children. "Plants growing in open sunlight are often warming, drying and cheering (Calendula, Lemon Balm, St. John's Wort, and Rosemary)" (Wood 1997, p. 25).

Plants Growing on Compact Soil

My first herbal teacher said "plantain loves if you walk on it." It does thrive on compact ground, from which it is able to draw its nutrients. Wood considers that the signature for it being one of the best "herbal drawing agents" (ibid., p. 26).

Snow and Cold

Some plants have so much innate heat, they can generate it and be several degrees warmer than the surrounding area. These plants are called *thermogenic*. Skunk Cabbage is a good example—even in deep snow, a field of Skunk Cabbage will be on barren ground having melted the snow around it. In Chinese terms, these plants have strong internal *yang* or fire. Pickers have noticed that the plant can screw itself into the ground, and it has been used for asthma, corresponding to this cramping state and its shape resembling a thoracic cavity. The tissue state correspondence (hot and cold) has not been worked out. Matthew Wood observes that Bloodroot leaves in early spring feel warmer than the surrounding area, and it being a remedy for migraine where the hot blood violently rushes to the head. These warm leaves wrap around the nascent flowers in an unusual and remarkable way, protecting them from the harsh early spring gusts. Kate Gildae who developed the flower essence attributes to it the quality of feeling protected on one's path forward.

Desert Plants

Desert plants have unusual ways of preserving their life in the face of lack of water; this is thus what they can teach us. They form bulbs, other succulent forms, or Aloes, which are essentially water storage organs with plump, water-logged tissue that preserves water for dry spells. These plants moisturize dried out tissue, and are cooling. Heat stroke is prevented in Haiti by washing with water into which either cactus or Aloe leaves have been crushed. These plants are heat stroke resistant for sure. Aloe is also a most excellent sunburn remedy.

The Influence of the Environment on Medicinal Properties

The influence of the environment on the medicinal properties is well known. Plants are usually the most potent when grown in their ideal climate and soil conditions. Dioscuried already points out that the medicinal properties of plants vary according to soil and climate. For example, Rosemary grown in different climates yields an essential oil of different "chemotype," which also has different medicinal properties. Manuka essential oil is considered at its best if grown on a particular peninsula in New Zealand. Most plants that come from the Mediterranean basin will grow in the more temperate and wet climates, but their warming and drying properties will be less pronounced. This is equally true for wild versus cultivated plants: the wild ones can chose their place by germinating or not germinating, by finding the conditions suitable or not, as they go through the hard "school of nature" with its trials and tribulations. Cultivated plants are pampered in comparison, and thus may grow in a soil or climate that is not at all conducive to the formation of the inner healing principles.

Plants that Suppress other Plants' Growth

"No plant will grow under the shadow of [Elder], being affected by its exhalation" (Grieve 1982, p. 267). Walnut trees excrete substances through their roots that are herbicidal, and kill many other plants. Pine needles are so high in turpentine that a thick layer of them, as of other conifers, will inhibit other plants to grow beneath them. While Bach saw this as a signature for being free or freeing oneself from the influence of other people in the flower essences of the latter two, Elder dispels poisons of all kinds from the body—being free from their influence. Plantain, "when growing in good soil, one notes that a span of two to four inches of bare earth encircles the herb. The plant has drawn from the soil and unto itself a great deal of the nutrients which rightfully should have been shared with other plant life" (Harris 1985, p. 146f). This is a nice illustration of its power as a drawing agent for poisons, venom, pus, and splinters.

The Movement of Leaves and Flowers

Flowers open and close, leaves fold and unfold in reaction to stimuli from the environment. Flowers that open and close with sunshine denote a strong relationship to light, as well as sensitivity (they behave almost like a sense organ). The same is true for flowers that trace the Sun's journey across the sky—showing a strong link to the Sun as a "planet." Night blooming flowers such as Evening Primrose and Nightblooming Cereus shrink from sunlight and have a strong relationship to the Moon as a planetary force. Scarlet Pimpernel was called "Poor Man's Weather Glass," because it closes its flowers before the onset of rain. Wood sees this as a signature of this fire dominant plant to protect its inner heat and fire nature against being flooded by excess water (2008, p. 88).

Witchhazel petals roll up and unfurl with the temperature of November/December when it is blooming, curling in self-protection in the frost. It is a remedy for becoming harmonized with natural rhythms. Bloodroot leaves wrap themselves around the flower buds before they open to protect them from the frost of the spring nights. The flowers open in the mornings and close around noon, so the Bloodroot migraine is worse from morning to noon.

Mimosa trees and other plants from the *Leguminosa* family fold and unfold their leaves with the Sun, as well as when being touched (see photo of Silktree leaves). This earned them the name "Sensitive Plant." By contrast, Germans call an overly sensitive person a "mimosa." We will not be surprised to find they are healing plants for nerves and sensitivity, and to know that these leaf movements occur from electrical impulses running through the plant tissue in a quasi-nerve-like fashion. The Cherokee call the sensitive plant *bashful;* it is used in formulas for people who are too shy (David Winston).

Persian Silktree

THE ELEMENTALS

Elementals are invisible beings traditionally associated with the elements. Their description varies from culture to culture. A clairvoyant Scottish man, who lived his life in the presence of nature spirits he could see and talk to, explained to me as follows: they are curious and playful beings, who are attracted to humans especially if they have a luminous and colorful aura. Their outer appearance changes with the seasons, much in the folk way of dressing the fairies in the leaves and colors of the surrounding natural habitat. One could say that since they are one with nature, they are an external expression of it. Traditionally, they are depicted as gnomes, dwarfs, trolls (earth) and undines, nixes, mermaids, and sirens (water), fairies, sylphs, and wind gods (air) or salamanders (fire). A friend of mine says she sees them clearly with details such as the gnome wearing a mouse pelt jacket, but she acknowledged that this kind of almost caricature-like clairvoyance was a rather low type of clairvoyance. Other people see the elementals more as energies moving about, having the colors of the associated element. Thus, the water beings look wavy and water-colored, the fire beings flame-shaped and orange-red and so on. In Tibetan Buddhist culture, which still preserves a lot of the old shamanistic traditions of central Asia with its relationships to beings of other realms, the water beings are described as having the shapes of fish, mermaids, snakes or reptiles and wearing clothes of "water silk" (Harding 2003). This difference in what is perceived in dependence on the person's type of clairvoyance is another reminder of the principle that our perception of nature depends on the observing mind and its qualities—we have to question the existence of an objectively discoverable reality "out there" independent of the observer.

Historically, belief in elementals figured predominantly. There are teachings on the unseen beings in the *kabbala*, in which Paracelsus was well versed. He professes to have encountered elementals in dream-like states, which might refer to the altered state of consciousness that most people require to perceive them (Rivière 2000, p. 93ff). His *Treatises on Nymphs* gives vivid and detailed accounts of their nature, being, habits, etc., which sound alive like the accounts of someone talking of a foreign country he or she visited.

Those creatures have four kinds of homes: aquatic, airy, earthy, inflamed. Those that live in the water are called *nymphs,* in the air *sylphs,* in the earth *pygmies,* in fire *salamanders.* I don't think that those names are really those that they use among themselves, I think that they were given to them by people who never met them; but since they are in use among us, I will employ them, although one might also call the water creatures *undines,* the air beings *sylvesters,* the earth beings *gnomes,* and the fiery ones *volcanes.* In the end, it matters little what we call them; one has to know that these four sorts of beings inhabit very distinct environments (different elements), and that the nymphs, for example, have no business with the pygmies. Thus, man can understand the wisdom of God who did not leave one single element empty or uninhabited. (ibid.)

He goes on to describe how just as we are amazed to find that nymphs can live and breathe in water, they, in turn, are amazed to see us live in the air. Thus, in a sense, we are closest to the air beings, which is maybe the reason why we hear about them most under the name of fairies. He illustrates that the air elementals live in the air, drown in water, suffocate in earth, and burn in fire. Possessing subtle energetic bodies, they do not, however, have a soul (ibid.).

Elementals are rather small (Paracelsus specifies that gnomes measure the width of two hands) and have less of a range of action than other invisible beings in nature related to plant growth, such as landscape angels, devas or angels, or devas related to bodies of water; Pan or other entities related to virility in nature; or planetary spirits believed in some cultures such as Tibet and ancient Greece through the Middle Ages to be responsible for causing epidemics. Due to their lack of a dense physical body, they possess a certain degree of clairvoyance. Elementals live in what one might call symbiotic relationship with one element. They could also be called the living, conscious or spiritual aspect of that element. Marco Pogačnik describes this as follows: "It is important to understand that in dealing with the elemental world, nature, and environmental spirits, we do not mean that we encounter individualized beings like humans. Such an understanding of the elemental world is basically incorrect. Perceiving a consciousness dimension within a given landscape in the form of elemental beings means to perceive holographic units of a single consciousness, the consciousness of *Gaia,* the Earth soul. As holographic units of the all-embracing Gaia-consciousness, even if we do encounter elemental beings as individual light-and-consciousness phenomena in the landscape, from their point of view they are always an indivisible part of the whole" (2007, p. 101). Pogačnik describes various excises to strengthen our perception of elementals. He describes the water elementals as "beings related to the water element first of all represent the consciousness permeating rivers, lakes, oceanic waves, water drops, and so forth.... Their task is to distribute the life-sustaining qualities of water throughout the surrounding landscape" (ibid., p. 104).

Rudolf Steiner described the interaction between the elementals and plant beings in detail, having observed them by virtue of his clairvoyance. Wilhelm Pelikan elaborates on these indications in his third and last volume of *Heilpflanzenkunde,* to date not translated into English. It becomes clear that we do not need to be clairvoyant to understand the workings of the elementals in the plant. Quite simply, if the fire element is present, so are the fire elementals; if the water element predominates, so does the work of the undines. If the plant shows an integration of fire and water, we are witnessing a collaboration of fire and water elementals. Steiner describes closed, defined forms with sharp outlines as the hallmark of the gnomes, the earth elementals. He points out that undines cannot be perceived in fixed forms, but that the very essence of their being is one of continuous metamorphosis, transformation of shape. All chemical and biochemical processes of transformation of one substance into another in the plant are their dream-like workings. He describes the air elementals or fairies (he calls them by their old-fashioned name "sylphs") as beings of which we could not even say that they have a continuously changing form, but who "do not quite have any shape." They light up like tiny shooting stars and are gone the next moment, like "tiny meteors" or fire flies. Steiner does not describe what the fire beings look like, but just tells us we can observe that they act in the stages of ripening by way of heat in the plant. Their hallmark is the transformation of inorganic into organic warmth (Pelikan 1984, p. 21ff). He points out: "No wonder, the earthy and fluid elements are tending much more toward form (behind which stand the gnomes and undines), the air element however, and even more so the fiery [realm of the salamanders] toward dissolution, even destruction of form" (ibid., p. 14). We can appreciate these descriptions from contemplating the corresponding element. Not surprisingly, the folk image of fairies even in cartoon movies shows fairies as hovering around with wings (air), uncatchable and flashing about, giving off sparks and fireworks of light in puffs from their magic wands. These images appear to be shaped by the folk wisdom in our collective subconscious.

Maude Grieve states that folklore explained the spots on the flowers of Foxglove and Cowslip, as well as on butterfly wings and peacock's feathers, as marks left by the fingerprints of the elves. She accounts that Foxglove was originally called *Folks-Glove,* meaning the fairy people. Foxglove was said to grow in the areas where the fairies love to dwell (1982, p. 323). It is true that places in Scotland where Foxglove thrives have an enchanted feel to them. Elves are the elementals of the air element. Pelikan would tell us that the spots in Foxglove are an expression of its overly strong astrality, giving rise to the toxic glucosides. What is astrality but the air element? Hence Foxglove flowers have traditionally been seen as most suitable to clad fairies—although they have also been seen dressed in Cowslip blossoms or Harebell flowers.

In the light of the elementals, the colors and shapes of the plant are not just arbitrary, nor a mere expression of the survival of the fittest type of selection in reaction to the trials and tribulations of its environment, but rather a direct result of the work of the responsible artists: it is the elementals who sculpt and paint the different plants under their influence according to their preference. Rather than a signature being a feature stamped upon the plant by God as the Christian mystic Jakob Böhme thought, we could say that the characteristic is a result of the character that the elemental stamped upon the plant. In anthroposophic botany also, the elemental predominance in a plant is the creative result of the elemental creating it, weaving its energetic form as it were. The elementals are at the same time correlated to plant parts where they are most active, or one could say: whose guardians of wellbeing and growth they are. Those correlate to parts of the human whole, as well as the four kingdoms:

fire	fruit	the "I" (individuality)	human beings
air/light	flower	the astral body (feelings)	animals
water	leaves	the etheric body (life force)	plants
earth	roots	the physical body	minerals

As an illustration of what we could call the *signature of the elementals,* we can consider Ginger. Pelikan begins the description by setting the stage: Ginger is a member of the Monocots, within which we hardly find any spice plants. The Lilies can offer Garlic, Onion,

Leeks, Chives (more sulfuric than truly spicy), and the Orchid's Vanilla. That is it among 20,000 species. So, Ginger with its pungent taste is truly an exception among the Monocots. Pelikan points out how these plants, among which we also find the grasses and cereals, are usually very earthy, forming patches that cover the earth like a firm carpet. In the Ginger plant, however, the fire process within the plant, usually present in the flowering, fruiting and ripening processes, has descended all the way to the root of the plant. It is thus a plant in which we find a predominance of the fire and earth elementals who meet and work together. Another example is Mistletoe, quite specifically *Vscum album*, not other mistletoes. It cannot germinate in the soil, but only high up in the branches of a tree, bathed in air and light. Not only will the seed die if it falls to the ground, it has to take a journey though the air to germinate: swallowed by the bird, the berry is digested and the seed set free. When excreted by a bird onto a branch with suitably soft wood, this airborne seed can spring to life. It thus has no relationship whatsoever with the earth elementals, as Rudolf Steiner puts it, it repels them. Being a leafy plant with no flower as such and berries that are ripened by the cold of winter, it obviously also is not the workplace of the fire elementals. Mistletoe is thus a co-creation of the water and air elementals (Pelikan, 1984, p. 9ff). It is of interest in this context that the European tribes who used this as a sacred healing plant held that Mistletoe should not touch the ground when cut, or else it would lose its medicinal properties. This correlates with Steiner's view that the elementals who shape the plant abhor the earth and its elementals (ibid.). Pelikan compares the task of the botanist or pharmacologist to that of the anthroposophic doctor—the doctor has to infer the state and function of the energy bodies from the physical appearance of the person, while the plant scientist has to guess the activities of the elementals from the comportment and other characteristics of the plant. He points out that in this way, we can say that the Mistletoe hinders the earth and fire spirits to enter a relationship with one another, which would correspond to a state in which the "I" is severed from the physical—the perfect configuration for cancer as a disease to arise. Mistletoe, as a tumorous, parasitic growth that kills the host tree, is the perfect illustration. In holistic medical terms, we can say that cancer takes over when a person has abandoned their life (the "I" has withdrawn from inhabiting the physical body).

THE SEASONS

The significance of the seasons is most pronounced in the temperate zones, since it is there that the four seasons play out the most clearly. In a sense, the tropics are in a state of eternal summer, the poles in eternal winter, and the climate zones in between swing between these two extremes, giving rise to the four seasons. In the temperate zones, we find a fourfold rhythm of spring, summer, fall and winter. In this circle, the energy is at its lowest at winter solstice and at its highest at summer solstice. The time between winter and summer solstice is the time of increasing daylight (reverse for the Southern hemisphere) and the rising sap, and the time from summer to winter solstice the time of decreasing length of daylight and falling sap. Spring equinox is the time of fastest increasing daylight and an almost euphoric rushing increase of energy, while autumn equinox is the time of fastest decreasing daylight and a call to detach from life and move into the death or hibernation of winter. These outer events strongly shape the energy of the seasons, and the energy and healing qualities of the plants that mature at those times.

Pelikan talks about the "etheric rhythms of spring." While I am not sure what that is supposed to mean exactly, I find the term poetically descriptive of the energy of spring. Being German, the lines of Eduard Mörike's romantic poem "Er ist's" (It's Him) arise in my mind each time I feel spring in the air:

> *Er ist's*
> *Frühling läßt sein blaues Band*
> *Wieder flattern durch die Lüfte;*
> *Süße, wohlbekannte Düfte*
> *Streifen ahnungsvoll das Land.*
> *Veilchen träumen schon,*
> *Wollen balde kommen.*
> *—Horch, von fern ein leiser Harfenton!*
> *Frühling, ja du bist's!*
> *Dich hab ich vernommen!*

It's Him!
Spring displays His ribbon blue
fluttering through the air again,
sweet aromas well familiar
touch with hope the lands anew.
Violets are already dreaming,
dreams of soon appearing.
—Hark! soft sounds of harps, it seems!
Yes, my Spring, it's You!
You I have been hearing!

This is the most concise, poetic rendering of essential spring I know, at least in the original German version, and I admit having altered the above translation to be closer to the original imagery in the German wording. Spring has sprung we say; it is the time of a new beginning, of renewed energy, of something etheric, not yet earthy. This expresses itself in the simple and joyful flowers of spring: Crocuses, Primroses, Tulips, and Daffodils. These flowers are all simple and without conceit. They are bringers of light, hope, joy, youthfulness, and uplifting in quality. Heralding spring, they herald a new beginning and new energy. Crocuses bring a sense of rebirth; Primroses and Tulips open the heart to joy. Windflower (*Pulsatilla*) is one of the earliest spring flowers and has as its keynote symptoms easily changing emotions, "like an April day." It is hence "the weather cock remedy." In this way, it embodies the quality of the weather of the season of its bloom.

As spring grows fuller, the energy becomes earthier. The plants grow taller and bigger, and the ethereal quality of their colors and the spring green darken, and they become earthier. As summer arrives, so do the first fruits—nature is slowly maturing. Summer has the energy of matured, grounded, warm, sunny energy. Since it is most natural for a plant to mature and peak in summer, this is not remarkable as a signature.

As the year rolls on and autumn arrives, all of nature prepares for fruition and going to seed, or to store up reserves for the winter. The energy that had been moving outward and extroverted up to summer solstice starts to go inside, giving us plants that as flower essences have to do with nurturance, thanksgiving, and abundance for the first part of fall (Amaranth, Sunflower) or awareness of impermanence and death for the later part (Meadow Saffron, Aster, Witch Hazel). With the sap descending into the roots, it is the best time to harvest medicinal roots, which have stocked up nutrients for winter. Meadow Saffron is a very interesting plant, in that it blooms in autumn; however, the leaves and fruit appear above ground in the spring. The symptoms calling for it in its homeopathic preparation interestingly have the keynote "dysentery worse in autumn, rheumatism worse in spring" (Murphy 2000, p. 524ff).

As the life force of nature slips away and we go into winter, we herbalists also can take a break, because there is not much left to do outside. Plants that are evergreens and do not "die" in the winter have of old been regarded as signs of immortality, since they defy winter's grip on nature. The Christmas tree is a remnant of the Germanic belief that it stood for immortality, symbol of the hope for renewal at winter solstice. Herbalist David Winston told me that the Cherokee hold that evergreens are stronger, more powerful plants than the others. Cherokee lore has it that the Creator had almost finished creating the world and its beings, the plants and animals. Something was still missing in creation: the human race. In order to create the power to finish His work, He asked all plants and animals to do a four-day fast. After two days, many creatures started to fall asleep, and even more on the third. Only a few were able to stay awake and conscious throughout the entire four days, because they were stronger and had more power than the others had. Those were the evergreen plants and the animals that do not hibernate nor migrate for winter. The most important among those plants in Cherokee medicine is the Cedar. We might also recall the Celtic significance given to Holly. Interestingly, many of those evergreens yield valuable medicines for the colds and flus of winter, and the needles of Pine and such were used by the Native Americans of the northern latitudes to combat the threat of scurvy during this time of scarcity. The leaves of evergreen shrub *buxus* (Boxtree) is used as an infusion for colds and flus in rural France. Heralding the end of winter, Snowdrops pierce the cold white blanket: Snowdrop flower essence is the essence for seasonal affective disorder (SAD), bringing back a sense of inner light, an attitude of seeing the light at the end of the tunnel.

THE ANIMALS IN THE ENVIRONMENT

How a plant relates to the animals around it, and the animals to it are also part of the signature. This is covered in the chapter below on animal signature.

CHAPTER ELEVEN

THE PLANETARY SIGNATURE

"The stars are the model, the ruler, and the blueprint for all plants. Each herb is from its side an earthly star and belongs to the sky, and each star is a heavenly plant in spirit. Herbs have to be divided according to the nature and manner of the stars into seven classes [for the seven planets]. The different organs of the body need corresponding herbs. That which belongs to the Sun, serves the heart; and that which is ruled by the Moon will be good for the brain." —PARACELSUS

Since the dawn of time, astrology has been tied to medicine—to the medicinal plants, medicine making, and disease classifications. During the Hellenistic period of ancient Egypt, this was compiled in the hermetic writings and passed down to us mainly through the practice of the alchemists. To reduce the planetary signature to a mere matching of plants with planets is too narrow and understanding. The quote above reminds us of a common notion that flowers are stars on earth looking back up to the cosmos. Rather, planetary signature is a witness to an entire worldview in which *as above, so below* meant that we can find the cosmos in everything, that all of nature and its creatures around it is ruled by the stars. Paracelsus writes in his *Paramirum*:

> Thus there is the firmament in man, with the course of the planets and the stars in his body, their exaltations, conjunctions, oppositions, etc. And all that astronomy has achieved with great pain and effort by contemplating the stars, you must apply to the explication of the bodily firmament. Who among you ignores astronomy will not achieve anything in medicine.... The Sky acts within us, but to understand the essence of this action you must know the external Sky. The doctor does not merit his name if he only knows the external Sky, he is but a mere astronomer or astrologer. But if he knows to apply that science to man he knows both skies. Finally, understand that the star above and the star below are one and the same and not separate. It is the external Sky that points the way to the inner Sky. Can he be a doctor who ignores the external Sky? The external situation only gives knowledge of the internal....

You should not say about your art: "Lemonbalm is an herb for the uterus and marjoram for the head." This is the talk of those who are ignorant. Their effect depends on Venus and the Moon. This should be conjoined to a favorable constellation if you wish for their medicinal effect to have the effect you wish for. This is the error that has invaded medicine. (Rivière 2000, pp. 45, 60)

Paracelsus goes so far as to say that the medicinal preparation itself should become a star, or rather: carry its archetypal energetic force. He based his entire medical work on astrology, and as we see from the quote above, this was his way of practicing in a truly holistic way, in which man and the universe were one. The influence of astrology on health becomes clear in time of special Saturn conjunctions (Saturn rules the bones), when an unusual number of people break their bones or twist their ankles. Paracelsus also applied this to questions of public health, epidemiology and the like, investigating under which constellation say a cholera outbreak had occurred. We should remember that he was also a mineralogist and alchemist, and that he applied the same principles to his mineral medicines, and often fashioned compound medicines from herbs and minerals considering the person's birth chart and the present day constellation, trying to see the workings of the planetary archetypes, star signs and constellations in everything. This is the point of crossing over into the doctrine of signature as applies to metals and minerals, with the seven metals being assigned to the seven planets.

When I was trained in anthroposophic massage, we were instructed to align our consciousness to the planetary force inherent in each of the different strokes, thus aligning our awareness with the cosmic forces. This is another meaning of "planetary medicine." The eighth alchemical principle in *Emerald Tablet* illustrates this point: "It ascends from the Earth to the Heaven. It extracts the lights from the heights and descends to the Earth containing the power of the above and the below, for it is with the light of the lights." Thus, Paracelsus instructs us that the stars teach us to understand disease, and the plants how to heal them (ibid., p. 59f). It has to be added, however, that to Paracelsus the stars were not what determined our life in a definite manner, but rather an influence, a force that could or could not sway the course of events. This is clear from the fact that he thought that human thought and action could, in turn, influence the stars, because of their natural mutual positive resonance (Rivière 2000, p. 76).

The classic herbal for working with planets and the zodiac is *Culpeper's Herbal* (1653). In recent years, Robin Murphy has assigned planets to all remedies in his homeopathic *materia medica* following this ancient tradition. I have found more disagreement among herbalists as to which planet rules which plant that on all the other aspects of signatures. From antiquity down to the renaissance, and maybe even today, herbalists generally considered one signature per plant. I am proposing that each *quality* is one signature, and that they can be the same or contradictory, and—in the manner of an artist mixing different colors to obtain a new shade—will communicate the ultimate essence of the plant. It seems to me that, ultimately, plants are ruled by more than one planet—many, the form by one planet, the taste by another—and that this leads to the valid ascription of different ruling planets. Paracelsus often assigns more than one planet to the same plant, such as Mars *and* Mercury to Basil and Garlic and Venus and Moon to Plantain (Rivière 2000, p. 61).

Paracelsus and Nicolas Culpeper were two of the herbalists most devoted to astrology in healing. They considered astrology an archetypal language of underlying energy patterns. Both were accomplished astrologers, as well as herb doctors. They made a chart for the disease to determine the planet causing the disease and how to counteract it. "Since how are the stars, so is the sickness, and he who knows the stars also knows the sickness," Paracelsus wrote in his *Paragranum* (Rivière 2000, p. 58). They classified all herbs by planets and star signs; for instance Eyebright and the Sun and Leo (ruled by the Sun), because the Sun rules the eyes. Thus, Eyebright should be picked in July and August when the Sun is in Leo (Graeme 1997, p. 203). In his *Herbal,* Culpeper uses astrological categories to describe disease and healing herbs. Tobyn Graeme, herbalist and astrologer, presents all the details on practicing humoral medicine with astrology in his excellent book *Culpeper's Medicine.* To give an idea of the complexity of this kind of medicinal practice, "If, for example, Mars was the afflicting planet and was conjunct with Saturn, and the disease was not in a part of the body ruled by Saturn, herbs which are in antipathy to Saturn would have to be used since Saturn aggravates a disease of Mars."

Culpeper matched zodiacal signs and planets by means of both contraries and similars:

> [Agrimony] is an herb under Jupiter, and the sign Cancer, and strengthens those parts under that planet and sign, and removes disease in them by sympathy; and those under Saturn, Mars, and Mercury, by antipathy if they happen in any part of the body governed

by Jupiter, or under the sign Cancer, Sagittarius, or Pisces, and therefore must be good for the gout, either used outwardly in an oil or ointment, or inwardly in an electuary or syrup, or concreted juice. (Culpeper 1653, p. 14)

It seems that the classification of coming under a planet was based not so much on outer signature, but rather on the physiological effect of the plant taken as medicine. Culpeper writes about Bryony: "They are furious Martial plants. The root of Bryony purge the belly with great violence, troubling the stomach, and burning the liver, and therefore not rashly to be taken" (ibid., p. 55). Similarly, he says of Dragons (red *Arum*): "The plant is under the dominion of Mars, and therefore it would be a wonder if it should want some obnoxious quality or other." Not to our surprise, however: "It is excellent good against the pestilence and poisons. Pliny and Dioscurides affirm that no serpent will meddle with him that carries this herb about him" (ibid., p. 113). *Arum* sports a snake signature, so this does not come as a surprise. Ancient Greek indications are positive natural magic. Culpeper explains Celandine thus: "This is an herb of the Sun, and under the celestial Lion, and is one of the best cures for eyes that is. All that know anything in astrology, know as well as I can tell them that the eyes are subject to the luminaries. Let it then be gathered when the Sun is in Leo, and the Moon in Aries applying to his trine; let Leo arise, then may you make it into an oil or ointment which you please to anoint your sore eyes withal" (ibid., p. 74). Leo is ruled by the Sun, along with Aries, a fire sign. So Culpeper links the light of the Sun and fire to that of the eyes and teaches how to use the stars to make especially potent medicine. Because Celandine loves moisture and shade, we would not have assigned it to the Sun based on the environmental signature. However, Celandine has a warming and drying effect, which makes sense for a plant governed by Sun. About Solomon's Seal, Europe's best bone-mending herb, he says, "Saturn owns the plant, for he loves his bones well" (ibid., p. 258).

A nice example of how Culpeper explains the healing effects is with Nettles: "This is also an herb Mars claims dominion over. You know Mars is hot and dry, and you know as well that winter is cold and moist. Then you may know as well the reason why Nettle tops eaten in spring consume the phlegmatic superfluities in the body of man that the coldness and moisture of winter has left behind" (ibid., p. 202). The energetic qualities of the planets (hot and dry) were matched to the tissue states (cold and moist) in this way by contraries.

Mugwort

While Thistles come under Mars because of their spines, Culpeper develops a different reason:

[Blessed Thistle] is an herb of Mars, under the sign Aries. Now in handling this herb, I shall give you a rational pattern of all the rest, and if you please to view them throughout the book, you shall to your content find it true. It helps swimming and giddiness of the head, or the disease called vertigo, because Aries is in the house of Mars. [Mars rules Aries, and Aries has as its assigned body part the head, because rams push with their horns.] It is an excellent remedy against the yellow jaundice, and other infirmities of the gall, because Mars governs choler [bile flow]. It strengthens the attractive faculty in man, and clarifies the blood, because one is ruled by Mars. Continually drinking a decoction of it helps red faces, tetters [vesicular skin problems], and ringworms, because Mars causes them. It helps plague sores, boils, and itch; the biting of mad dogs [rabies] and venomous beasts, all which infirmities are under Mars. Thus you see what this does by sympathy. (ibid., p. 71)

In terms of the doctrine of signature, we would say that Blessed Thistle heals the gall by way of its bitterness, and vertigo by way of its pronounced flower heads and long tap root, grounding the energy and giving a firm stance.

The elements are said to be ruled by the following planets:

> **Earth**—Mercury and Saturn
> **Water**—Moon, Venus
> **Fire**—Sun, Mars
> **Air**—Jupiter

Examples of planetary signatures are:

Moon—rules all the water on Earth; thus it is related to watery and cooling plants and places, night blooming flowers (Evening Primrose), flowers that open only with the full moon at night (Nightblooming Cereus), silvery whitish colors and moon-sickle shapes (Mugwort foliage), and so on, healing affinity to the internal fluids, brain and reproductive organs, governing conception, pregnancy, and growth. Culpeper regards Water Lily under the rule of the Moon, and therefore as cooling and moistening. Paracelsus names Water Lily and Watercress (the latter by taste surely ruled by Mars).

Mercury—asymmetric shapes (Elm), swiftness in going to seed (Elm), relationship to the air element and so on (flying Elm seeds), finely divided or feathered leaves, winding plants, healing affinity to the lungs and respiration, swiftness of thought, mobility, digestion. Paracelsus names Fennel and Wild Carrot.

Example: European Elm

Steiner said the European Elm embodies the mercurial principal most perfectly among the trees. Mercury, or Hermes, the Greek messenger of the Gods, is associated with a caduceus, which has two snakes intertwined around a staff. The bark of the European Elm is patterned in waves, like those snakes. These waves show the eternally dynamic energy underlying mercury: swiftness, efficacity, mediation. The Elm tree blooms in February, even before the Sun has really warmed the air—its precocity being mercury's swiftness. The tree whose large branches make the most unpredictable asymmetric curves show the mercurial principle of asymmetry, and this is carried through the shapes of everything within the tree: the buds and flowers are asymmetrically curved, and so are the leaves; one side of the leaves is round, the other one S-shaped, twisting the entire leaf into a kind of spiral. Even the flower buds are asymmetrical like conches. The bloom of elm heralds those of the other trees. It soon looks covered as if in light green young leaves. Upon closer examination, these "leaves," among the very first of the springtime tree realm, turn out to be the winged seeds: delivered by mercury with immense swiftness. Remember that the messenger of the Gods has winged shoes! They already flutter off carried by the wind (the element associated with the planet Mercury is the air) as the leaves are stirring to unfold. The first tree to be sown and germinate in the yearly cycle is therefore the Elm. We could find no better image of swiftness and dynamic asymmetry begetting dynamic motion in a tree. William

From the top: The asymmetric Elm leaf (photo by Sandra Lory); Elm seeds; Elm flowers; the asymmetry of the Elm tree

Coles used it for mending broken bones and shrinking overstretched sinews, very suitable for a mercurial tree (Coles 1657, p. 602f). Elm wood fibers intersect like feathers, rendering the wood virtually impossible to split. These last characteristics might be why Paracelsus classifies Elm as ruled by Saturn, the planet of bones and hard structures (Rivière 2000, p. 61).

Dr. Bach developed the flowers of the Elm tree into a flower essence. It is for very capable people, quick in thought and action, capable of tremendous multi-tasking of course, who find themselves burnt-out and overwhelmed (over-*elm*ed as my friend Tammy says). Discouraged by the incredible workload ahead, they feel like hiding. One dose of Elm flower essence usually restores them to their dynamic, getting-things-done self. It is amusing to note how upon spilling elm flower essence, it forms a little intense ball of energy that puffs and dissipates fast: this is a wonderful image for Elm energy—bursts of energy, but not persistence. That quality pertains to Oak (see below).

Its Northern American cousin, the Slippery Elm, yields one of the best mucilaginous substances found in herbalism. It lubricates the passages and thus speeds the delivery of a baby, the passage of kidney or gallbladder stones and dried feces, and coughing up dried mucus. It speeds up and helps movement.

> **Venus**—pink and pastel colors, lovely scents, beautiful showy flowers, harmony, softness, loveliness, copper color or content of the metal copper (European Birch), healing affinity to eyes, skin, kidneys and sexual organs. To give an idea of Venusian plants, we get a sense that the feminine softness and fineness of Birch leaves and branches are akin to those of Maidenhair Fern, also called "Venus' Hair" in German, used to beautify the hair, for the kidneys and to regulate menstruation. Paracelsus names the kidney-shaped beans, as well as the Venus-shaped pear.
>
> **Mars**—bright red, spines, thorns, plants with a relationship to fire or iron, possibly burning such as the pioneering plant Stinging Nettles, rich in iron, upright in growth and very well defended by glassy hairs that burn upon touch—and which loves iron-rich soils. Healing affinity to blood and body heat, muscle and will power, and gallbladder. Culpeper attributes nasty, sick-making effects of herbs and violent poisoning to Mars. This would be considered *pitta* in Ayurveda. Paracelsus puts other spiny plants into this category, such as Sloe (Blackthorn), Berberis, Hawthorn, as well as pungent Garlic, Horseradish, and Basil.

Example: European Oak

Assigned by Steiner, the European Oak represents the Martian principal in the tree realm. Mars standing for male virility, we are not surprised to find that Oak seeds are gland-shaped, exactly as the Indian tantric symbol for male virility, the *lingam*. These heavy seeds hit the ground, where they lie on the surface and sprout the following spring: straight upright in a pointing gesture, as one would expect from Mars. The maturing tree, however, does not have the straightforwardness of a spear, but rather is twisted and gnarled. This is because the new sprouts of the European Oak, *Quercus robur,* are very tender, are easily damaged by passing insects etc. and become thrown "off course." This reminds me of the fact that boy are more tender than girls. It is interesting to note that other Oaks, such as the Northern American Red Oak, do grow in Martian straightness and redness. The *Quercus robur* tree, however, matures

Ruscus hypoglossum (above);
Wild Rose hips and thorny stems

into what reminds me of a muscular bodybuilder displaying his grandeur: a huge, strong tree, posing like a bodybuilder twisted for the photograph. I was intrigued to receive the following account from my friend Peter Schell: "This weekend I climbed a Pin Oak tree (about twelve inches in diameter) and got twenty to thirty feet off the ground in the forest—loved hearing exactly where the birds were singing from and all the other heightened perspective wonders. But an interesting thing from a signature point of view was feeling the trunk of the Oak tree twist and untwist in the wind—it was a wringing-like action—there was some swaying but the twisting was more pronounced—reminded me so much of muscular twisting of the body. The effect is very profound when you are up in the tree hanging on to the central trunk to keep from falling!"

Oak bark is used for the musculoskeletal system whenever re-calcification or strengthening of broken-down tissue is needed, such as in osteoporosis, hernias (external), or varicose veins. Oaks make very thick barks compared to others trees, an image of strong boundaries and pointing to its tannins strengthening our outer boundaries—the skin and mucosa. Oak trees can live to be five hundred years or older, a sign of the resilience of its wood and its innate strength. The wood,

European Oak
(right photo by Rieko Oshima)

admired for its strength and unsurpassed as such in timber frame building, Oak has of old been a sacred tree to ancient people. To the Germans, it was the tree of Thor, god of war—or, as we could say, the Germanic Mars. Thor is the heavenly wielder of lightning, and it is interesting to note that Oak trees are often struck by lightning. This is due to the fact that they like to grow on veins of underground water. The German saying *"Buchen sollst Du suchen, Eichen sollst Du weichen"* (search for Beech trees and flee Oak trees) bears witness of this: I was taught this ancient lore as a child by way of explaining what to do during a thunder storm. Germanic tribesmen held council under mighty Oaks—at a time when council was held only by men and was often a war council. The Oak was likewise considered the tree of Zeus, or Jupiter, another wrathful father god who hurls lightning. The German Oak was often found on a warrior's coat of arms to symbolize his strength. The German Oak, a sign of Germanic strength similar to the American eagle, is still found today on the coins. The medicinal properties of this plant are expressed perfectly in the saying , "The mighty Oak is broken down"; it heals strong structures broken down from long overuse. The rigidity of the wood parallels the rigidity of the mental state calling for Oak flower essence.

The red color associated with Mars is found most purely in the Northern American Red Oak, but occurs in all Oaks but the Cork Oak in the new foliage. Red also streaks its flowers, stems, and glands. While the main element associated with Mars is fire, we should not be confused that Oaks grow on underground water—one could say that their innate fire element is so strong that it overpowers the water, thus the water not harming the roots that grow in it. Cork is another completely water-resistant material.

Oak yields valuable medicine for strong people with tremendous endurance who have gone beyond their breaking point, but keep struggling on. The same holds true for broken down tissues, yielding to a long period of overuse. "Oak is the great remedy when integrity of mind or body has been broken down by long, arduous suffering or usage" (Wood 2009, p. 294). The bark, very high in minerals, can be used to strengthen the teeth and even cure cavities. A friend of mine, who has very strong teeth in general, was told by his dentist he had a tiny spot of caries—maybe. In the weeks before his scheduled appointment to have it drilled, he poulticed the tooth with powdered Oak bark. Upon his return, the confused and frustrated dentist could not find the spot. Angrily, she drilled all the same in the spot where she thought it had been. She, too, had needed the Oak—to teach her to let go of the struggle! Overall, the medicines yielded by this tree are strengthening and rebuilding. The glands, equally astringent as the bark, have a reputation of being therapeutic for alcoholism (a macho Mars disease), as well as liver disorders, including cirrhosis of the liver. This is also related to disturbances such as hemorrhoids, varicose veins, and distended gallbladder (Wood 2009, p. 292ff). William Cole in his *Adam in Eden* views acorns as a signature for gallstones.

Similarly, Dr. Bach made Oak into a flower essence and found it suitable to "the beaten warrior who never gives up the fight." Oak teaches such people to give up and end struggles that cannot be won, to manage their energies and save them for struggles that *can* be won. Oaks grow very slowly, making an extremely hard, durable wood. This ability of the Oak to contain and husband its energies can be our guide.

Wood thinks Oak are also ruled by Saturn, owing to the hardness of its structures, while Paracelsus has it ruled by Saturn and Jupiter (Rivière 2000, p. 61).

Jupiter—Golden colors and crown-like shapes such as of Maple leaves, edible plants, fruits and nuts, healing affinity to the liver. Steiner considers Apple, Paracelsus Sweet Chestnut, Agrimony (liver healing and yellow), Burdock, and Fig.

Saturn—stiff and rigid structures as of old age or the skeleton, "sclerotic" or hard structures such as bones and teeth, killing off other plants around oneself (Pine), healing affinity for hardening such as Prunes which soften hard stool, and the spleen. Paracelsus list Rhubarb (laxative), and the hard fruits of Quince.

Sun—bright yellow, golden radiant colors and shapes, affinity to sunlight and sunrise/ sunset. The Sunflower not only looks like a sun, but traces its path with its flower head. It is therefore called *tournesol* in French, "Turns-with-the-sun." Flowers that open and close with the Sun also belong here; Culpeper names Centaury (Graeme 1997, p. 203). They may be radiant in appearance. Healing affinity to the heart, circulation, and depression. Heating plants such as Cayenne were also listed under solar influence. Pelikan states that many spice plants belong into the "Sun classification" (1984, p. 217). Paracelsus and Steiner consider Ash to be ruled by the Sun, and Paracelsus further names Saint John's Wort and Chamomile, very sunny flowers indeed.

The Sun is of course not a planet, nor is the Moon in the truest sense; however, for the alchemists they were classified as such. We have to remember that this system predates the discovery of the Sun as the center of the solar system. (For extensive listings of organs, diseases, humors, and so on, categorized by planets and star signs, see Tobyn Graeme, *Culpeper's Medicine*.)

The tradition of associating plants with planets is deeply rooted in the alchemical tradition. This section would be lacking without pointing out that the alchemists did not only strive to classify plants by the planets, but any other substance, such as metals or precious stones, too. This approach to making medicine remains alive today in anthroposophic medicine (see Wilhelm Pelikan, *Sieben Metalle* (Seven metals).

Culpeper says in his *Complete Herbal* that, after identifying which planet causes the disease, one could then cure it by choosing an herb governed by the opposing planet.

I am skeptical of these classifications, rather thinking that there might be one or more planets ruling the plant more strongly that the others. This kind of fine tuned approach would seem valid to me, in the same way as one will not classify an apple as sweet or sour only, but as sweet *and* sour.

The planetary signature is intimately tied in with that of the elements, the environment and weather. This is because the planets have come to be associated with a predominant element, and have been found to influence the weather accordingly. The planets are said to rule the elements: Moon rules water; Venus rules air; Mars rules fire; Jupiter rules warmth; Saturn rules cold; and, obviously, the Sun rules light warmth for the Earth! We should not be surprised that thousands of generations of shepherds observed that one planet or other pulling in front of a star sign changed the microclimate or brought about a complete change of weather. Cloud formations, strength of dew, fall, etc. all point to the interaction of the elements. In a way, weather is simply dynamic expression of the elemental qualities. While it was known to all cultures through all ages that the planets modulate the elemental balance, hence weather, the environment, and plant growth, Maria Thun has demonstrated in more than fifty years of scientific research that these changes repeat and are thus predictable.

The idea that characteristics of a plant reveal under the dominion of which planet it grows go as far back as the Middle Ages at least. Hence, attributes of Mars such as bright red and sharp points when found in a plant are the planet signature. This is another example for the thought that there is a correlation between macrocosm and microcosm. *Ruscus* (Hardy Butcher's Broom), for instance, a member of the Lily family which is generally under the rule of the Moon, has fire engine red berries and is the only Lily with spiked leaves. Hence, it is thought to be ruled by Mars. Wild Roses, of course, are also sharply thorned and have bright red fruit. While some people say that its strong roots and very fierce growth making impenetrable tangles and barriers also point to Mars, others argue it is ruled by Venus, because of the light pink heart-shaped petals. I have seen a circular diagram of Venus' course around the Sun, the line making a perfect rose shape. There is also a German folk song *Sah ein Knab ein Roslein stehn,* about a boy seeing a rose blooming in the heather, the rose being symbolic of the maiden. Maria Thun, in her research into relating plants to their most favorable planetary constellation, found that roses set flower buds under the rule of Mars (Aussaattage 2009, back cover). Thus, I like to think that roses are ruled by both Mars *and* Venus, and therefore became the flower symbolic of erotic love.

While obviously an herbalist would need to know astrology very well to read the planetary signatures, I have found the present day works of the anthroposophic researchers on this of great interest. Starting with Rudolf Steiner, who knew astrology and astronomy very well, he pointed out seven European trees archetypal of the planetary forces of the classical seven planets: Oak for Mars, Birch for Venus, Pine for Saturn, and so on. (The Northern American cousins do not necessarily represent those planetary aspects as clearly as the European one.) Anthroposophists have also measured the angles of one-year-cycles of the planets around the Sun, and then related those to the angles between leaves up the stem on a plant shoot. Considering the appearance of one leaf after another along the stem as a spiral, Steiner pointed out that the planetary rhythms express themselves in those spirals. If the angle is matching, the plant is said to be under the rule of that planet. The only true scientific research with regards to this that I am aware of are found in the works of Maria Thun and allies who have systematically cultivated plants under certain planetary constellations and recorded whether or not it stimulates those plants to better growth—if yes, the plant is said to be ruled by that planet. Some of the results, especially for trees, are listed in her yearly publication of the biodynamic gardening calendar. The medieval astrologer's way of determining the right moment for harvest was different, and we find some examples above. This is in part because Culpeper considers medicinal plants, and seeks to enhance their therapeutic action in a specific way.

I personally find the attempt to fit a plant under the rule of one planet somewhat limiting. Astrology states that each planet plays a role in our personality make up, as well as rules different body parts and functions—so why would that be all that different for a plant? I therefore suggest to take the classification of plants according to planets lightly and with the understanding that *the* planet is maybe just the most obvious or strongest one in the orchestra. In a way, the research of planting trees and so on by the planets as conduced by Maria Thun supports this idea—she will indicate under which constellation the plant will unfold its strongest potential, set the most fruit or flowers. This makes sense, since the act of bloom or fruition is just one aspect out of many in the life of a plant, albeit maybe its highest "destiny."

Ayurveda gives another angle on plants and planets: "Plants transmit the vital-emotional impulses, the life force that is hidden in light." This light is all cosmic light coming from the stars (Frawley and Lad 1986, p. 4).

> Plants bring us the love, the nourishing power of the Sun, which is the same energy of all stars, of all light. These cosmic energies emanated by plants thus nourish, sustain and make grow our own astral body. In this way, the existence of plants is a great offering, a sacrifice. They offer us not only their own nutritive value but the very light and love from the stars, from the cosmos whose messengers they are. They bring us the universal love so

we can enter the universal life. They exist for psychological, as well as physical nourishment. Our feelings, then, are our inner plants, our own inner flowers. (ibid.)

Ayurveda sees plants as connected to the principle of feelings.

THE ASTROLOGICAL ENVIRONMENT

The constellations of the planets in their changing formation is part of the environment, and gives different impulses to plant life; at one time favoring germination, at other times not, on one day favoring the formation of big roots, on another that of abundant flowers. While not a part of the signature, I will briefly allude to it here, since the ancient herbalists have used this knowledge to wildcraft with the planetary rhythms.

Just to give one example: the results of the planetary constellation research of Maria Thun and her staff in *Hinweise aus der Konstellationsforschung* provide the fact that the Moon being in front of a zodiacal sign will communicate the qualities of that sign to living beings on Earth. The zodiacal signs each rule one of the four elements. It is interesting to note that the Moon, when in front of Leo, the most fiery of fire signs, gives a particularly positive impulse to the part of the plant related to heat/fire: the fruits and seeds. By contrast, the two other fire signs, Aries and Sagittarius, favor fruits more, Leo favors seeds and small fruits such as Raspberries and Rose hips. If we bear in mind that Leo has been associated with the heart and the metal gold (a prime healing substance for the heart), then we can see how relevant it is to harvest our seed heart remedies under such a constellation; *Cardiospermum* comes to mind, as does Hawthorn berries and Rose hips. Their vital forces will be heightened above normal by such a constellation, becoming imbued especially with an energetic imprint favoring the healing of the heart.

CHAPTER TWELVE

ORGAN AND PHYSIOLOGICAL SIGNATURES

"Within the plant is the potential of the human being. Conversely, within the human being is the underlying energy structure of the plant. Our nervous system, it could be said, is a tree whose plant-essence is human. Therefore, plants communicate directly to that essence."
—FRAWLEY & LAD (*The Yoga of Herbs*, p. 4)

"Does a plant grow in swampy or mucky soil? Then that might help remove hardened mucus from the ailing body. The color of the plant is yellow? Then, generally, its therapeutic properties are directed toward the liver and gallbladder. Herbs with hollow stem are indicated as cleansers of the human hollow tubes, alimentary and bronchial; others that display sharp thorns or spines are indicated as relief for sharp pains." —HARRIS (*The Complete Herbal*, p. 38)

There are different ways of categorizing the organs with the signatures. Contemplating the profound correspondence between plant- and body-organs, this system of organ signature equals certain plant parts to certain body parts—the bark to the skin, for instance. It acknowledges that the bark *is* the skin of a tree. "The [Native American] Indian herb gatherer recognized the roughly spotted and lenticelled barks of Elder and Sumac as healing agents with which he prepared decoctions and ointments to apply to all affections of the skin, which is the "bark" or outer covering of the body" (Harris 1985, p. 32). We are reminded of the use of Birch bark for skin disorders in the European tradition.

Another general analogy is that of coagulated saps and resins to healing wounds—the sap and resin being the substances that close and heal the wound of the plant, in exactly the same way that the blood does in humans. It is amazing to see how many resins are high in essential oils, which will disinfect, and other substances that will speed wound healing. From pinesap to myrrh, they have been priced for this purpose throughout all cultures and ages.

Another system looks into which organ shapes the plant parts "imitate." An example would be the rhythmic expansions and contractions in plant organs, pointing to the rhythmic expansions and contractions of the heart and lungs.

When considering the doctrine of signature, we find that it can point either to the seat of action of the plant substance in the body (such as the jaundiced sap of Celandine to liver and gall bladder) or to a general action it exerts all over the body, touching upon all tissues. Thus, while Hawthorn is an herb we could consider an organ specific for the heart (heat in the heart, in fact), the signature points to the heart and blood; the hips being red is the traditional signature for heart and blood, and all herbaceous parts being sour means they sedate heat (which overrides the warming signature of the color red). The five-petalled flower making the gesture of fivefold human being points its theme being the center of the five-star (the heart) as well as the five tips—circulation into the limbs. While it is indeed a very well known organ specific herb for heart disease, it reduces heat in the body wherever the blood goes—true to the signature pointing to the blood. Going beyond what we would consider physiological, the energetic gesture follows one of the pranic flows called *vayu* in Ayurveda, the one that is seated at the heart and governs circulation (see the section on *energetic signature* below).

It is outside of the range of this book to repeat every signature already listed under color, shape, and so on under the appropriate organ system here. Please refer to the extensive index for cross references.

TISSUE CORRELATIONS

Ayurveda graces us with a detailed analogy between plant and mammal tissue. They appear here in the traditional order of one human tissue leading to the next:

- *plasma*—juice of the leaves —>
- *blood*—resin and sap —>
- *muscle*—softwood —>
- *fat*—gum and hard sap —>

- *bone*—bark —>
- *marrow and nerve tissue*—leaf —>
- *reproductive tissue*—flowers and fruit

The plant tissue will heal its corresponding body tissue. "The seeds of plants thus treat congenital diseases and dysfunctions by virtue of their affinity with our own seed and congenital root" (Frawley and Lad 1986, p. 16ff).

It is important to notice that Ayurveda also calls all of the nervous system our "inner plant"—in other words, these categories work and are useful, but to apply them as a rigid dogma is taking it too far.

There are countless examples illustrating the above list—such as Oak bark helping to recalcify demineralized bones, or resins being used as the chief "blood moving" remedies in Traditional Chinese Medicine—substances with the power at once to stop bleeding, and to break up internal "congealed" blood.

TISSUE HEALING AND TISSUE STATES

Plants with remarkably fast tissue healing also help to heal human tissues; the succulents, Sea Onion (Sea Squill, *Urginea maritima*) (Pelikan 1980, p. 349), Boneknit (Comfrey), the Aloes etc. Red points to wound-healing herbs and plants that stop bleeding (St. John's Wort).

Succulents and juicy plants have a "damp tissue state" and are often moisturizing, Aloe again being a prime example. Sweet plants are also moisturizing.

Plants that are a little juicy often grow in dry places where it is hot; they are often aromatic and drying.

Pungent plants are heating and induce a hot or warm tissue state; we may think of Ginger. Other plants do not freeze off in the winter because of their inner heat; they are thus healing to colds, as is Mullein, for example.

Plants that grow in cool, shady, and thus moist places tend to cool the body; we may think of Peppermint. Plants that are cooling may do so through several mechanisms. Rosemary, for instance, stimulates circulation, so it assures that the body's core heat gets distributed evenly throughout the body. Thus, it can both warm cold hands and feet and bring inner heat to the surface to be radiated out and cooling the body (especially in larger doses).

Salty plants tend to grow in or near the sea. They increase the water and salt content of the tissue, making it damp and plump: Celery.

The tissue state of stagnation has a relationship to both plants that grow in stagnant, swampy environments and those that contain a lot of essential oils or resins. Cedar would combine these two qualities.

The atrophic tissue state is symbolized by skinny, atrophic plants. "The bean symbolizes being skinny in an unsurpassed manner, and bean pods are sold for a price worth of gold in gel caps for weight-loss cures. A regular consummation of the vegetable would certainly have the same effect!" (Lepage 2007, p. 6). Nations that feed on rice and beans such as the Indians or Mexicans are skinny, indeed. It is counteracted by plump plants such as potatoes.

Another way of looking at tissue signatures would be to say—well, Artichoke and Celandine are very bitter, so is liver tissue—hence the correspondence. Mallows are soft and in all plant parts turns very soft when prepared—hence it softens the tissue. Linseed has a lot of oil—so it lubricates in the oily sense and so on.

THE DIFFERENT ORGAN SYSTEMS, HEAD TO TOE

As we move from the tissues into the organ systems, we will see that there is more than one signature type applying to each. This is because organs are made up of several tissue types—the lungs, for instance, are made up of bronchial tubes, lobes, alveoli, nerves, lymphatic tissue, serous membranes, and fat. In addition, the lungs have a characteristic overall shape. Depending on the similarity of the plant signature, it might be a lung–nerve, bronchial–tubular or alveolar remedy. It can gravitate to different aspects, depending on its picture, the intuitive image that matches.

The signature can manifest in two ways: by looking either like the healthy or like the diseased body part. Pilewort roots similarity in appearance to hemorrhoids is in fact a *disease signature,* whereby the plant looks like the disease it will heal. It does not look like the healthy tissue, but like the unhealthy body part.

Head

The head signature is flowers that come to a head, making large, round buds (Peony, Poppy, Iris), as well as hard-shelled nuts or seeds that look like the skull (Walnut, Nutmeg). They all effect the head in different ways, from how the weight is held up to the functioning of the nerves in the brain, the clarity of mind, or, in the case of Mistletoe, giving at once the image of the circulation in the brain as well as being a good remedy for epileptic seizures. Peonies are used equally for epilepsy, as well as head trauma, poppies and Nutmeg narcotics. Coles writes that the many layers and membranes of Squill bulbs resemble the layers and membranes of the head, "and it is very effectual in divers distempers thereof, but especially the Falling-Sickness, Headache, and dizziness" (Coles 1657, p. 19). He considers the fact that Wood Betony has hairy roots as a head signature, praising the herb as a cure for headaches and epilepsy (ibid., p. 14). Coles recommends a decoction of Quince, a large, head-shaped fruit covered in down, to restore hair that has fallen out (ibid., p. 29) in a typical example for the signature of a remedy for alopecia.

Bones, Joints, Tendons, Teeth

There are many bone signatures—chalky white roots or structures (Wild Yam, Boneknit, Solomon's Seal, Mullein [withered stalk], Boneset [flowers]); mineral-rich, hard, tough, fibrous structures (Rue, Oak bark [according to Ayurveda barks in general], Solomon's Seal, Wild Yam [bone hard chalky white roots]); stiff hollow tubes like the large bones (Mullein, Teasel); leaves clasping the stems (Solomon's Seal, Boneset, Mullein, Teasel); joint socket shapes (Solomon's Seal); plants rich in calcium (Oak bark, Wild Yam—but this signature is not highly specific to the bones until found with one of the others listed here); rhythmic structure and symmetrical alignment (Mullein, Boneset, Horsetail Grass (used also for broken bones [Lepage 2007, p. 7]), Solomon's Seal); and fern shapes unfurling (various ferns) and other wave or snake-like motion (Black Cohosh). The signature for arthritic bone deformation is gnarly, knobby growth and outgrowths (Devil's Claw). Action on the calcification of the teeth may be indicated by toothed leaf margins (Sweetfern, various ferns, Oaks). The stem-leaf insertion corresponds to the tendon-muscle-bone insertion (for example, Solomon's

Solomon's Seal, Mullein, and Horsetail Grass

Seal, Mullein, Horsetail Grass, Oak, Black Cohosh). Considering this, we find that Solomon's Seal is represented in more of the categories than any other of the herbs. This makes it the supreme "herbal osteopath."

The action of Snapdragon on the trans-mandibular joint is owed to its remarkable similarity in shape to that part of the body—jaw to jaw.

Solomon's Seal

Snapdragon

As I apprenticed with plants, I noticed that many of the bone or tendon remedies are very hard to pluck off, even when the stem is thin—Rue and Solomon's Seal in particular. I understood that a tough, thin string-like stem stands for a tough, thin string-like tendon.

The bone-and-tendon herbs, which have a highly rhythmical structure, seem to have the ability to set bones; they are herbal bone setters. This makes sense when we contemplate the rhythmic structure of the skeleton, and how bone setting means restoring that order. Boneknit (Comfrey) does not share this structure, nor does it set bones so much as it causes quick callus formation—a quality that makes it a dangerous herb to use *before* the bone has been reset. Boneset has opposing leaves that fuse where they clasp the stem. "The Indian medicine man, noting that the two leaves are joined together as if to indicate a fusion of broken leaves, used the plant in healing broken bones. Indeed, it is much recommended as a "rejuvenating tonic" for broken health. But the name Boneset is derived from its unquestionable value in treatment of breakbone fever. Recent herbal literature also declares the worth of this herb in the treatment of muscular rheumatism" (Harris 1985, p. 71).

Unquestionably, the name *Boneset* is a translation of the Native American term, and more certainly this is because of its power to help set bones. Because it is believed in recent times that herbs cannot set a bone back into its rightful place, this action is stubbornly ignored. My herbalist friend Jacquelin Guiteau described the action of Boneset lucidly when treated with external and internal application of the tincture thereof for his freshly dislocated collarbone: "It sends an intelligent energy into the bones that makes them change place. You apply it to one spot, but then it resets all the bones in the body." This energy entering the bones and starting to shift them can be felt under the hand of a sensitive body worker. It is also visible from the outside as the body moves and the bones change position, sometimes causing the necessary healing crisis the Chinese bonesetter is looking for; all the muscles that hold the bone in place or pull it out and were effected by the blow of the original injury cramp up into the position of the original shock, and, after what appears to be an ensuing energetic fight, relax and allow the bone to slide back into its original position as the muscles assume their normal tension. In modern terms, once the cells have released their memory of the trauma fully, the healing can begin.

My acupuncturist friend Peter Schell informs me that traditional Chinese bone setters will not even attempt to put the bone back into position until this crisis has occurred. Herbalist Lise Wolff teaches that the stems of dried Boneset snap easily, like a bone breaking. Matthew Wood adds that the dried roots of Spikenard do the same. William Coles rec-

ommends them as a poultice on broken bones. He writes that Crowfoot-Cranesbill has the form of a hip bone, and therefore heals all broken bones (Coles 1657, p. 601).

Heart shapes may point to the hips (Gabrielle Simon), such as the heart-shaped leaves of Wild Yam, specific for pain in the hips, especially when caused by a lying position or from osteoporosis, as well as Bleeding Heart flower essence for hip alignment.

Black Cohosh

Spine Images

Plants that act on the spine have a spinal look—they are elongated and very rhythmically structured—examples are Solomon's Seal, Mullein, Black Cohosh (the flower spike), Weeping Cherry (which I use as a flower essence to relax the spine when hanging forward), Motherwort and Horsetail Grass.

Harris offers an unusual spine signature, describing the stalks of Madder that "appear very weak, for they are usually found growing prostrate upon the ground." Madder was once used in rickets, a disease in which the

The Royal Fern shows its rhythmic structure as a remedy for the back, rhythmic organs, and skeleton. (photo by Sandra Lory)

bones turn weak, which affects the spine and long bones (Harris 1985, p. 125). (For a more on bone setting, see *Bones, Joints, Tendons, Teeth*, page 256.)

Hands and Feet

The five-lobed leaves have of old been seen as signatures for the hands, and thus as a symbol of "power over" and magic. The palmate leaves of the Fig tree were used for ailments of the joints of the hands (Coles 1657, p. 140). After discussing how the juice of Fig leaves removes warts, he continues, "The decoction of Fig Leaves doth also avail much to do away any other malady that infects the hands, by Signature; the Leaf being commonly divided into five parts, as the hand into five fingers; and because the hand is a place full of joynts it hath therefore been applied to the Joynts that have been pained, and found effectual." The same could be said for the palmate leaves of the Castor plant, commonly called *Palma christi* (ibid., p. 309). The seed pods of Devil's Claw look like hands crippled by arthritis, and they are useful in arthritic pains. Our ordinary Figwort with its knotty, knobby roots contains the same medicinally active compounds as Devil's Claw and has of old been used for swollen, arthritic joints. The unfolding leaves of both Oregon-Grape and Black Cohosh go through a fleeting moment of looking like demon's claws. They are remedies for fear and paranoia, the feeling others are out there to get you.

Oregon-Grape leaves: clawing in, left; unfolding, center;
Devil's Claw (Harpagophytum procumbens), *right*

I do not know of many foot signatures; however, Lady's Slipper offers one used for a flower essence that helps to know when the shoe fits right. It is also a remedy for edema caused by ill-fitting shoes. While not foot-shaped, Mandrake has one of the most pronounced roots in the vegetable kingdom, an incredible downward gesture. It is useful for gout, a disease that affects the base joint of the big toe worst of all.

Skin

The tiny oil-gland pores of St. John's Wort are the signature for the pores, pointing to it as an excellent skin-healing plant. The sunburn signature is said to be that it first flowers at St. John's, or summer solstice, when the Sun is highest and burns most directly (Lepage 2007, p. 8). I would add the red color of preparations in all their forms are red like a sunburn. Hence, its traditional use as a remedy for sunburn and other burns. It is still widely produced for this purpose in French farm homes.

Sweet Leaf, also called Wild Bergamot or Bee Balm

The plant part that corresponds in general to the skin is its own skin, often the barks that are rich in tannin and toughen up the skin. Oak bark wash is helpful to cut profuse perspiration (but should be used only after the inner imbalance is addressed). Other barks with lenticels, such as Elder, mark diaphoretic remedies. Birch bark is the image of the smooth skin of a fair lady.

Other skin images include the peachy skin of Peach, and the porous Elder flowers for a diaphoretic, as well as the tubular flowers of Sweet Leaf, Melissa, and so on, for diaphoretic flowers.

Harris gives a list of signatures for skin healing herbs: "Skin healers are indicated in various ways. The signature of the following herbs is their thin, thread-like stems and roots, suggesting the sewing up of skin lesions—Bedstraw, Cleavers, Septfoil, Cinquefoil, and Gold Thread. (Spider webs are also good for this purpose.) Lenticels (openings in the outer layer of cork and tissue stems) also represent skin lesions. White Birch, Elder, Cherry, and Sumac are indicated" (Harris 1985, p. 45f).

Coles names Strawberries as a cure for leprosy by signature; we can appreciate the similarity of skin lesions to those on an overly ripe strawberry (Coles 1657, p. 178). He recommends it both internally and externally for the disease.

Coles states further that Beech heals blisters by signature. I assume he means that the nuts are blister-like (ibid., p. 569).

The classic Aleppo soap, an olive-oil-based soap, enriched with Bay Laurel essential oil, has been used traditionally for all kinds of skin afflictions, from psoriasis to eczema. The hard surface of the leaf might point to the skin as a signature (Wood).

See also the entries for latex, galls, resins, and gums, as well as lichens and molds. Parasitic plants can indicate cancer, and black Chaga tree mushroom on Birch (the tree that stands for smooth, beautiful skin) is a remedy for skin cancer. The Bloodroot leaf wraps around the dainty flower in the harsh spring frost—an image of a protective layer. Bloodroot has proven curative for countless skin abnormalities and cancers, restoring health to our protective layer.

Brain and Nerves

The nerve signature has to do with long, fine, thread-like structures: the tufts of *Mimosa* and Silktree flowers, sometimes in the stamen as in the case of St. John's Wort, the "nerves" in the leaves of Plantain and its long, fine parallel rootlets, and the fine roots of Valerian. The signature for nerve pain is the thorns that could injure or puncture. Matthew Wood considers square stems, such as of Passion Flower or the Mint family, to be a nerve signature.

The brain signature is that of the hard outside shell with the nut meat inside (look under *Nuts* for more details). The archetypal brain signature is that of Walnut.

Skullcap has a flower that looks like a cap over a skull; it is an excellent nerve remedy for the brain. William LeSassier has said it is good for those who over-think (Wood 2009, p. 324). It is also called Mad Dog Skull Cap, because it is a traditional cure for rabies, a viral infection of the brain that is, of course, inside the skull.

Cleavers have the square stem and are long and thread-shaped like nerves. Once they go to seed, they are covered with little seed "balls" that could be likened to synapses, or else Morton's neuroma, which it treats.

Eyes

The Eyebright flower looks like an eye and is one of the most specific herbs for conjunctivitis. It was the most widely used herb in European folk medicine for eye troubles. Harris notes that the yellow center of the flower is a signature of the jaundiced eye, for which Eyebright is curative (Harris 1985, p. 93f). Coles sees it as similar to a bloodshot eye (Coles 1657, p. 46), possibly meaning the dark veins of the flower to be the signature for the red capillaries in conjunctivitis. He also says of Hawkweed flowers, which are undoubtedly luminous, that they bear the eye signature (ibid., p. 50). Coles further lists the Marigolds, Anemones, Scabious, and Wild Tansy as "cure the Eyes by Signatures" (ibid., p. 50). Chamomile has traditionally been said to look like an eye. The tea is invaluable for rinsing inflamed eyes. Also yellow at the center, it has a therapeutic action on the liver. In Ayurvedic and Chinese medicine, the eyes are the sense organ related to the liver. Coles considers the reddish spot on Clover leaves a signature that indicates its therapeutic value for bloodshot, inflamed eyes (p. 562).

Atropa belladonna

Cornflowers, or Batchelor's Buttons, were said to look like eyes because of their strong luminous blue color. They were used to strengthen and heal the eyes, especially blue eyes. If we consider that blue eyes are a sign of *pitta,* or fire constitution, then it makes sense that the cooling blue Cornflowers would heal conjunctivitis in blue-eyed people who have too much inner fire. Chicory flowers are also light like blue eyes. Wood reports the use of Chicory for amaurosis, loss of visual power of the eye, and cataract (2008, p. 189ff).

The eyes have been acknowledged by many healing traditions to be connected to the wellbeing of the liver. Thus, many plants with a liver rather than eye signature are healing here. A special eye signature comes from the animal realm: swallows pick pieces of Celandine to rub the eyes of their young to open—hence its name Swallow Wort. Effective as it is, Celandine is primarily a liver/gallbladder remedy.

The black shiny fruits of Deadly Nightshade (*Atropa belladonna*) look like black eyes. They are poisonous, and in small doses will widen the irises of the eyes, so the pupils appear large and black, like the fruits of Deadly Nightshade. It was called Belladonna, because women used it to widen their pupils and thus look more beautiful. It is still used in modern ophthalmologists' offices to widen the pupils. It thus transforms the eyes into "night eyes," as if adapted to seeing in the dark—very suitable for a member of the plant family that ancient wisdom has called the *Nightshades* and that thrives in shady places.

Rose water from red roses is for red eyes and conjunctivitis (as a wash).

Coles writes, "The Flowers of Vervein in some sort representing the Eye, are no small Argument, that it is thereunto to be appropriated. The distilled water of the Herb when it is in full strength, cleanseth them from Films, Clouds, or Mists that darken the sight, and wonderfully strengtheneth the Optick Nerves" (Coles 1657, p. 37).

Ears, Nose, Mouth

These organs are covered by many of the throat-shaped flowers, many of which are just as orifice-shaped as any orifice would be. The section on *invaginated flowers* gives a list of examples. Sweet Leaf (*Monarda fistulosa*) not only sports the square stem as a nerve signature, the flower head pointing to the head, but also the invaginated flowers indicating the ears. It is generally good for colds and coughs, and a specific for tinnitus.

William Coles graces us with a very interesting signature: assuming that he meant the same as we do by polyps, he writes of Arum it "helpeth the stinking sores in the nose, called *Polypus*" (ibid., p. 65). In this case, the polyp-shaped spadix inside of the spathe would be the signature for the polyp inside the nose.

Strawberry allergy can cause strawberry tongue, and other allergies causing strawberry tongue or other hives (like the surface of a strawberry) might respond to the anti-histaminic action of the Strawberry family.

Coles says of Houseleek that it has the signature of the gums, and uses the pressed juice for scurvy (ibid., p. 92). While I am not sure how Houseleek looks like gums, rather than teeth, Coles quotes Crollius in his *Book of Signatures* as saying that the scales of Pinecones are the signature of teeth, and recommends the boiled needles thereof for scurvy. This was also an old Native American scurvy medicine (ibid., p. 100). Similarly, he points to the seeds of Pomegranate and Coral to look like teeth, using them to fasten loose teeth (ibid., p. 102ff). The husks of Henbane seed looking like a "Jaw Tooth," so a warm gargle of it was used to allay tooth aches (ibid., p. 112; please note that Henbane is toxic).

Mucosa

The mucosa is best illustrated by the pink and red-veined flowers of *Impatiens*. A succulent mucilaginous plant, it is useful in lubricating inner mucosa. In general, mucilaginous plants heal the mucosa. Another famous pink-flowered herb is Mallow and Marshmallow.

The nostrils are hairy, and so are the main bronchi. Thus, many respiratory remedies have velvety hairs: Hoarhound, Mullein and Coltsfoot for instance.

Phlegm production of the mucosa is illustrated and healed by gums and resins.

Neck and Throat

If we talk about a flower *head*, then the stalk beneath it should be the flower neck. Some flowers with pronounced flower heads yield valuable neck remedies: *Iris versicolor* opens the throat chakra and relieves a lot of throat and neck tension, straightening out the neck (flower essence). Yucca flower essence equally inspires us to carry our head high above our shoulders. Maude Grieve recommends the juice of Thistle for a crick in the neck. A bigheaded flower, Coles recommends Blessed Thistle for "swimming of the head" (ibid., p. 209). Black Cohosh, excellent for whip lash injury, sports the signature of the cervical spine.

Jack-in-the-Pulpit has an old reputation for curing sore throats, and it is about as close to the shape of the voice box as a plant can get. Self-heal has a "throated" flower and is a plant that can draw poisons out of a wound, like a "sucking doctor." "The compact flower clusters of Sumac, Self-heal, and Hardhack indicate an accumulation of pus sacs in the throat or tonsils and are often employed by the commercial herbalist and in folk medicine as an astringent gargle for tonsillitis and sore throats. The peculiarly shaped corolla of Throatwort appeared to the early herbalists as a most reasonable facsimile of that part of the body, and they found it to be of good service in the treatment of throat irritations" (Coles 1857, p. 116f; Harris 1985, p. 47).

Daffodils are curiously throated flowers, and we can appreciate them being an emetic (Coles 1657, p. 237).

Lungs and Thorax

Talking of a bronchial tree, it is remarkable how the bronchial tubes look like an upside-

The leaves of Lungwort (pulmonaria officinalis) are mottled with whitish dots, giving them a lung-tissue-like look. It has excellent moistening properties for dry lungs (photo by Sandra Lory).

down tree, and the lungs like the foliage. While the lungs take in oxygen and give off carbon dioxide, the leaves "breathe in" carbon dioxide and "breathe out" oxygen. While bronchial tubes and lungs are hollow, trees are filled out. They are positive–negative images of each other. In that sense, tree-shaped plants, those with tubes, bags or puffed-up structures, as well as large leaves (standing for large gas exchange areas) can point to lung healing plants. Wood considers large leaves (Mullein) to be a signature for the large gas-exchange areas in the lungs. The fuzz on the leaves stands for the cilia in the bronchus. Finally, the lungs are a rhythmically breathing organ, and so rhythmically structured plants are often lung and heart remedies.

The thallus (plant body) of lichen and algae respectively of Island and Irish Moss resembles the lungs. They are also mucilaginous, therefore indicated in dry lung conditions.

Pulmonaria officinalis has leaves with whitish spots that resemble lung tissue with alveoli, and was once used a lot for lung ailments. Coles names Sanicle for the same signature (Coles 1657, p. 161). Yerba Santa leaves collect dirt on the sticky surface as they age, giving them a mottled appearance, the way lung tissue appears dirty after inhaling too much smoke and dust, which sticks to the moist inner surface.

Gingko biloba leaves resemble the two-winged lungs. Gingko seeds have of old been used in Chinese medicine to moisten the lungs.

Thistles have been used of old as a remedy for stitches in the sides, especially those of pleurisy, by way of signature (ibid., p. 209).

Chinese Bellflower as a bud and *Lobelia inflata* seedpods look like the overly inflated alveoli of asthma, which they treat.

Celery and Fennel bulbs when cut in half will display a dome-shaped structure at their base that looks like the diaphragm. Both are excellent respiratory remedies (Harris 1985, p. 79). They also benefit the organs below the diaphragm, as well as those benefitted by the movement thereof. Skunk Cabbage, when cut transversely, resembles the human thorax. It is used in various chest complaints such as asthma and whooping cough (ibid., p. 168).

Thyme, such an excellent respiratory remedy, is said to grow in the form of an upside down thorax with the stems paralleling the appearance of the ribs (ibid, p. 181).

"The rough spots that are on the under sides of the leaves of *Polypody* [fern], as also the Knags, or Excrescences on each sides of the Roots, is a sign that it is good for the Lungs and the exulcerations thereof" (Coles 1657, p. 167).

I did not realize that the name *Chest*nut of Sweet Chestnut might actually be *nut for the chest,* until I saw an old herbal talking about its use for coughs and blood-spitting of tuberculousis (Delaveau et al. 1980, p. 80). An astringent remedy that is nurturing and rebuilding does make an awful lot of sense for open tuberculosis. The nuts are shaped like a heart, pointing again to the chest, and as a flower essence treats the deepest despair of the heart. Coles recommends them for cough with spitting of blood, due to their binding (astringent) nature. "The *Horse Chestnuts* in Turkey and other Eastern countries where they grow plentifully are given to horses to cure them of the *cough, shortness of breath,* and other *diseases,* whence it had its name" (Coles 1657, p. 43). Sweet Chestnut and Horse Chestnut are similar in appearance, but not botanically related.

Calamus root is an excellent remedy for colds, tracheitis, and laryngitis; the rhizome looks like a trachea.

Hollow Tubes

This signature bridges several organ systems, pertaining to the alimentary canal from mouth to anus, the bronchus, and in some cases even the blood vessels and urinary canals as well as the birth canal. Plants with hollow stems clear those hollow passageways—classical examples are Angelica, Elder, and Onion, here in this image looking like food going down the esophagus.

Heart and Blood

We find the last remnants of the doctrine of signature in Traditional Chinese textbooks stating something like "the red color of the plant points to its action on the heart." Red color in plants pertaining to blood, circulation, the heart, bleeding, wounds, and inflammation is one of the most universally agreed upon signatures. Prime examples are red Roses and the red sap of St. John's Wort as well as the red latex of Bloodroot.

The rhythmical structure of plants echoing the rhythmical expansion and contraction of heart and lungs is another strong signature—Lily of the Valley and Foxglove.

Coles names heart-shaped fruits as heart remedies—Strawberries for heart palpitation and Pear spirits make the heart glad (Coles 1657, pp. 178, 260).

The local variety of Wild Yam root used in Belize with the stems attached is said to look like the heart with the arteries. It is used as a heart remedy (Kimberly Hart). Creeping rootstocks are another circulatory signature next to vines. The heavy venous blood is portrayed by the heavy, drooping branches of Horse Chestnut.

Onion

Angelica

Bleeding Heart has a very clear heart organ signature. Composed of two individual flower which fused to make one blossom, it is the prime flower essence for codependence: "I cannot live without you, because you are my other half!" Appearing split through the middle, it is also the remedy for a broken heart from codependence. Heart remedies with heart-shaped petals are the Primroses and Mallow. A great heart remedy with heart-shaped leaves is Linden.

Ayurveda relates resins and saps to the blood, since they circulate through the plant in the way the blood does in the body. Resins are often rich in essential oils that dispel *kapha* and thus liquefy thick, stagnant blood. They are also excellent wound healers: what is resin other than the coagulated blood of a tree?

Craig Wright points out that as the heart-shaped fruit of Cayenne ripen turning red, this follows the same "motion" as a contraction of the heart. Cayenne is a valuable remedy for heart and circulation.

Circulation and Veins

We covered the role of resins in thinning the blood in the above paragraph. Red color, vines (Harris offers vine/vein as a memory aid and points out that vines take the shape of blood vessels in the body; 1985, p. 44) and creeping rootstocks also point to the circulation. An example would be red Cayenne Pepper, which stimulates and equalizes the blood circulation. According to Eva Graf, it also stems bleeding, even in extreme cases (a pinch of Cayenne powder under the tongue, in lecture notes, 1978).

Another signature is offered by Yarrow, the leaves of which are reduced to mere veins, and it is one of the best herbs to stop bleeding from fine blood vessels, or tone the circulation through them.

Hemorrhoids are illustrated by the hemorrhoidal roots of the aptly named Pile Wort (*Ranunculus ficaria*). Hazel and Witchhazel make strong, pile-like underground root tangles. These two astringents heal hemorrhoids, and effect the circulation in general. The heavy and pronounced root of Stone Root is also a hemorrhoidal signature. Its shoots emerge from the ground as livid purple hoops in early spring, making livid purple hoops like hemorrhoids that are strangulated. Purple veins on the plant often indicate varicose veins. In the case of Horse

Chestnut, the heavy branches droop like veins. *Polygonum bistortum* with its twice-distorted root that looks like varicose veins is a strong astringent and very helpful in the condition.

The colors blue, purple, and sometimes black in a plant can indicate an herb for venous blood stagnation. Coles writes that the berries or flowers of Brambles (Blackberry) heal hemorrhoids having that signature, leaving us to wonder what that might be—however, they are purple for sure (Coles 1657, p. 22).

Oak branches resemble the black-blue varicose veins and hemorrhoids it treats.

Immune System

While the immune system is not something that can be perceived with the senses, its effects can. The signatures that are related to the functioning of the immune system are red and sour for histaminic overreaction, spines and prickles as well as stimulating taste for stimulation of the immune system (stimulating substances make the tongue tingle, such as Echinacea), and latex, gums and resins for wound care and immune defense in wound areas or areas of internal infection with pus. In fact, plants use essential oils and resins to protect themselves from microbial invasions. Since thorns make a plant well self-defended, it makes sense that thorny and spiny plants make our system better defended against outside intruders, be they energetic, microbial, or otherwise. Ayurvedic *Kalmegh* (*Andrographis paniculata*) is a spined, immune-stimulating plant used against malarial fevers and the like. Other examples of immune stimulants or tonics include Eleutherococcus and Echinacea. See also the above section on *Spines and Thorns.*

Yin deficiency according to Chinese medicine causes immune weakness, so *yin* tonics build immunity. They are characterized by a sweet taste and often show the human signature; they are fivefold human-shaped roots. Eleuthero (Siberian Ginseng) is an interesting example; the leaves are fivefold, pointing to it being a tonic for all of man, while the branches sport thorns, pointing to its immune enhancing properties. While this might not be via increasing the white blood cell count, there is so much more to immunity than that. Echinacea is another spiny immune enhancer.

Breasts and Milk

William Coles in his 1657 herbal *Adam in Eden* considers latex to be a signature for a galacta-gogue. He names Rampions and Lettuce as examples (p. 129ff). While the validity of this signature remained unclear for me until I read his elucidation, other herbalists have stumbled across this same question. Harris quotes Milkweed as being an example of associative or symbolic therapy—the milky white sap of the plant resembling mother's milk, and it therefore being employed by Native Americans "to treat or prevent faulty lactation" (Harris 1985, p. 31). The Milkworts (*Polygala* spp.) were used in the same manner (ibid., p. 128). Wild Lettuce (*Prenanthes alba*) was considered a "milk root" by Native Americans and used to increase the milk flow after childbirth (Harris 1985, p. 122f; Foster and Duke 1990, p. 80). This is the only point in Harris' masterful herbal on signatures where he himself does not seem to believe a signature. Some other plants containing milk sap act on the balance of the sexual hormonal balance—Dandelion helps the liver break down the sexual hormones, and allays breast congestion, hardness and mastitis, as well as PMS (Wood 2008, p. 482). Annie McIntyre teaches that Dandelion root has a very strong relationship to breast health, and David Winston says the Cherokee consider it a galactagogue. Not all latex-containing plants are a signature for milk flow (see under *latex*). Coles clarifies the question of latex being or not being a reliable signature for breast milk by tying it into the energetics:

> The Milky juyce which issueth forth from the wounded stalks and [Lettuce] Leaves is a sufficient Signature, that this Herb, if it be eaten boyled or raw, maketh plenty of milke in Nurses, who through heat and drynesse are not stored with a competency thereof; for it breedeth Milke by tempering the drynesse and heat; but in Bodies naturally cold, it does not ingender milke at all but is rather a hinderance thereonto, so that it is necessary to examine the Constitution of the party before any thing can be prescribed. If this defect happen in a dry body, there is nothing better then Lettuce, but if in a cold one then hot things as Nigell Fennel and Dill will be proper, because diseases are cured by their contraries. (Coles 1657, p. 131)

In other words, most latex plants are cooling and moistening, and if that is the appropriate energetic constellation, will increase the flow of milk. For the opposite, the milk increasing seeds of the *Umbelliferae* family are useful.

It is interesting that Milk Thistle bears not only the name Milk and has variegated leaves—as if milk spilled over them—but also the tea of the crushed seeds, which is the substance used in healing, yields a milk-colored brew that tastes milky and increases lactation. Milk Thistle is "thought to be a great breeder of milk, and proper diet [the leaves] for women who are [wet] nurses" (Grieve 1981, p. 797). It is, again, no wonder that legend was assigned to this plant saying that Mother Mary spilled some of her breast milk onto the leaves of this plant on her flight from Herodes, hence the variegated leaves. Whereas latex is white and high in proteins, Milk Thistle seeds are high in oils, and the milky hue of tea or tincture is caused by the oils forming an emulsion, like milk.

Milkweed as a flower essence has been shown to deeply nurture the soul, like a wet nurse. It is suitable for people with extreme dependency and regression, who often flee into drugs (Kaminski and Katz 1996, p. 341). The person does not take adult responsibility, but rather stays infantile, asking to be bottle-fed by life. It nurtures the soul like breast milk.

Several flowers and seeds of the *Umbelliferae* family can be seen as an image of the female breast with the milk glands and ducts—the point where the umbel's stems attach to the main stalk would be the nipple into which the milk ducts unite, and the flower petals or later the seeds would be the milk glands. Hence, Fennel seeds etc. are galactagogues. I successfully treated a case of a three-year-old girl of foreign adoption who had developed a breast fetish in her play (her mother had abandoned her at birth at the hospital) with Queen Anne's Lace flower essence based on this signature. Coles writes of Turnip roots, "They increase natural seed and milk in women's breasts by Signature, there being a neer resemblance between a womans breast and a Turnep" (Coles 1657, p. 117). This would hold true for the other members of this plant family. See the section below for the lymphatic signature of the breasts.

Lymphatic System

The roots of Figwort form strings of white knots that resemble swollen lymph knots. It was Europe's prime lymphatic remedy, even employed in eczema of lymphatic origin. Day Lily (Wood) and Peony roots when pulled up from the ground equally look like white lymph knots, and are arranged like the lymph knots in the female breast. Both remedies have been used to heal the breast's lymphatic tissue. Red Clover and Red Root similarly develop nodes on their roots. Other lymphatic remedies such as Cleavers have duct-like structures. Pokeberries, when young and surrounded by the pink aura of the flowers, also look like a string of tender lymph nodes. Hippocrates recommends Mistletoe for lymphatic swelling and the spleen (Storl 2010, p. 233). This signature needs a little more artistic imagination, but then it is easy to see how Mistletoe with ripe berries in the winter has both the lymph node as well as a spleen/glandular look.

Stomach

Coles cites Crollius saying that Ginger roots look like the stomach (Coles 1657, p. 247ff). This wonderfully warming stomach agent shares the sack like look with other stomach remedies: Cardamom and Lobelia seed pods, and the root-stock of Calamus is not too unlike that of Ginger. He lists Pears as closing up the mouth of the stomach and fortifying digestion (ibid., p. 260).

Sack-like flowers such as those of Contribo (*Aristolochia triloba*) are useful for stomach pain and gastric disorders, while the enzyme-rich sack-like organs of the pitcher plants also enhance digestive action—for example, California Pitcher Plant flower (or Cobra Lily) essence.

The stomach working properly only with parasympathetic nervous stimulation, a whole lot of herbs with nerve or solar plexus signatures should also be considered here, such as St. John's Wort. Lobelia acts on the stomach also by way of its nerve quality.

The stomach being the seat of the digestive fire according to most traditional medical systems, it also has a great affinity to warming spices to increase the digestive fire such as Ginger, Cardamom, or Calamus, or else cooling herbs should there be too much (Marshmallow root).

Spleen

This classic illustration of Hart's Tongue Fern from Fuchs shows what Coles and Wood consider to be the spleen signature (small, serrated indents along the edge of the leaf) in a similar way—here it is the pattern of the spores below the leaf that give an indented, serrated appearance (1543, chap. 111). According to Traditional Chinese Medicine, the spleen is in

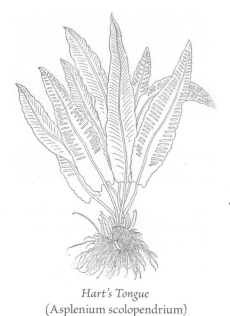

Hart's Tongue
(Asplenium scolopendrium)

charge of regulating dampness in the body. When there is too much dampness, the tongue swells and becomes serrated by imprints of the teeth, looking like the leaf of the Red Oak. The two shapes typified by (a) Wood Betony and (b) Red Oak leaves are analogous to (a) a water droplet increasing in size and expanding and (b) a water droplet shrinking as it dries out. Fuchs says of Hart's Tongue Fern that, prepared in vinegar, it is healing to the spleen. "Therefore those who have a spleen disease should use this herb often and industriously" (ibid.). Wood's other examples would be Royal Fern and Sweetfern (not a fern). I could add Wood Betony to the list. Ferns were traditionally called Spleenwort or Miltwort (*milt* being an old term for spleen, related to the German *Milz* for spleen).

Their Latin name is *Asplenium*, again derived from spleen, pointing to their use for the spleen going back at least as far as ancient Greece.

Coles credits "the learned Crollius" with recognizing in Spleenwort the spleen signature, however without specifying what that would be. According to other sources, it refers to the *sori* (pl. of *sorus*) on the underside of the compound feathered leaves of ferns. The clusters of *sori* make a special pattern that is the spleen signature. He says these ferns, including Hart's Tongue and Royal Fern, reduces an enlarged spleen in humans and animals alike (Coles 1657, p. 322ff), recommending their use for too much openness or hardness of the spleen. The German medicus and alchemist Oswald Kroll also credited Lupine with having the spleen signature, and again Coles does not say what that would be. I am wondering whether it is again the shape of the leaves (ibid., p. 334). Coles also writes that Black Hellebore is a spleen remedy by way of signature, which is the blackness of the flowers indicating a melancholy remedy—melancholy as a humoral imbalance being related to the spleen (ibid., p. 318). Wood points out that the leaves of European and Burr Oak also sport this signature, and that Oak bark is a fine remedy for enlarged spleen.

Liver and Gallbladder

The planetary signature for liver and gallbladder is yellow, sometimes bile green (extract of fresh Oregon-Grape root), or yellow-black like stagnant bile (David Winston). "The unsaturated oil of safflower is today employed in medicine for jaundice and malfunctioning of the gallbladder, although such use originated in folklore which read the "signature" for this very application in the orange-red flowers and the yellow coloring matter of the herb" (Harris 1985, p. 11f). "Those herbs with yellow flowers generally are indicated in disorders of the liver and gallbladder" (p. 43). He continues: "Dandelion, jewel weed, wild snapdragon, hawkweed, tansy, and gentian are examples of this type of remedy" (ibid.).

This photo exemplifies the typical liver signature of a golden yellow. Dandelion flowers look like a solar plexus chakra, and the root is one of the greatest liver and gallbladder tonics.

We might add Oregon-Grape, Safflower, Celandine, Saffron (cooling), Turmeric (heating, might overheat an already hot liver), Goldenseal and Yellow Dock, some of which yielding strongly yellow-colored saps. It is indeed striking to see just how many of the classic liver/gallbladder remedies are intensely yellow, just as are those two organs to which they gravitate, due to them being saturated in bile. Bile being bitter and yellow, sometimes green, we find that a whole range of remedies effective in this sphere are yellow and bitter. Nausea usually originates from the gallbladder, so many of the above herbs are nauseatingly bitter.

Plant parts that are thought to look like the liver are Horse Chestnuts, leaves of European *Hepatica* as it emerges in early spring, and the "jaundiced" leaves of Celandine.

Goldenseal, well known for the strong yellow dye in the roots and its intensely bitter taste, marking it as a liver remedy, here shows the fine-threaded flower—a nerve signature. It thus becomes a remedy also for the innervation of the digestive organs and the mucosa (photos by Sandra Lory).

Traditional Chinese Medicine assigns yellow color to Stomach and Spleen, but I feel that this springs from a need to assign five colors to five organs within the Five Element Philosophy, rather than on nature observation and doctrine of signature.

Bladder and Kidneys

Kidney shapes and plants that grow in or by water have of old been regarded as plants healing to the kidneys and bladder. We may think of Kidney Bean and other beans, Self-heal with kidney-shaped leaves, or Gravelroot, to name a few. The stone signature is a matter apart, and will be mentioned below. Harris also mentions round, kidney-shaped leaves in pairs on both sides of the stems.

Pelikan describes the kidney healing plant archetype (1982, p. 228ff). He quotes Rudolf Steiner, who equated Horsetail Grass with the anabolic kidney processes. Hence, Pelikan takes Horsetail Grass to be the archetypal kidney healing plant. He points out how much oxygen the kidneys use, making them an organ with a special relationship to the air. Horsetail Grass is one of the few plants entirely aerated—the stems are hollow, as are the rootlets. Pelikan names the *umbelliferae,* which includes Celery and Parsley, as one of the few plant families that shares this signature, and both are kidney healing plants. He points to other plants families that imitate the Horsetail Grass in shape and are also diuretics—plants equally reduced to stems: Brooms, Asparagus, and the Madder family, with Cleavers and Sweet Woodruff, which have leaf whorls, as Horsetail Grass does. We could say that tubular plants have an affinity with the urinary tract.

Physalis

When I was in medical school, I was impressed how much a cross section of a kidney glomerulum looks like the cross section of a Zucchini, or of any *cucurbitacea*. In fact, the entire Pumpkin family expresses a theme of storing water—the fruits are, as it were, edematic. They make good diuretics, and Pumpkin itself, looking like a huge prostate, yields seeds that are healing to prostate enlargement, which leads to withheld urine. Watermelon juice and seeds have been used for a kidney flush. Pipssissiwa, also called Prince's Pine, has a flower that resembles the kidney glomeruli, too. It was one of the most important kidney remedies of the woodland Native Americans in the Northeast.

The funnel-shaped leaves of Pitcher Plant, which fill with water, point to it as a kidney remedy.

The prime herb for urinary infection, Bearberry, has bladder-shaped flowers. *Physalis* has a fruit enclosed in a "paper lantern" that resembles a bladder, and it is a very fine diuretic. Dried Corn silk resembles pubic hair, so it helps in cases of urinary-tract infections (Lepage 2007, p. 7). Coles writes of the Common Nightshade that "the Berries of Nightshade, having some similitude with a Bladder, are of excellent use to provoke Urine, and to expel the stone, especially the Seeds contained in them" (Coles 1657, p. 60).

Coles credits "*Crollius* that excellent Author in his book of *Signatures*" with the explanation that the soft pith in Elder twigs, which pits under slight pressure, points to the use of Elder juice for **dropsy**, and, I assume, pitting **edema** (ibid., p. 296). He also cites Crollius as saying that Bryony has the signature of dropsy, but it remains unclear what that means (ibid., p. 300).

Stone formation in kidneys and gallbladder has its own signature; sometimes the plant will have a stone-like seed, such as Gromwell, *Lithospermum officinale*, or Burdock. Others grow in stony ground and are called Stonebreakers: *Saxifragae*,

These Blueberry flowers are identical to those of its botanical cousins, Bearberry and Cranberry, and display the bladder signature. In the case of Blueberry, a powerful eye tonic, they can also be seen as eyeballs or eyes. (photo by Sandra Lory)

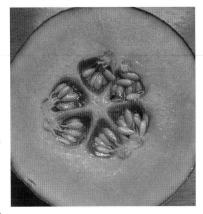

Along with Melons and Zucchini, all fruits of the Cucurbitaceae family show a pattern in their cross-section akin to that of the glomerulus in the kidneys. These fruits are water-storage organs of the plant and are diuretic.

European Stoneseed (Lithospermum officinale)

Parietaria officinalis, and Sassafras. Other plants grow on wet or wet and gravelly ground, and heal gravel in the urine, the precursor of the stones: Sevenbarks (*Hydrangea*) and Gravelroot.We see that these deal with the process of mineral deposits versus a liquid phase. When the concentration of minerals in the liquid becomes too great, they precipitate as crystals. Plants that live in such a milieu and live in harmony with such a process can bring that process into harmony within us.

Plants growing in or at the edge of water are related to the body's water system—the kidneys, urinary tract, or water held in the tissue or liquids in general. Examples for those are Gravelroot, Staghorn Sumac, Sycamore, and Hydrangea.

Intestines

Red Root is considered an intestinal remedy by Native Americans, because the S-shaped root looks like the intestines, all the more so since it is surrounded by nodules like the intestines by the lymph knots (Wood 2009, p. 104). Solomon's Seal root equally looks much like the intestines, and is most useful in lubricating dry and malnourished guts. False Solomon's Seal does share this signature, but being yellowish in addition adds a degree of action on the liver to the former. Since the healthy colon produces some mucus to protect itself and function well, all mucilaginous herbs have a signature here (Linseed, Marshmallow, etc.)—they help to lubricate the colon when too dry. While Walnut is always quoted as the perfect signature for the skull and brain, the surface of the nutmeat also looks like the intestines curled up inside the abdominal cavity, as well as worms. It is one of the best remedies against intestinal parasites, covering bacteria and worms. Crollius said that the turning and winding of Bindweed very much resembles the turning and winding of the guts, making it a good remedy for colic thereof, as well as to kill and expel flat and round worms (Coles 1657, p. 394). In general, winding plants indicate cramp remedies.

Reproductive Organs, Sexuality, and Fertility

Mistletoe was used in Celtic fertility rites. The image of a pregnant woman in a tree hanging full of Mistletoe is striking—all the more when one ponders that how mistletoe sinks its roots into the branch, taking nourishment from the host without relinquishing its cellular identity being so similar to the way the child's organism attaches to the mother via the placenta. Mistletoe "was used in times gone by in cases of sterility, because the berries, once crushed, resemble human sperm" (Lepage 2007, p. 7). The druids used it to treat barrenness in animals. Interestingly, Native Americans also used it "as oral contraceptive" and "to stop bleeding after childbirth" (Foster and Duke 1990, p. 296). Its Cherokee name was *It Is Married* due to the symbiosis of root and wood of the host (Mooney 1992, p. 420).

Isla Burgess in close up photos shows that Red Clover flowers have a vulva color and shape. Lata Kennedy, the owner of Flower Power herbal store in Manhattan uses them as one of the chief herbs for gynecological issues, especially for lack of estrogen.

An interesting Candida signature is that of Red and White Deadnettle, which very easily develop whitish fungus on their leaves and are used for vaginal Candida infections. So do European Oak leaves, and the bark has been used as a wash to toughen skin and mucosa against infections.

Red Clover (photo by Sandra Lory)

Cleavers has the kidney signature in the leaves, while the seeds point to it as an excellent remedy for the lymphatic system, as well as for male health. It is useful for cystitis extending to the testicles, for inflamed, enlarged prostate, and, as the signature would have it, hydrocele and orchitis. (the latter refers to swollen testicles and inflammation of the serous membranes in the testicles). Matthew Wood sees them as a signature for Morton's neuroma, which they treat (photo by Sandra Lory).

Showy Lady's Slipper (left); while this species looks like an ovary, with the fimbriae of the fallopian tubes, this is not the species that looks the most testicle-like (photo by Sandra Lory); (right) Pink Lady's Slipper (Cypripedium acaule), its lower section showing the male sexual signature (Wikipedia, public domain)

Phallic shapes such as of Broomrape, Yucca, and Solomon's Seal and others indicate herbs that increase male virility. They can also denote sexual vitality for females (the ability to engage with the male). Knotweeds with their pink phallic flowers increase male sexual potency. Orchids with their testicle-shaped flowers and roots are also sexual tonics. The Central American Wild Yam sports round, pink tubers that, with their rootlets attached perfectly, look like testes. The Mayas used them for infertility of men and women (Arvigo and Balick 1998, p. 225). Mandrake, Ginseng and other tonics of virility have groin-shaped roots. Female sexual tonics often have three petals or three-lobed leaves. The section on vining plants offers the image of a couple embracing in intercourse for several of those, such as Chinese Cornbind, to strengthen sexual performance.

Coles in his section on plants that increase sexual desire in *Adam in Eden* lists Artichoke, Sea Holly, Potatoes, Peas, Rocket, Mustard, Cotton, Pistachios, Sweet Chestnut, Chocolate, Orchids and Arum. These are but few of the plants in the herbal that he credits with increasing libido. It is evident that some in the list are heating, increasing sexual fire (and we might add Onions and Garlic here), while a good number are very nutritious. Remembering the

Chinese concepts of *yin* tonics, as well as that this list stems from a time when people tended to be malnourished and skinny rather than overweight and overfed, this makes a lot of sense. Coles names Orchid roots, Pistachio nuts and Sweet Chestnuts as having resemblance to testicles, thus working by signature. Arum is evidently phallic in shape. Chocolate or Cacao pods not only look like a pregnant belly, the seeds are highly nutritious and connected by a slimy white matter called *la placenta* in Mexico, which looks like sperm. This signature is given for the crushed berries of Mistletoe, as mentioned.

Solomon's Seal is called thus, because there are round impressions on the root as if someone had pressed a seal upon them. This is said to be the signature of the root closing back the abdominal cavity after it ruptured in an inguinal hernia, allowing the intestines to break into the scrotum. In this case, it should be used inwardly and outwardly. It is also used to stop nocturnal emission in men, as well as to heal leucorrhea and excessive menstruation in women (Coles 1657, p. 598). The opening buds, flowers, and berries viewed in succession depict ovulation and the shriveling of the *Corpus luteum*. Its root is a fertility tonic.

Once thought to be a supreme sexual tonic but now used little because it has been over-harvested, Lady's Slipper sports both a male and female signature: while the scrotum-like bags hanging below are the male signature, the petals above those look like the clitoris. The nerved leaves and fine rootlets mark it a tonic for nervous sexual tonic of first rank.

Australian herbalist Dorothy Hall considers the leaves of Mugwort to have the shape of fallopian tubes, making it a female remedy.

Uterus and Menstruation

Some tuberous roots are said to look uterus-shaped, like that of Maya Wild Yam and Cyclamen. They also act on the uterus. Indeed, a very uterus-shaped flower is Crocus, and I and my Maya Uterine Massage students have verified many times that its flower essence can reposition a subluxated or prolapsed uterus. The prolapse signature *per se,* however, is the heavily drooping flowers of Windflower, Tiger Lilies, and *Trillium* (Wakerobin), which as flower essences, whether in herbal or homeopathic form, have been used to lift the uterus back up. In the case of the latter, it is also a signature for bringing down the baby. This signature, shared also

Wild Ginger (top);
and a Hazelnut flower

by American and European Wild Ginger, can also stand for a remedy that brings on delayed menses (that is, it activates the downward voiding wind, *apana vayu*).

The juicy, gel-filled pads of Nopal, or Paddle, Cactus resembles a juicy uterus. "Drinking a cup of juice from a fresh pad at onset of childbirth is said to ease delivery. Midwives also recommend ingesting ¼ cup of the juice daily for seven to ten days prior to delivery" (Arvigo and Balick 1998, p. 187). Thus lubricating the passage makes a lot of sense.

Coles states that the red stalks of Mugwort are the signature of menstruation, and uses it to provoke, stop, or correct menses; while red-flowered Amaranth is against the "perilous flux of period blood" and red-rooted Madder regulates the period, hemorrhoids and bleeding by signature (Coles 1657, pp. 58, 566, 585f). Since menstruation is a shedding of blood, all the blood signatures and blood remedies act on this sphere. For instance, the tiny uterus-shaped flowers of Hazelnut look like they are spilling forth menstrual blood. I had observed this for almost 20 years, when I read in Coles' herbal that he used the Hazelnut skin over the nut, especially the red kind, to stop excessive menstrual bleeding by signature, as well as the dried husks, shells, and other parts of the tree (ibid., p. 570). Coles also names the red resin of the Dragon Tree to stop the period (p. 567). In China, the red resin called *Dragonblood* is used to stop bleeding. Red Hibiscus and Rose are used in Belize for postpartum or uterine hemorrhage (Arvigo and Baclick 1998, p. 123 and 177).

Since menses is also a rhythmical event, a number of menstrual remedies have a marked rhythmical structure, such as Motherwort. The word mother here means uterus. Ruled by the Moon, silvery leaves such as those of Mugwort may point to a remedy to regulate menstruation.

Since so many plants act in one way or another on the hormonal environment, or more directly on its balance, thin or thicken the blood, or influence the upward or downward traveling energies (*apana* and *upana vayu*), we should not be surprised that the old herbals list an effect or other on the menstruation for almost every medicinal. The only **hormonal signature** that I am aware of is that for the hypothalamus, which reigns over all the other hormonal glands. Matthew Wood considers *cloud medicine,* herbs that show a signature of vapor, to be the signature for a hypothala-

mus regulator, and gives *Pulsatilla* as an example. Hormonal glands were not know in traditional medicinal thinking, hormones an unknown concept, so they do not figure in the tradition of the doctrine of signature. The red flower in the umbel of Queen Anne's Lace has been seen as the third eye chakra with its corresponding pineal gland, which Queen Anne's Lace acts on. Besides various gynecological uses, it acts on thyroid problems caused by low pituitary thyroid stimulating hormone.

Drooping Wakerobin (Trillium); *the uterine prolapse signature (photo by Sandra Lory)*

Birth

French folklore holds that the leaves of Lady's Mantle form a round form similar to that of a cradle ready to receive a newborn, so it was used by pregnant women to prepare and facilitate birth (Lepage 2007, p. 7). The drooping flowers of *Trillium* and Windflower denote both, the withholding of energy in the pregnant belly, thus the swelling and "stagnation" as it were of the pregnant state, and the coming down of the baby in labor. The threefoldness of *Trillium* also illustrates the trunk with the legs astraddle.

In medieval Europe, it was *Aristolochia* that was graced with the name Birthwort, while in Northern America this name (Birthroot or Bethroot) fell to *Trillium.* Crollius points to the round root being uterus-shaped, and using the plant for the ease of delivery it imparts, helping the expulsion of the afterbirth, and being useful as an abortefacient (Coles 1657, p. 581). The flowers of the poisonous European Birthwort, *Aristolochia clematitis,* are said to have the signature of the birth canal. Coles specifies that they be given to women who have carried to full term, and best who are already in labor for an easy and speedy delivery. This must have proven very efficient, since the entire plant family bears the name of *aristos* for best and *locheia* for childbirth. It acts strongly on *apana vayu.*

Coles considers another signature, that of Sabina (Cypress) and the inner bark of Birch bearing the signature of the veins of the womb, making the first an emmenagogue and abortefacient, and the latter useful to expel the afterbirth (Coles 1657, p. 593ff). In birth, the passage has to be well lubricated, so also all lubricating plants such as Slippery Elm are indicated here. See also the above section.

The cover over *Allium* species flowers such as kitchen Onions has been taken as a signature for the amniotic bag covering the fetus. Onion helps expel the afterbirth. A beautiful example of the multilayered truth of the signatures, these images could also point to Onion's male fertility enhancing properties and show an ejection with sperm emerging.

Queen Anne's Lace is a powerful menstrual remedy; the umbel changes from a concave to convex and back to a concave shape, imitating the menstrual cycle of reception and expulsion

THE SIGNATURE OF POISONS

In Ayurveda, *pitta* or fire predominant plants are said to tend toward being poisonous (Frawley and Lad 1986, p. 15). Since *pitta* includes the characteristics of being pungent or burning, we can think of the Stinging Nettle, which is burning and poisonous. So are other acid or caustic plant saps. Other pungent plant agents such as raw garlic can burn the skin upon prolonged contact, or the inside of the stomach if ingested.

Maude Grieve cites old sources to explain the spots on plants or animals as the fingerprints of fairies marking the plant as their own, sign of the air elementals that are related to astrality. Dotted plants can point to poison—Foxglove, Castor plant seeds, Poison Hemlock, Magic Mushrooms, and Primulas to name a few. If the spot be purple, pointing to toxic tissue states, Matthew Wood ties the signature in with witchcraft, as in the case of Poison Hemlock. He also considers Lady's Thumb with its spotted leaf a witchcraft herb. Ancient Indian lore has it that the beautifully dotted feathers of peacocks, who are said to live in the jungle unharmed although feeding on poisonous berries, are a result of them eating poison. The Ayurvedic signature does not explain the presence of chemical poisons such as strychnine in a plant.

Wilhelm Pelikan offers a better image: according to anthroposophic thought, poisons arise in plants when the plant's astrality, its emotional aspect as it were, does not remain outside the plant as it should for a being below the animal realm, but enters into the plant's body. This gives rise to dirty, often spotted colors (Pelikan 1980, p. 157). A plant's body, not equipped to serve as a base for astrality like that of animals with internal organs, reacts by producing poisons instead. When this happens, we often see plant shapes that are pushed down, as if held down by an invisible force, as is the case of Thornapple (*Stramonium*). It grows up fast and strong, only to suddenly come to a halt as if pressed down by an unseen force. This forceful entering of the astral into the plant is thought to create the poison. Interestingly, the Nightshade alkaloids have the opposite effect on animals and humans: they sever the link between the astral body and the physical, thus causing hallucinations and sensations of lightness, including that of traveling through the air—which make them part of many witches' potions. If we consider that the fairies stand for the astral, the fingerprints do not seem so unrelated to this thought. The astral body in humans is the source for emotions and, if restricted in its flow, said to cause cramping.

Monkshood (Aconite)
(photo by Sandra Lory)

A lot of these plant poisons from "astral forcefulness" stimulate exaggerated emotions, even hallucinations, and severe cramps. The more forceful the flowering process is pushed down into the plant, the more toxic the plant of the Nightshade family.

Let's look at this anthroposophic idea of poison and astrality a little closer. Pelikan reminds us that the plant undergoes a big metamorphosis when it progresses from the leaf to the flowering process. This is because, before there can be a flower, the external astrality needs to enter the plant. We can get a feel for this when we watch the green bud of a Tulip slowly turns pink—it does not feel like the touch of pink comes from the inside, nor from below, but it appears first at the top, and as if gently breathed in by the bud or into the bud, sinks down as the petals let go of their green stiffness and become soft and ethereal. If we take a few days to watch the process, it does appear as if an ethereal force from above and outside the plant slowly enters into it, uplifting it beyond the green into a realm of color and shapes that speak to our feelings. In the case of the nontoxic Tulip, the astrality just touches the plant from the outside, gently entering the flower, interacting however without becoming tied to it. It aids the plant into blossom and fruition. The same process of astrality entering a body and becoming anchored to it that makes an animal an animal makes a plant poisonous.

Pelikan observes that all botanical families that have a strong flowering process and thus engage strongly with the astral, produce many poisonous plants. The main families that come to mind are the Poppies, with profuse and abundant blooms, and the Nightshades, with less flashy and big blooms; however, the flowering process often starts with the first leaf axel. In this sense, it is pushed low into the sphere of the leaves (1980, p. 148ff). Another example would be the Spreading Dogbane as used in homeopathy (*Apocynum adrosaemifolium*), a tall and towering plant topped by little white bells that seem illogical in the way they are hanging given the upright gesture of the leafy part of the plant. Spreading Dogbane is slightly toxic.

The stronger the plant realm lifts itself up and develops a strong flowering process, the more there are poisons. The Lily, Buttercup, *Euphoribiacae*, Pea, Carrot, Cleavers, Nightshade and Mullein families all contain a great number of toxic plants. All these plant families have a remarkably intensive and peculiar flowering process. The tropics with their abundance of bloom also produce more poisonous plants than our latitudes. By contrast, the vegetation of the high North and those of high alpine regions are almost free of poisonous plants. Plant families with unshowy blossoms

These Poppy seed pods look like the dilated pupils in someone on opiates, giving them a drugged or "zombie eye" look (photo by Sandra Lory).

like the grasses, the Amaranths, and trees with catkins are free from them. But also plants which live in water, especially in the ocean, are mostly nontoxic. (ibid.)

This last statement would make the Ayurvedic practitioners happy, because such plants would not be high in *pitta*. Pelikan continues:

> So we see: a *dearth* of floweriness means nontoxicity; too much of an abundance leads toward poison-forming processes. Too much, too early or otherwise abnormal a flowering process are the hallmark of typical poisonous plants." (ibid.)

Again, these plants would be considered very high in *pitta*.

The most poisonous of plant families in temperate climates are the nightshades. If we look at those plants with an open heart, we can already feel that they are toxic: the colors are dark,

Poppy; the movement of the petals gives the impression of swaying, as one who is drunk or poisoned (photo by Sandra Lory).

purplish-black, earthen, dirty and mottled, the shape pressed down, ragged like bat wings, drooping, the smell stinking like animals. They flee the light and search for shade, often blooming at night and being pollinated by nighttime flying insects. There is nothing clean, fresh, joyful, or uplifting about those plants, unlike the Lilies, some of which are toxic in parts. Even the ancient name *nightshade* sounds ominous, and we are entering the zone of plants used in witchcraft. What we can already feel from the outer appearance is echoed on the chemical plane; these plants give rise to highly toxic alkaloids. These are plants that have helped murderers, so we should not be surprised that they were once deemed home of demons. My herbalist colleague Jacquelin Guiteau said upon seeing the dirty purple-veined blossom of Henbane (Stinking Nightshade). "That looks spooky." It does, especially with all those bat-wing-shaped leaves fluttering around it.

If then we read the homeopathic literature about the intoxication symptoms with those plants, we find "diabolical force seems to take possession of the brain preventing its function," "rage with desire to strike, bite, fight, insult, scold and to kill," "feeling possessed by the devil," "fearful hallucinations which terrify the patient, sees ghosts, vividly brilliant or hideous phantoms, animals, jumping sideways out of the ground running to him, wildly excited, as in night terrors, sees ghosts, hears voices, talks with spirits," "dread of darkness and has a horror of shining objects," and much mention of insanity with dread of the dark and symptoms like delirium tremens etc. (Murphy, *Hyoscyamus* and *Stramonium*, 2000, p. 848f and 1669f). As pushed-down as the growth of these plants are, we will not be surprised to hear that they cured depression. If we compare this language to the descriptions of Opium poisoning, for instance, while there is delirium, the dark demonic dimension is missing altogether.

Pelikan points out that whereas plants such as Mandrake, Henbane, Jimsonweed, and Deadly Nightshade all have similar alkaloids within them, their medical actions are distinctly different. They correspond to the dynamic process of growth of the plant and its signature, and does not reflect in the chemical analysis of their poisons. For instance, Deadly Nightshade (*Belladonna*) aims its process of becoming toward the black shiny berry that peeps at us from its dry, papery chalix, like a strange one-eyed creature. Steiner explains that *Belladonna*, in thus allowing astrality to enter too forcefully, acts as though wanting to become endowed as a sentient being, with sensory organs such as eyes. Owing to this "eye formation" of the berry, Deadly Nightshade acts strongly on the eyes (see also *Eyes*, page 263). It also wilts immediately after being picked, because a tremendous amount of sap rises and quickly evaporates. Thus, it is a prime remedy for migraines caused by blood rushing to the head (especially with dilated pupils and light sensitivity). Mandrake, with its disproportionately large root, is traditionally dug up only with great care, because the plant demon that lives in it would utter piercing screams that might kill the one who heard it. Because its main energetic gesture is downward, it is active in the lower part of the body, being a valued aphrodisiac. In anthroposophic medicine, it is used for gout. Pelikan stresses that the language of plants, the signature, is therefore more important to know than its chemical analysis.

To develop a feel for the poison signature in this way takes a long time and much contemplation of plants, along with a very intimate knowledge of their growth cycles.

CHAPTER THIRTEEN

DISEASE SIGNATURES

While most signatures are images of organs or physiological processes, some depict disease and are what I would call disease signatures. For example, eruptions, wounds, and ulcers are marked by a wound-like spot or spots, or eruptions. Excrescences on the plant can

point to warts, other skin excrescences, or excrescences of arthritic joints. Swollen joints in plants heal swollen joints in people. And we could say that the most jaundiced plant in nature is Celandine, wonderful to cure the condition. It is a distinct experience to gather a plant and "see" the disease, such as when pulling up the roots of Pilewort, revealing its hemorrhoids. The disease correlation also often appears in the name of the plant, such as Pleurisy Root. Nature is impartial, and whether the signature points to the diseased or healthy state does not change the value of the healing plant to bring about the cure. Let us consider some examples.

Pilewort, a plant with hemorrhoids

TISSUE STATE IMBALANCE SIGNATURES

We can match plants by tissue states. That is, red-hot inflamed tissue states will be cured by fire-engine-red plants (such as Hibiscus, Cherry bark, Rose hips, or Peach leaf), which turn bright red in the fall. Tense and cramping tissue states can be healed by healing plants that are tense or cramping; we may think of vines that "cramp" themselves around other plants like Passion Flower or Dodder. Poke root, which treats pale, waterlogged edematic tissue with lymph stagnation, looks just like that. The pods of Baptisia turn black when touched and heal necrosis where the flesh turns black.

INJURY SIGNATURES

The classical injury signature is that the plant "bleeds" as it is injured. This means it releases a red sap, such as St. John's Wort. (This signature could also stand for hemorrhage or other disorders of the blood, such as the red sap of Bloodroot standing more for the blood rushing to the head in migraine, for example.) St. John's Wort also has the little oil glands that look like it has been perforated, thus making it the best herb for perforations: puncture wounds. Together with the signature of nerves, the fine tuft of stamen, it becomes the prime herb for nerve injuries. Tree resins and gums that exude and crust up when the plant has been injured just like blood oozing from a wound are excellent wound healing substances, highly disinfecting at that. Charles Ben Harris gives plants with fine, thread-like structures like Goldenthread as a signature for the thread to stitch the wound back together.

Another one is the wound signature, that of fast tissue regeneration. Many plants of the Lily family, succulent Aloe and other, as well as succulents from the *Sedum* family such as Houseleek regenerate their tissues remarkably fast and stimulate fast tissue regeneration in us. Comfrey could be said to be unkillable and have proliferating tissue regeneration, happily overgrowing the garden and coming back with a vengeance after each attempt to rip it out. Comfrey is an excellent tissue-regenerating herb that can cause tissue overgrowth.

PAIN SIGNATURE

In the homeopathic sense of "it must be able to cure what it can inflict" (Matthew Wood), a lot of plants with sharp thorns or spines are great pain remedies. Examples go from Prickly Ash (torturous pain), via Hawthorn (angia pectoris pain) to *Aralia spinosa* (arthritis pain).

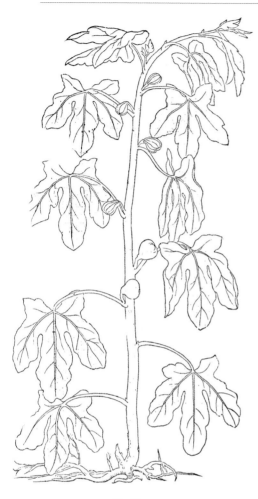

Fig Tree

MUCUS AND PUS SIGNATURE

Apart from being taken as an injury signature, the saps, resins and gums that exude when a plant is injured also look like mucus and pus, and are highly healing to colds, coughs, phlegm, infected wounds, and so on. We may think of Pine resin or Myrrh.

ABSCESS SIGNATURES

There are two basic abscess signatures: Coneflowers and bulbs. Other bulbous or bulging plant structures might also point to it. Within the *Compositae* family, there are a number of flowers with a bulging center as if of an abscess coming to a head: Chamomile, Echinacea, Spilanthes, and Black-Eyed Susan, for example. They are all highly anti-inflammatory and healing to bacterial infections such as found in an abscess. The bulbs of Lilies and their sub clan, Onions and Garlic, have in the past been much employed baked, roasted or boiled as poultices on boils. The bulbs look bulbous like the abscess.

SKIN DISEASE SIGNATURES

There are countless examples for this, and each time the plant looks like the skin affection. We find the use of various lichens for skin affections that look like lichen, Thuya for warts that look like Thuya berries, as well as Mugwort used for moxa. The Mugwort flowers look like warts, and in TCM, warts can be moxed off—the healing agent being the Mugwort resin. Galls are the result of insect bites on leaves, such as the gall wasp on Oak leaves. Oak galls "are, and do, represent excrescences" and are used for skin disease (Harris 1985, p. 133). Grieve names them for swollen tonsils and hemorrhoids (swollen tissue heals swollen tissue; 1982, p. 597). Chaga is a black tree mushroom that cures skin colorations and excrescences, even skin cancer—things that look on the skin like Chaga looks on the bark of a tree.

I was amazed to see how the red seeds of the Guaiacum tree popping out of its orange yellow seed coat looks like a chancre, primary syphilitic lesion. Guaiacum resin was the most important herbal cure for syphilis used by the Caribbean Indians.

Prolapse Signature

Many prolapse remedies are plants with heavy, drooping flowers—flowers that literally prolapse. Some of the famous examples include *Trillium*, Solomon's Seal and Tiger Lily (homeopathic).

Asthma Signatures

I am aware of two asthma signatures. One is that of the *Lobelia inflata* seedpod or the Chinese Ballon Flower bud before opening, image of the inflated alveolus that cannot release the air. Lily of the Valley flowers also resemble inflated alveoli. The other is that of Dodder vining around the host plant and choking it. This is an image of the cramping and choking in the bronchi (use as per Oliama Derivière, Haiti).

Epilepsy Signature

Formerly called the falling sickness, the signature imitates the act of sudden falling in a seizure with the head crashing onto the ground. Classic examples include Peony root (its heavy flowers crash to the ground), Passion Flower (its heavy fruits pull the vine toward the ground), and Lily of the Valley (the drooping flower is said to be the image of the humors "having fallen into the ventricle," the cause of epilepsy, according to the Greek humoral theory). Fuchs says of Lily of the Valley that it should "especially be used in case of fainting, dizziness, and falling sickness" (1543, chap. 88). Gotu Kola, Ayurvedic herb for epilepsy, has flowers that hang on the ground. Interestingly, Fuchs says of Bryonia that it is the remedy for falling sickness, dizziness and stroke and similar diseases (ibid., chap. 32). Bryonia is a vine in the *Cucurbitacea* family with small, berry-size fruits. Their size or weight would not pull the vine downward. So maybe just the lack of standing upright out of its own power of a vine can indicate the weakness of falling over in disease.

ARTHRITIS AND RHEUMATISM SIGNATURES

Arthritis can be depicted as the hand crippled by the disease or the sharp, clawing pain: Devil's Claw can either be seen as the crooked member, or else the hooks penetrating the flesh, causing torturous pain. Thorns and spines can also be an arthritis pain signature, as those of Prickly Ash. Unfurling ferns have been seen as the stiff rheumatic patient slowly stretching his or her curved back. The racemes of Black Cohosh, so valuable for rheumatism of the big muscles, contract into a distorted shape as they ripen—image of the spine distorted by rheumatism.

Plants with swollen joints can point to a plant that heals swollen joints in people, such as the Knotweeds or Solomon's Seal or Figwort.

CANCER SIGNATURES

Wishing to mention the cancer signature, this category contains many parasites. From Mistletoe via Broomrape to Indian Pipe (the latter being not so much of an anti-tumor, but rather a cancer pain remedy), we can appreciate the correspondence between a parasite feeding off of the host plant and the tumor feeding off of the host person, often eventually killing the host. Coles also mentions Sundew as a cancer remedy "by signature" according to Crollius, without naming what he considers to be the signature (Coles 1657, p. 153). We could imagine it to be the fact either that it is a meat-eating plant, and cancers eat the body's flesh, or that, since it can digest meat, it can also digest the cancerous growth.

Another cancer signature may be invasive growth. Sheep Sorrel, famous from the Essiac formula, grows very fast and covers large areas with its mat. This growth is not even slowed down by a thick lawn, which it simply invades. Sweet Violet rootstocks can also overgrow wherever they are. Day Lilies spread very happily, and have a traditional use for cancer in Korea. Periwinkle is an even more invasive ground cover that chokes out everything. It is said to slow the growth of tumors (Arvigo and Balick 1998, p. 159). Grape vines have an explosive growth that covers everything around; chewing the Grape seeds well to release the antioxidants is a traditional cancer cure. Japanese Knotweed is so invasive that it must be called a pest. Although it is listed as an invasive species today, it is nevertheless becoming well-known as a new cancer herb.

INVASIVE DISEASES

Apart from cancer, there are other invasive diseases that are indicated by invasive plants. Japanese Knotweed is also used as an herbal co-treatment for Lyme disease, the spirochetes of which invade the deepest and most inaccessible layers of our tissue.

LYME DISEASE SIGNATURES

We saw above how the characteristic bull's-eye rash, the early stage of Lyme disease, is exemplified by the circular flowering patterns of Teasel and Black-Eyed Susan roots, the Cherokee remedy for Lyme disease. In terms of Traditional Chinese Medicine, Lyme disease is due to weak kidney *yang*. The thistle-like growth makes Teasel a *yang* enhancing plant. It holds water in a cup formed by the paired leaves clutching the erect stem. The plant can absorb nutrients from dead insects that have drowned in the water. This puts them on the road to becoming a flesh-eating plant in terms of plant development. If we understand that Lyme is a disease similar to syphilis, and how syphilis destroys tissues, this makes intuitive sense for a plant that cures Lyme disease.

Teasel (Dipsacus fullonum)

The water-holding basin is also an image of the kidney *jing,* the most essential life force, being held by the kidneys on both sides to the spine. This is depleted by the disease. Furthermore, the spines of this spiky plant point to its ability to drive poisons from the body (an outward gesture). It is debatable whether Lyme disease is caused by the spiorchetes themselves, or the toxins they emit (Storl 2010, p. 172). One way or another, to overcome Lyme disease, it is essential to excrete those toxins. Last, Teasel helps overcome self-destructive tendencies, which would be regarded as the mental aspect of the syphilitic miasm in homeopathy. This is the mental aspect of healing from this disease (ibid., p. 158). It is not astounding that a plant with so many Lyme disease signatures is the best candidate for curing it. My friend the animal herbalist Swanie Simon told me the story of a dog she treated successfully with Teasel. While undergoing the treatment, the dog shed its fur in wandering circles around its trunk!

Matthew Wood remarks that flowers with circular patterns, such as Teasel and Black-Eyed Susan (David Winston), are employed for Lyme disease, which gives rise to a bull's-eye rash.

SNAKEBITE SIGNATURES

Snakebite remedies used to be of prime importance in all pre-modern cultures, because there was no anti-venom that could be injected upon demand. Those who knew snake remedies or how to treat a bite were held in high esteem, and often kept the remedy a family secret. I have found the snakebite signature to be very reliable. It is in almost all cases not just a remedy for the snake venom, but also for the bites of other poisonous creatures, such as scorpions, spiders, insects, and sometimes rabid dogs. With the exception of the latter, all animal venoms are chemically almost identical. The main signature is that of a bud, shoot, or sprout looking like a rearing snakehead, or the body of a snake. When researching and pondering this signature, I realized I knew many plants with very snake-like, phallic shoots without ever having heard of them as snakebite remedies. However, I just had to leaf through enough medieval herbals to find entries listing it as a sure remedy for the bites of venomous creatures. Snakebite remedies also often cover such entries as "expels poyson" or "bite of a mad dog" (Coles 1657, p. 135f). Coles recommends Nettle seeds for the "stinging of venomous creatures" (ibid., p. 165), and while Nettles do not make snake-like shapes, they do "bite." As is so common, this also covers being bitten by a dog with rabies (or nowadays: a dog vaccinated against rabies). Again, Nettle hair contains formic acid, the same substance as in the bite of an ant, thus giving the signature of like curing like. Classic examples for the snakebite signature would be Plantain, with its flower in snakehead shape, and Self-heal, which is regarded as having a flower head that looks like a snakehead by some Native American tribes. Both are also classics for the treatment of insect and spider bites. Northern America still points to a lot of the snakebite remedies by way of the names that stem from native tongues—Snakeroot, Rattlesnake Master, Rattlesnake Plantain. In the latter case, it is the patterning on the leaf that resembles the patterning of the scales of the Rattlesnake. Viper's Bugloss is an example of a snakebite remedy from European culture, and the signature is the snake-like unrolling of the flower raceme.

European and American Wild Ginger root-stock snake over the ground like a nest of vipers—Fuchs says "drunk in wine, it is useful for those bitten by poisonous animals" (1543, chap. 3). Wood Betony, with as much of a snake-like head as Plantain of Self-heal is quoted as "put on as a poultice externally is useful for those bitten by snakes and grass snakes" (ibid., chap. 132). About a plant of the *Arum* genus with very snake-like flowers, he remarks, "Putting the leaves onto the

These Garlic buds display both the snaking snakebite remedy signature and the phallic image (a good example of those two often occurring together). This makes Garlic a remedy that enhances virility, wards off poison, and detoxifies the body. (photo by Sandra Lory).

bites of poisonous animals pulls out the venom" (ibid., chap. 86). He calls this plant *snake herb,* a translation of the Medieval Latin term *Serpentaria.* In modern German, it is still called "Grass Snake Tongue" for the shape of the leaves or "Snakeroot." While there are countless other examples, we can note that a lot of these plants are either drawing herbs with the power to pull poison out of the body, herbs that prevent or treat the necrosis following a bite (here the signature might be that of the necrotic purple or black, as in *Echinacea purpurea* as a snakebite remedy), or great wound herbs needed to heal the bite. A rare and curious signature is that of Black Cohosh, also called Black Snakeroot, of which the ripened seedpods rattle like a rattlesnake. Sound signatures like this are seldom found!

THE SIGNATURE OF THE HEALING PROCESS

In some rare cases, the signature shows the process of healing that the plant will bring about. The fruit of Sweetgum are round, hanging balls, much like prickly Christmas decorations. Intensely spiky, they get entangled with the other fruit and form impenetrable barriers. Not only is this the signature of the coagulated blood Sweetgum heals, but Sweetgum fruit also actually looks like blood cells. Spiny and spiky as they are, they resemble dehydrated red blood cells, lymphocytes, natural killer cells, as well as clotting platelets. Clotting platelets are of course the reason for blood coagulating. Sweetgum is also a cancer remedy, and natural killer cells attack cancer cells. Sweetgum fruit furthermore promote the opening of the body's eliminating channels. So, while the signature points to the image of clotting and blocking as the fruit ripen, they pop open and eject their seeds. At that stage, they look like an inflated starfish with wide-open mouths all over. This is why it is called "all roads open" in Chinese; it is covered by openings like wide-open orifices. Sweetgum is efficient in promoting lactation, urination, eliminating edema, moving coagulated

Fiddleheads (photo by Sandra Lory)

blood, and aiding menses. It opens all roads. In this case, watching the plant depicts the healing process—the opening of the obstructed roads and the emptying out.

PLANT DISEASE AS THE SIGNATURE

A different twist on the disease signature is to take the disease of the plant as the signature—which we already saw for galls on leaves. The soft leaves of White and Red Deadnettle are easily invaded by a whitish fungus, or mildew, that looks like thrush, and they are good vaginal candida remedies. Oak tree are also easily prone to mildew, and Oak bark is great to strengthen the skin and mucosa against candida. Water Lily flowers are easily infested with "lice" (aphids), and Water Lily is a remedy for head lice.

Parasite Signatures and Parasitic Plants as Signature

A lot of the *worm-expelling plants* have a work-like shape—unfurling ferns, the Corsican "worm" Algae, and Pinkroot (also called Wormgrass or Wormroot), to name a few. My herbalist friend Sandra Lory of Vermont got freaked out for a moment when preparing Fiddleheads for lunch, Fiddleheads being the name for the local edible fern sprouts collected in spring. Rolled up like the head of a violin, she thought for a moment that they had within them the larvae of some spooky looking big insect. This is the worm signature.

As we have seen above under *cancer signature,* a cancerous tumor is akin to a parasite growing in the host body. Thus we should not be surprised that many plant parasites such as Mistletoe, Broomrape or Chaga and other tree mushrooms have of old been used as cancer remedies.

There are countless other examples for you to discover, such as the tight-jawed Snapdragon flower, which as a flower essence heals TMJ and grinding one's teeth.

Cure Signatures

If there are disease signatures, then of course there must be signatures of the cure. While we could say that every signature that displays health is a signature for the effected cure, there are more specific cure signatures. One is that of the Stonebreaking remedies. These are plants the roots of which will grow through, and break up, stones and rock. Much employed for breaking gall and kidney stones, these plants include Sassafras, several Stonebreaks (*saxifragaceae*—from the Latin *saxum* for stone and *frangere* for breaking), and Pellitory-on-the-Wall (*Parietaria off.*). The image of breaking up the stone is not an image of a healthy state, but that of the process of the cure. Gravelroot growing in gravelly soil and curing gravel in the urine, as well as breaking up stones into gravel to be passed in the urine is similar.

CHAPTER FOURTEEN

ANIMAL SIGNATURE

This signature comes to us from the Native American art of healing. While it is easy to talk about Native American medicine as one entity, this would not do justice to the richness, diversity, and individual freedom of the peoples of such a vast continent, bearing in mind that North America was home to some five hundred ethnic groups, all having their own systems of traditional medicine in the US territory alone. Though spread over large geographical regions, Native American cultures where related. Nonetheless, we still find several large distinct cultural groups. Northern American native culture has been organized around totem animals, which functions as categories to create clans, societies, and lodges and to determine the spiritual place of individuals. Traditionally, such animal designations are more powerful as categories for structuring society than are family and tribe. Representing innate skills and gifts, member of a clan dream about the totem animal, which then indicates ones place in life.

I am indebted to herbalists Karyn Sanders (Choctaw) and Matthew Wood for helping me to understand *animal signatures.* Sanders explains that, whereas there where individual differences in the use of animal medicine among the various healers, there has been a certain consistency within each Native American nation, which nonetheless differ from one another. Wood was taught a basic principle by Karyn Sanders: "When a plant looks like an animal or is eaten a lot or used by it, it has special power; it is a *spirit signature.*" "Spirit," in this context, means that it is more profound than physical medicine. Its action is not on the physical level. He further learned about animal signatures from Paul Red Elk (Sioux) and Yagho Tahnahgah (Mohawk and Anishinabe). Animal signature is a way of grouping the qualities of animals, their *animal medicine power,* to use the Native American term, together with corresponding qualities in the human and plant realms. Thus, the Dakota term *wakan* for "medicine power" can at the same time mean power, wisdom, medicine, and skill, as well as refer to a charm. The Cheyenne medicine man Bill Tall Bull said, "It is not the ingredients; it is the spirit of the plant that heals us"

(Storl 2010, p. 156). We can transfer this understanding of healing to animal medicine. It is the animal spirit associated with the plant that is the healing principle.

Clara Niiska (Ojibwe) explains that belonging to an animal totem indicates that this is your family. In a healthy society, all beings live together in harmony, each having their own kind of wisdom. It is the diversity of these different kinds of wisdom that make for the richness and health of this living web of society. The bear knows the plants and has its wisdom. The wolf also knows the plants and has its wisdom. So do the deer and rabbit and human beings. All the different kinds of wisdom form the living whole of a healthy society. Belonging to an animal totem means not only sharing that animal's spiritual power and wisdom, but also means being part of that family. All of the different families together make the tribe. Plants have their wisdom and power. They have been in existence so much longer than the animals. The animals have been around so much longer than the humans. Therefore, their relationship to the plants is thousands of years old, and much older than that of people. This means we should respect it.

Karyn Sanders was taught animal medicine by her grandmother, as handed down by her ancestors. She explains that plants carry animal medicine—the medicines of snake, watersnake, deer, hawk, bear, badger, and hummingbird. They are related to the personality traits in those animals and in human beings, as well as to typical disease patterns. The fact that a plant has an animal signature does not necessarily make it more powerful than other plant medicines. However, if one should find a Bear Root (Balsamroot) that has been dug up or chewed by a bear, that particular root is more powerful than the others of the same kind. Karyn recalls an occasion out in nature when she was harvesting elk medicine. She felt an electric sensation traveling down her back, as if someone was watching her. When she turned, a whole group of elk stood there watching her. "This particular batch is a lot more powerful than an ordinary one," she explains. Similarly, if you find a plant with a shape like the face of a wolf on it, this would be thought to give that particular plant specimen special power. Bear people, for example, would thus carry bear medicine as a totem.

In Western society, animal medicine is akin to grouping personal characteristics, body parts, and disease according to zodiacal signs, such as the Ram, Taurus, or Cancer. Animals have also been used on the coat of arms to invoke such qualities in warriors or a noble family, and appear in names such as King Richard Lionheart, or in names such as Bjørn (Bear) or Wolf. The animals considered most powerful in Europe were probably the lion and eagle, whereas in Northern America it was the bear and the wolf. Being born under the sign of Scorpio, or belonging to a family with lions on the coat of arms, is a Western form of totem, or animal medicine. Western astrology predates the Egyptians and stems from a time when deities were depicted with animal heads to express their characteristics and powers.

It is a teaching of the Midewiwin (*Midē Wiwin,* or Grand Medicine Society) that every tree, bush, and plant has a use. A country of such bountiful vegetation as that of the Chippewa presents a great amount of this material. Although the Midewiwin was a repository of knowledge of herbs, it did not have a pharmacopoeia accessible to every member. The remedies are individual, not general, and an individual when questioned invariably replies, "I can tell you about my own medicines. I do not know about other peoples' medicines nor their uses of the same plants." Thus, it is frequently found that different people have different names and uses for the same plant. Members of the Midewiwin were not taught many remedies at once, except at the time of their initiation. Their instruction at that time was comprised by what might be termed "ground work in the practice of medicine," with the identification and use of a number of plants. The same sort of instruction accompanied their advancement from one degree to another, and was made more extensive as they went into the higher degrees. Aside from these times of special instruction, a man learned one or two remedies at a time as he felt inclined to go to the old man and buy the knowledge. Among the Chippewa, as among other tribes studied by the writer, it is not common for one man to treat a large number of diseases. (The writer as well as many of the interviewed medicine "men" for this study, as well as the research carried out in the early 1900s, were women.)

A Sioux said:

In the old days, the Indians had few diseases, and so there was not a demand for a large variety of medicines. A medicine man usually treated one special disease and treated it successfully. He did this in accordance with his dream. A medicine man would not try to dream of all herbs and treat all diseases, for then he could not expect to succeed in all nor to fulfill properly the dream of any one herb or animal. He would depend on too many and fail in all. That is one reason why our medicine men lost their power when so many diseases came among us with the advent of the white man. (Densmore 1974, p. 323)

This gives us a good idea of how personal the totem of the healer and one's ascription of animal medicine power can be.

Other medical systems have also applied the doctrine of signature to animal substances, such as Traditional Chinese Medicine, which might use a seal penis as a kidney *yang* tonic. The tissue state in this case is too cold and watery, leading to lack of erection. Seals live in cold water but retain the ability to procreate. However, the term *animal signature* does not denote applying the law of correspondence and doctrine of signature to animal substances, though this was not unheard of among Native Americans. The following account survives from homeopathic history.

In 1847, a homeopath was called to the bedside of a boy who had been suffering for several months from severe, prolonged high fever, accompanied by profuse swelling of the abdomen and thorax. All the other local doctors had already failed the case. "The secretion of urine was nearly suspended; the skin was dry and hot, the pulse rapid and weak, respiration short and difficult, great tenderness of the abdomen, dryness of the mouth and throat, thirst, excessive restlessness and anxiety, short irritating cough, and an almost entire inability to sleep." The homeopath was also unable help, and the boy was about to die. As in so many American stories from those times, it happened that a "strolling Indian woman" (one of the few survivors of the Narragansett tribe) suggested to the family that they use roasted honeybee as the remedy. She showed them how to roast the bees in an oven in a tin can and how to powder them and work the powder into a syrup. The boy largely recovered within twenty-four hours, and was cured entirely within a few weeks.

The homeopath quickly recognized the "like cures like" principal. The boy had been sick as if stung all over by bees, indicated most particularly by the dry, red, hot swelling and intense restlessness. Thus, "roasted honey bee" entered the homeopathic *materia medica* under its Latin name *Apis mellifera* (Tyler 1942, p. 71).

I find it remarkable how many of the old case histories tell of a pioneer invader at the brink of death being saved in this way by a passing indigenous survivor of the genocide wrought by European settlers. We may give thanks to them for their compassion and selflessness in sharing their medical knowledge, which continues to enrich us today.

The term *animal signature* does not indicate how a plant relates to the animal world. Nevertheless, how plants relate to animals and how animals relate to plants is part of the environmental signature, and this will be discussed.

ANIMAL SUBSTANCES AS MEDICINES

In Traditional Chinese Medicine, animal substances are considered stronger and potentially more harmful than plant or mineral substances are. In the words of my acupuncturist friend Peter Schell, they hit home with more vengeance. The homeopathic *materia medica* echoes this tendency, in part because so many of the animal substances included there are venoms or from venomous creatures. In the previous section on plant poisons, we saw how plant poisons relate to the plants having assumed animal characteristics. Poisonous plants tend to make the most potent medicines when used in small enough doses. Likewise, venomous animals make especially potent medicinal substances, since they are in the class of poisons that need to be taken in very small doses.

Whereas some Native Americans sometimes attribute stronger medicinal power to an animal substance, this is not generally the case. Many animal substances used in making medicine—for example, using bear fat in salves—are common foods and considered especially potent medicine. Animal substances are often used for ceremony (Karyn Sanders) and assume a spiritual quality.

The doctrine of signature applies to all of nature—to the mineral realm as much as to the plant and animal realms. This example is from homeopathic literature: "As the fox is probably the longest-winded of all animals, the doctrine of signatures pointed to his lungs as a likely remedy for short breath." Thus, the homeopathic *Pulmo vulpis* (fox's lung) has persistent shortness of breath as its keynote symptom, and may be used to treat asthma (Murphy 2000, p. 1425).

DISEASES CONTRACTED FROM ANIMALS

This covers contagious diseases as well as bites. The term *animal signature* would be understood in Cherokee medicine as a disease received from an animal, such as *deer disease* (lymes). It is treated with Deer Eye (Black-Eyed Susan). Cherokee medicine employs Rattlesnake

Fern (its spore pods look like the rattle) and Self-heal (called Snakehead because the flower head resembles a snake rearing its head) to treat snakebites, even if they occur in a dream, because in Cherokee culture, dreams are real. You might also receive a disease from an animal because you failed to do the proper rituals and prayers while killing it, and the animal spirit strikes you down (David Winston). In the European tradition, animal bites were commonly treated with snakebite remedies. These often included bites by all venomous creatures, including snakes, scorpions, insects, spiders, and even rabid dogs. Snakebite remedies have the telltale snake shape in some part of their body, or "bite," as in the case of Nettles. By contrast, Hound's Tongue (*Cynoglossum*) has the signature of the leaves in the form of dog's tongues, and this points to them being wound healing in the same way that a wound heals faster and well if a dog licks it clean (Dominique Lepage).

ANIMAL OBSERVATION

Some healing uses are attributed to observing animals use them for healing. Celandine, for example, is also called Swallow Wort, because swallows take a sprig to rub the eyes of their young to make them open. It thus became an important eye remedy. The Chinese Horny Goat Weed is another example, as are the foods used by the bear (see below). This is very relevant to *animal medicine*, since plants are attributed to animals by way of

Black-Eyed Susan (above)
and Hound's Tongue leaves

observing that the animal uses or eats it, as well as receiving special power should the animal have used a specific specimen.

Plant Relationships with Animals

An unusual example for the doctrine of signature is Water Lily. The buds and flowers are often covered in a thick layer of aphids at the water line. Some European languages refer to aphids as "lice." Water Lily is a good remedy for head lice. I once contracted pyleonephritis (a urinary tract infection) and head lice at the same time. Water Lily was the remedy that covered both symptoms, and it brought me back to health. This was the only time I had head lice, though I have had long hair most of my life. It is as if kidney weakness (water—Water Lily) invited the bugs.

Plant Dependence on Animals

Dependence on certain animals for pollination or propagation of the seeds is a special relationship with animals for some plant, one of codependence. Mistletoe berries, for example, need to be eaten by birds and excreted on the branch of a tree with suitably soft wood before it can germinate. Thus, Mistletoe has a close relationship to birds; hence the air element. They are "airborne germinators." Indicated in people with lack of grounding, Mistletoe is also the flower essence for interdependence. Orchid flowers take the shape of the mate of their pollinating insect, which comes to the flower to mate. The sexual relationship to their pollinating insect points to them being sexual tonics. *Trillium* seeds have a fleshy appendage relished by ants, which carry them away to their nests. After eating the fleshy part, they discard the seeds with their garbage, where they lie protected in a rich growing medium until the next spring. Thus, *Trillium* (Wakerobin) flower essence is connected with relationships and is very grounding.

Animal Shapes in Plant Names

Many plants are named after animals or animal parts, based on their shapes. Adder's Tongue, Hound's Tongue, Hart's Tongue, Bird's Tongue, Crane's Bill, Larkspur, Staghorn Sumac, Goatsbeard, Lion's Foot, and so on. The relationship between the plant and animal is one of shape, and does not necessarily indicate a medicinal relationship in a direct sense. For instance,

Hound's Tongue is apparently not used for rabies or other diseases afflicted by a dog or to treat the tongue of a dog. It is, however, in the *Boraginacea* family of remedies for animal bites. As mentioned, the French herbalist Dominique Lepage explains that Hound's Tongue heals wounds in the same way that a dog licking a wound does. Fuchs lists it as one of the best wound herbs (1543, chap. 155). Others however point to the animal as the image around which the medicinal properties could be grouped: Cranesbill, whose seed pod resembles the head of a crane, points to the animal, water, and swamp, which, as we saw, is the environmental signature of kidney-healing plants; Cranesbill (a *Geranium*) prefers moist soils and is a kidney remedy. In such cases, the name leads to true animal signatures.

ANIMAL SIGNATURES AND ANIMAL MEDICINE POWER

Rattlesnake Plantain, "because its white-veined appearance, was said to resemble a snake's belly; the leaves were considered an 'infallible cure' for snakebite and for external conditions such as eczematous eruptions" (Harris 1985, p. 147). This is a true like-cures-like animal signature. One of nature's most striking imitations of snakeskin, it makes sense to call it the *infallible* cure; strong signature makes for strong medicinal action. The erect flowering spikes are also a snake-head signature. This animal signature still falls into the category of "like cures like."

Adder's Tongue (top); Crane's Bill

The real animal signature is to recognize the likeness of a plant to a particular animal and its medicine powers. This includes some things that are not animals, such as "Cloud Medicine," in which the likeness is to steam, fog, and clouds. The whole idea is that every entity in the cosmos holds its own power or essence, which when understood correctly can be used as a medicine. The word for "medicine power" is *wakan* in Dakota language, which could be rendered "spiritual power." I am reluctant to translate it as *chi* or *prana*, since in my understanding it includes what might be called a "magic" dimension in which everything in the cosmos is alive and ensouled—something beyond mere energy in motion.

Matt Wood explains that in American Indian medicine the major problems of life, social, spiritual, psychological, or physical, are associated with animals that personify problems and solutions. The social habits, psychological tendencies, physical strengths and weaknesses of the animal became the symbol around which to group and in which context to understand spiritual, psychological, community and physical health. The correlations were often established by watching what plants the animals used for food and medicine. He gives the example of Osha root (*Ligusticum poteri*) which looks like the paw of a bear. The name "Osha" means bear in Spanish, hence it is a *Bear Medicine*. Going beyond mere "like cures like," sour berries are Bear Medicine, because they are a bear food, and not because bears are sour. Wood points out that most of these especially powerful animal medicines act on the endocrine (*Cloud, Elk, Deer,* and *Bear Medicines*) and autonomic nervous system (*Panther Medicines*).

Bear Medicines are some of the most powerful medicines, worthy of one of the most powerful animals. Bear is the food provider, healer and herbalist, since the mother bear takes such good care of her cubs. The Bear was regarded in many native systems as the herbalist, since he digs the roots with his huge claws and thus has knowledge of them. Bears eat oily roots in the spring to fatten up, and sour berries in the summer to keep cool. Thus, some Bear Medicines are oily roots that are brown, fuzzy or fury like Osha, Angelica or Burdock, others are sour berries like blueberries and rose hips. Wood points out that two kinds of people might need Bear Medicines—either thin, malnourished people who need to fatten up like the famished bear out of hibernation (oily plants), or else heavy people with a bear-like body build to lose weight (sour fruits). Since the most ferocious creature in the wild is the mother bear with her cubs, Bear

Medicines include the idea of taking care of people. Bear medicines act on the lungs, heart, and liver—the aeration, circulation, and metabolism of the body. Clara Niiska explains that bears have a special wisdom connected to dreams—unlike human beings, they spend half a year dreaming. So imagine how the world looks like when you come out of a whole winter of hibernation. Thus the bear has a special wisdom humans do not have. The oily bear medicines include Angelica, Osha, Balsamroot, Lomatium, Burdock, *Allium ursinum,* Spikenard, Sunflower seed; and American licorice as an adrenal tonic.

Cloud Medicines have soft, fuzzy, hairy structures that are often silver white, like vapor or clouds. Related to the penetrating principle of vapor that will go through the smallest crack, they clean the inner waters and help hormonal movement through these: Windflower (Pulsatilla), Corydalis, Lady's Mantle, Queen Anne's Lace, and Smoke-of-the-Earth. The names echo the theme—wind, smoke, lace, the feminine. These medicines often act on the hypothalamus and pituitary, and have a strong influence on the signals to the sexual hormones.

Elk Medicines are the domain of elk, who dig through the swamps with their antlers and are thus related to kidney and water-regulating remedies. The kidneys are under the rule of Venus in the European tradition, and the elk is the animal of love charms and sexuality. It is the gift to attract people to you, including those whom you do not want to be attracted to you. In Traditional Chinese Medicine, it is the kidney *chi* that determines sexual strength and health. Elk Medicines such as Staghorn Sumac, the branches of which look like antlers, Blue Vervain which grows in damp lowlands, and Dogwood give sexual stamina, facilitate sexual partnership, balance the sexual hormones, especially the androgens, and aid fertility. Elk remedies control water loss via the skin and ensure strong bones—a characteristic related to the kidney function. Elk medicines are beautiful, sweet, perfumed plants

Above: Staghorn Sumac "antlers" (photo by Sandra Lory); below: close-up of the antler-like appearance of the branches before they shed their velvet

Staghorn Sumac branches, showing the antler shape

such as Sweet Leaf, also called *Indian Perfume.* Hunters ,who need to possess some elk medicine to be successful, use these plants to rub on them to cover their own odor when hunting. While elk medicines act more on the kidneys, related deer medicines act more on the nerves.

Deer Medicines are for delicate, nervous people with a *vata* constitution like deer. These are often nervines. Wood mentions Sweet Leaf (*Monarda fistulosa*) as a deer medicine. Karyn Sanders teaches that deer medicine is for the heart and veins, and has a softening action. Deer love to make their beds in sweet smelling Cleavers to cover their smell. Deer and elk medicines are related, and stand for hunting knowledge and medicine. Deer medicines and people are thin, fine structured and sensitive. They include nervines and remedies that sharpen the senses.

Crane Medicines such as Wild Geranium moderate the inner waters, home of the water bird. The bird's loud cry earned it the name "echo maker" in some Indian languages, and the crane clan was in charge of big tribal events and dealing with the outside world. People with crane medicine are great orators. Crane brings Spirit into the sweat lodge and accompanies spirits back to the other world. Our image of the stork bringing the baby still points to this function of the water bird mediating between the two worlds.

Panther Medicines (Catnip, Valerian, Hops, Cramp Bark) all have a smell that entices cats, especially those with valerianic acid. They relax the smooth muscles, so that one can assume a feline-like smoothness of movement and relaxation. The medicine man Sun Bear and Wabun assign the puma and Plantain to Pisces in their book *The Medicine Wheel: Earth Astrology;* Pisces standing for sensitivity as do cats, and Plantain is a prime nerve remedy that has to do with sensitivity to pain.

Turtle Medicine is carried mostly by women. The energy is feminine; it is medicine for women, and turtle lodge is a woman's lodge. Turtle medicines can be used to mediate, since they help to penetrate the veils, get in and out of shadowy worlds, and thus receive messages and healing. They give endurance and sustenance in life-and-death situations (Karyn Sanders). Matthew Wood names Gravelroot and its ability to dissolve or precipitate solids in liquid. Turtle is connected to the kidneys and bones. Wood explains that in the same way that the turtle lives inside of its hard shell, Mother Nature lives inside of the planet Earth.

Rabbit Medicines are nutritious, such as Wild Yam (Wood 2009, p. 132) or Bittersweet Vine. Rabbits are thin-boned and have twitchy muscles. Wild Yam strengthens the bones and calms muscular spasms. Many emergency and starvation foods are associated with Rabbit Medicine. This is the only animal available for hunting in a hard winter since it is light enough so it can walk on snow. "There is an old story that Nanabozho, the Trickster (who is a rabbit in the Great Lakes region), was walking across the ice on a lake in northern Minnesota when he noticed something clunking around on the ice behind him. Oops! His intestines had fallen out and were already frozen. He grabbed a piece and threw it to the shore, where it snagged on a tree branch" (ibid., p. 108). This is how Bittersweet Vine came to be, and it is still hanging over trees and hedge rows. Its bark is an emergency food that has saved people from starvation in hard winters.

Snake Medicines have to do with the ability to get into places. They help people to get into their heart and stay there, to go into the trauma and transmute it (Karyn Sanders). These are plants that are used for snakebites or the bite of other poisonous animals, such as spiders, and toxic poisonings. The Cherokee will use them even for having received the bite in a dream (David Winston).

> One of the most important in this category [of animal signatures] are the Snake Medicines.... Because of the necessity of using good snakebite remedies on the frontier, and also because the Europeans had a tradition of using plants which resemble snakes (Bistort, Plantain) for snakebite, this nomenclature was adopted by the pioneers. Snake Medicines known to the Indians and the pioneers include Plantain or Snakeweed, Black Cohosh or Black Snakeroot, Virginia Snakeroot, Senega Snakeroot,.., Rattle Snake Master, Echinacea, Rattle Snake Plantain, Button Snakeroot, and Corn Snakeroot. (Wood 1997, p. 29)

We might add European Wild Ginger (see photo, page 124), the rootstocks of which snake over the ground (Fuchs, 1543, chap. 3). These are plants that counteract the tissue depression induced by the venom, and combat necrosis and sepsis. Some of them are plants with the power to draw venom out of a bite in external application, such as Plantain and Self-heal.

Badger Medicine is medicine for the healer. It gives the strength to maintain the healing process the whole way through, as well as to go against the grain. Badger medicines are mostly medicinal roots (Karyn Sanders). Matthew Wood names Yellow Dock and Turkey Rhubarb (see drawing, page 102) as Badger Medicines, explaining that badger burrow deep into the earth. Similarly, these roots are huge and burrow very deeply into the ground. They move things down and out, hence are excellent for constipation. The badger person can attack others by saying something that will hit them in the solar plexus and dis-empower them in that manner.

Wolf Medicine embodies the spirit of the pack and the strength of the group. Wolves have absolute loyalty to the group and mate for life, rearing their young and hunting as a group; a lone wolf rarely survives long. The group spirit is crucial for their survival in the harsh wilderness. Wolf fights are harsh, but they are careful not to hurt one another. Choosing an alpha male means choosing a benevolent, wise leader, and strong leaders are in the best interest of the pack. Wolves and dogs will eat Burdock and Wormwood in the wild. They have extremely strong digestive and immune systems. All these qualities are typified by Solomon's Seal, marking it an archetypal wolf medicine. Such group consciousness and cooperation is illustrated by flowers that grow in clusters, both on the stem and in groups on the ground, such as Onion, Solomon's Seal, Burdock, and Comfrey (Swanie Simon). Wolf medicines teach respect and draw boundaries. wolf medicine is good for couples (Simon). Karyn Sanders teaches that autoimmune diseases are related to wolf. Lupus is an autoimmune disease that gives the face a wolfish appearance. Wood sees the signature as right angles between root and stem, meaning a complete change in direction, profound transformation, or adapting to change (Spreading Dogbane, Solomon's Seal). Right angles also represent the joints, which stand for changing direction in life (Wood).

Hummingbird Medicine is used for love charms (Karyn Sanders).

These are only a few examples to invite the reader into the spirit of animal medicine. Other animal medicines include **Spider** (creating webs of confusion, setting up webs to trap others, symbol of the witch doctor) **The Underwater Panther**, or Watersnake, is presented in part one of this volume (page 14). Its medicine is not commonly used (Karyn Sanders).

✧

CHAPTER FIFTEEN

THE ENERGETIC SIGNATURE

A fter having looked at the signatures in the light of the four elements, we end on the most refined of elements, the fifth: ether. Ether is the element beyond the material world, the one we could call energy or mind or consciousness.

When working with plant signatures on the energetic level, we are faced with the chicken-and-egg question: Which comes first, the physical plant tissue or the plant's energetic body? For those who can see the plant's energetic body or aura, it is clear that the energetic body unfolds first, and the cells grow into it like plaster being poured into a mold. So to understand the energetic pattern of unfolding holds the deepest secret to reading the plant. This flow of energy carries growth and matter/molecules along in its movement. When our energy body interacts with the plant's energy, it happens by way of resonance. We find that the healing herbs tend to reconstitute their energetic gesture or shape inside of us once we ingest them, stimulating our energy field to follow their energetic gesture. While this phenomenon is clearest in flower essences that are energetic preparations, it applies equally to any form of plant material that has some life force left in it. I learned this lesson when a yoga teacher friend asked me for a flower essence for a girl who was crippled by a very traumatic birth. Severely restricted in many movements, she also had a very hard time bending forward and letting her head and upper body hang. I did not have any idea what to give her in that moment, but realized the next day that we had been standing under a group of weeping cherries in blossom when she asked me. It occurred to me that, in the plant realm, there could not be a clearer "hanging over forward in a relaxed way" signature than in weeping cherries. So I made a flower essence from the blossoms and gave them to my friend. She reported that not only did the handicapped girl have an easier time stretching and bending forward after taking it, but so did the rest of her yoga class participants. From then on, Weeping Cherry flower essence has been in her bag whenever teaching a yoga class. I then started to use it in bodywork applied onto the body, and found, like her, that it helps the vertebrae separate from one another, as when in a forward hanging stretch. In the pant, it is as though each blossom along the stem were one of the vertebrae.

Ultimately, the energetic shapes in plants do not follow any fabricated scheme, but I find it helpful to match them to the patterns of the human aura. The chakras could be called energetic eddies in the aura, and flowers match them in shape. What a flower is on a plant, a chakra is to the aura. Thus, flowers and flower essences are wonderful for opening and balancing chakras. We have seen in the color chapter that they follow the correspondence of the aura as a rainbow in color, thus for example yellow flowers matching the solar plexus chakra. A prime example would be Dandelion. It is remarkable that the energetic branches of the channels that make up a chakra are traditionally called petals. We speak of a sixteen-petal chakra for instance, and the eight-petal heart chakra is traditionally depicted as an eight-petal lotus.

Similarly, the plant shapes themselves often correspond to the five *vayus*, or main energetic winds or movements within the aura. These five could simply be described as the upper part of the energy going up, the lower part of the energy moving down, all energy circulating out and around, heat energy being contained at the center, and the most basic, life-sustaining life force residing at the heart. *Vayu* literally means wind, standing for energetic movement or flow. In Sanskrit, the five *vayus* are called:

- **Prana Vayu** is the most basic and life-sustaining wind. If it stops functioning, we die. It resides in the heart area, from where it flows up with the breath that sustains our life and, according to some models, keeps the circulation moving. Lily of the Valley helps both the heart and lung energy-related aspect of *prana vayu*. It helps regulate the heart and heartbeat, and proves helpful for smoker's lungs.
- **Udana Vayu** flows upward and maintains exhalation, operating in conjunction with *prana vayu*, which helps with inhalation. It is also the energy we use to spit or vomit. Lobelia herb stimulates *udana vayu*. Lobelia herb is thin below and larger above, with proportionally large, inflated seed pods.
- **Apana Vayu** flows down and out through the lower abdomen. It is needed for all excretion, such as urination, defecation, menstrual flow, and childbirth. Rhubarb root stimulates and supports *apana vayu*. Also called *downward-bearing wind*, Rhubarb root bears downward, indeed, sporting an *apana vayu* signature.

- **Samana Vayu** resides in the abdomen below the navel. Related to the idea of digestive fire or heat, it aids digestion as well as digesting ideas and information. Hot and fiery Ginger and Cardamom increase *samana vayu*. Because the fire element is represented predominantly by pungent tastes, those are the ones that aid the digestive fire.

- **Vyana Vayu** flows through the entire aura, propelling the circulation of blood, as well as enabling the joints to move. Graceful dancers owe their movement skills to *vyana vayu*. Mistletoe and Rosemary aid this pranic flow. It also serves to hold the energy together and prevent it from leaking out, a function that is similar to *wei chi* in Traditional Chinese Medicine. This aspect of *vyana vayu* is enhanced by Calendula flowers.

Hawthorn flowers and berries nurture both *vyana* and *prana vayu*. It is good to understand that those five energetic winds are different functioning aspects of one energetic field rather than truly separate entities. Just as we cannot separate the heart and its action from the blood, blood vessels and circulation, it is often hard to differentiate between those two *vayus* and their overlapping functions. Hawthorn is a good example for a *vyana* and *prana vayu* signature. It is *vyana vayu*'s job to ensure proper circulation throughout the entire human periphery with the five limbs. Hawthorn flowers are five-petalled, looking like Leonardo DaVinci's famous drawing of a man standing in a pentagram. Hawthorn restores the blood vessels and heals the heart—center of *prana vayu*—nurturing the heart muscles and prolonging their life span.

The basic correspondence is that of the energetic upward flow in a plant stimulating our upward flow, the downward flow strengthening our downward flow, and so on. We can read those from the overall plant shape as outlines in the beginning of the shape chapter (see section on *basic plant shapes*). In the same way, we can detect their state and balance from a person's body shape and constitution.

I understood more about the energetic correspondences and signature when I started spilling flower essence on the floor and "saw" the energetic patterns created in space. Almost comically, a good number of them re-formed their own shape spatially; Lotus essence would form a large lotus flower shape in space, while Sunflower energy flows upward like its tall stalk and creates a round shape. Elm, the swiftness of whose energy we discussed in the section on planetary signatures, makes little energy puffs that come fast and are gone in an instant. When taken internally, these shapes "push" the body's energy to repeat their shape; taking Asparagus flower essence, for example, makes us stand more upright, as though pushed upward by the force of the asparagus shoot, reaching the top of our heads toward the ceiling.

With its long stem and clearly formed light-purple flower head, Teasel, when applied in the form of an herbal tincture to an injured knee, will energetically reshape its flower head in the

Fireweed

head of both the person receiving and the person applying the treatment, since both come into contact with the tincture. When considering energetic correspondences, the top of the plant and the flowers, if they are at the top of the plant, go to the head; the leaves and branches go to the center; and the roots go to the pelvic area, legs, and feet.

While the energetic signature might correspond to a chakra or a *vayu*, it might in other cases stimulate or correspond more clearly to one of the meridians. This is true if plants have strong organ signatures—Artichoke energy flows through the gall bladder meridian.

In anthroposophic medicine, the energetic signatures are described as corresponding to the ether body, astral body, or the "I." Patricia Kaminski correlates the color magenta to the etheric body, and she uses magenta flowers to strengthen it—Fireweed is just one example. Once an integral part of the Western herbal tradition, the suction of cupping with the hands in massage, though not an herb, also strengthens the ether body. We described signatures corresponding to the astral body in the *Poison Signatures* section. Rudolf Steiner relates the human "I," the Self, to the principle of warmth and attributes the healing powers of warming plants such as Rosemary to the integration of the "I" into the other human energy bodies.

THE ENERGETIC GESTURE

Besides the energetic signature by which the plant's energetic pattern parallels that of a particular aspect of the energy body, there is also the *energetic gesture*. This art of the signature is the poetry of the plant, its song and dance. If we were to give it words, then Thistle would say, "I stand self-defended" (see drawing, page 50, and photo, page 143). Scarlet Monkey Flower, a fire-engine-red relative of Snapdragon with an open mouth, shouts, "I am scream-

ing with red anger!" Weeping Cherry tells us, "Relax and release downward like I do." Mallow flowers are pink, with five heart-shaped petals that are exceedingly soft, and the entire plant is laden with mucilage that softens the tissues. Mallow says, "I soften the heart," and its flower essence softens the emotions and the heart. Lily of the Valley, with its tiny, sweet-scented bells on the arching stem, marks the gesture of humility or, letting its head hang, the gesture of depression. It bestows the former and cures the latter.

Goldenrod flowers

Looking at the gesture and dance of the plant, we find that again that there is a correspondence to the energetic gesture: Goldenrod flowers bloom from the top to the bottom along the raceme. This is quite rare. Blooming with the gesture of a warm glowing candle that burns downward, Goldenrod speaks of bringing in the energy. Hibiscus opens out wide, with the pistil and stamen protruding—speaking of sexual opening (Katz and Kaminski). Gorse blooms all year long, even in snow and ice, with an astoundingly tropical coconut fragrance. The flowers emerge among the spines that densely line the stems, shining their golden light through the winter. "I am self-defended light," they seem to say, and as a flower essence serve to enhance the inner light to fight off seasonal flus and colds.

Thus, we see that the energetic signature can follow the chakras, *vayus*, meridians, *chi,* or even mimic auric reactions. When we do not like certain people, our aura gets prickly in defense. This can become an ingrained habit, and the flower essences of prickly leaved Holly or Oregon-Grape can be of help us move beyond this. The energetic signature can also correspond to the emotional or mental gesture or stance.

HOLISTIC PLANT STUDY

So, how does it look if we apply the methods outlined in the book to plants, and study them in this holistic way? Taking Angelica as an example, we will consider them in their specific details as well as their larger context. As we become fluid in the language of nature, we will be able to think not only in terms of the signature of a certain plant, but also how that plant relates to its botanical family, what that botanical family stands for, and other plants from other families with similar or related signatures.

ANGELICA

Angelica archangelica is the angel plant of the old European pharmacopoeia (see drawing on page 321). Native to the cold parts of Northern Europe, it is one of the few warming aromatics from the cold countries of the old world. Angelica is a biennial plant from the *Umbelliferae* family, now renamed *Apiaceae.* Its name "archangel angel plant" already indicates the veneration for its medicinal properties, and Root of the Holy Ghost was an alternative name in old English. Native mostly to what is now Scandinavia, there is a smaller relative that grows throughout central Europe, equally loving cool, moist soil and half shade: *Angelica sylvestris.* This Forest Angelica is often found growing by streams, with its roots half in the water. Its aroma is not as sublime as that of *Angelica archangelica,* but the medicinal qualities are rather similar, and so it has long been used in folk herbalism.

Angelica archangelica, in German called *Engelwurz* (angel root), sprouts by unfolding its first pair of seed leaves with a gesture reminiscent of a graceful bird or an angel spreading its wings. Quickly growing into a big, lush, juicy cluster of green leaves, it is already penetrated by a fine, angelic scent. The leaves have three main stalks, graced by leaves in sets of three. The stalks are hollow and, when injured, yield an acrid yellow sap. In the second year, after the large underground root is established, the plant sends up one or more tall hollow

Angelica blossoms emerging like a newborn from the womb

stalks that, in late June or July, will be crowned by large light-green umbels of flowers. These stalks, easily higher than a person, are a good telltale sign to help differentiate between this Garden Angelica (*Angelica archangelica*), and its cousin Wild Angelica (*Angelica sylvestris*). The Wild, or Forest, Angelica blooms earlier, and the stalks do not become as high. The flowers are white rather than yellow-green, and the scent is far less refined. Its stems have more of a purplish hue. Angelica goes to seed, producing numerous light, serrated winged seeds that germinate readily in cool, moist soil, but quickly lose their ability to germinate. The Angelica dies off after going to seed, but can be prevented from doing so by cutting off the flower stalks before the seeds ripen. If Angelica encounters dry weather, it takes longer to build up its final size and may take several years before going to flower. Similar in appearance to Poison Hemlock, as well as several other botanical relatives, it is not a good idea to harvest Angelica unless one has trained well in botany.

Angelica has a long history of use as both food and medicine. Made into delicious flavoring for dishes, the stalks are still popular in confectionery today. The root has the most refined flavor and is the part commonly used in medicine. Since the dried root easily turns rancid, it is best prepared as an alcohol tincture or, as was customary, a liqueur.

Angelica probably attained the height of its popularity outside of its native range in Europe during the late Middle Ages, when it became known to protect from the plague that was ravaging the continent. While I have not tracked the name to an earlier time, it was called "Angel Root" already by that time, a suitable name for a plant capable of warding off such pestilence. Maude Grieve recounts how the name came into being when a monk had a dream in which Archangel Michael appeared telling the monk what herb he should use to help victims of bubonic plague, which was decimating Europe in 1665. Other sources say that Angelica was thought to be a gift of Archangel Gabriel. Either way—Michael being the warrior-like slayer of evil forces, and Gabriel the messenger of God—Angelica is a blessed plant. When it became known that having a piece of Angelica root in one's mouth all day long could effectively protect a person from the plague, it was quickly picked almost to extinction all over Europe. (Since the official Angelica is native only to the cold North, I must assume that "sylvestris" was widely used as a substitute.) Modern research has confirmed that Angelica heightens the immune system and is an efficient antibacterial, antiviral, and antifungal, effective against all kinds of infections. Gabriel is also the archangel who swept down to announce the Immaculate Conception to the Virgin Mary, so it is not surprising that angelicas have been used the world over for gynecological problems and to aid in giving birth. When the minor flowers emerge from their wrapping below the main flower, it looks like Angelica is giving birth, holding a baby wrapped in linen in her arms (emerging flower in the center of the photo).

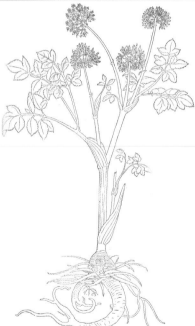

Angelica; above: emerging blossoms (photo by Rieko Oshima); below: the root and stalk are drawn bent to fit the original page

When we meet Angelica, she impresses us with her undeniably feminine character. There is sacredness about her, as she stands poised between Heaven and Earth. The light-green leaves and stems tinged in purple do not give in to gravity, despite their relative lack of refinement, but seem mysteriously uplifted and uplifting. Angelica forms a channel between Heaven and Earth, mediating energies between the two realms. It is thus not surprising that the Sami people of northern Finland use the hollow stems of Angelica in shamanic rituals for astral traveling. Energetically, Angelica tea or tincture opens the head chakras and refines the senses, as well as the emotions.

There are several other angelicas around the world, such as the Northern American *Angelica atropurpurea* and the Chinese *Dong Quai*. Nowadays, Japanese Angelica is becoming a pop herb, touted to heal pretty much everything. In Asia, the various angelica species remain the most widely used of herbs, with maybe the exception of Ginseng, and have been used since the dawn of medical history. While Ginseng is called "man root," angel root has a distinctly angelic flair about it. While Chinese Ginseng is a male or *yang* tonic, *Dong Quai* has been called the "female ginseng" for its use in any kind of menstrual disturbance. Commanding respect and awe, the tall plant seems to constitute an upright pole or channel between the earth and the heavens. The Forest Angelica bloom around May 8, the feast of St. Michael in the old calendar. Dr. Christopher writes, "Even though this herb is named in honor of a Christian angel, many angelica festivals are held in Livonia, East Prussia and Pomerania and celebrated in the pagan manner with dance and chanting of ancient deities in languages no longer understood. European angelica has been viewed as a magical herb for more than a thousand years. Peasants made angelica leaf necklaces to protect their children from illness and witchcraft. Witches were reported never to use angelica and if it was in woman's garden or home it was her defense against witchcraft charges."

Some angelica species, notably *Atropurpurea,* can cause vomiting when chewing the fresh root, and can cause abortion in larger doses. Native Americans used this Northern American cousin in much the same manner as archangelica in Europe, including one of its main uses in cases of lung ailments and even tuberculosis. The North American Angelica has a brown and furry root that looks like bear paws, and being a bear food is a classic *bear medicine* (see the section on animal medicine). A nutritious oil root, Angelica feeds the bear, which stands for nurturing and healing in the totem system. There is no creature more ferocious than a mother bear with her cubs, and we talk of mother bear wisdom—Angelica stands for fertility, birthing and mothering.

The most fragrant part of the plant is the root, second the seeds, followed by the stalk, while the leaves have a rougher taste. This is unusual, since most plants have the finest aroma in flower and leaves. This shows how the aromatic principle penetrates the Angelica plant deeply. Angelica stalks can be made into a delicious syrup. After cutting off the leaves, one slices the stalks into fine pieces and covers them with either liquid honey or Maple or Agave syrup. The concentrated sugar in the syrup draws the liquid out of the stalks, and soon the top portion will be quite watery. Stir this preparation several times over the next days. The result is a most delicious, medicinally active Angelica syrup. It will ferment unless kept in the refrigerator throughout this process. After a few days, the pieces of stem can be removed. One can also heat the syrup slowly and bring to a boil for a couple of minutes to pasteurize it so it will keep without refrigeration. Angelica root is quite acrid, as is the yellow sap throughout the plant. Chewing root or seed makes the mouth tingle and go numb, pointing to its analgesic action. In France, Angelica is called "the French ginseng," meaning that it serves as a panacea. It is held that the seeds are more suitable to treating nervous constitutions than are the roots.

Maude Grieve writes that the chief constituents of Angelica are about one percent volatile oil, valeric acid, angelic acid, sugar, a bitter principle, and a peculiar resin called Angelicin, which is stimulating to the lungs and to the skin.

When we step back and look at *Angelica archangelica* within the context of the other *Apiacae* species, we see that it is unique in its fragrance and royal pose. The other cousins have rather dull, or if pleasant and sweet nowhere near as divine a fragrance—thinking of Carrot, Anise or Fennel. While they follow a similar growth pattern overall, they do not seem to stand up straight and tall, nor do they take a dignified stance between heaven and earth. Angelica is also the only one to sport sets of three leaves. However, several of the other umbels do look like the milk glands and ducts of the breasts, the seeds of which such as fennel increase lactation. Queen Anne's Lace sports a pituitary signature and increases fertility by balancing the pituitary hormones, as well as by an aerating effect on the uterine lining.

When we put all of this together, we will not be surprised by the medicinal properties of Angelica. It is warming, aromatic, and stimulant, thus enhancing and ensuring good digestion on all levels, carminative and tonic, giving it a prime place among traditional alternatives. Being automatically warming, it helps to break sweat and lower fevers. Like all warming aromatics, it is wonderfully useful to settle a cold stomach. The hollow stem points to it clearing the tubes of the body, and it is an excellent expectorant and could be the signature for its diaphoretic action. Wood considers it the signature for opening all the sphincters, including the sphincter of the mind, inducing an open, intuitive imaginative state. Blood vessels are also tubes, and Angelica, as well as *Dong Quai,* are excellent remedies for blood stagnation, or "congealed blood" in Traditional Chinese Medicine. The hollow stems, as well as the winged seeds and lacy leaves, speak of Angelica's close relationship to the air element, which explains how it could aerate the lungs and blood. Its preferred cold and moist climate and soil environment betrays that it is a remedy for colds and rheumatism or any disease arising from exposure to cold and damp. Acrid in taste, it is an antispasmodic and helpful for colic and dysmenorrhea. Its large tap-like root speaks of increasing the downward, bearing wind, and points to it as an emmenagogue, part of its blood-moving quality. The sets of three leaves also point to the gynecological sphere. In this case, akin not to human beings but to angels. It remains a general tonic to all, much like Ginseng. A fine alterative, Angelica is also detoxifying.

The angelic touch of Angelica communicates in the way it holds itself, as well as by its divine fragrance. In my mind, rivaled only by the fragrance of Lily of the Valley, both are sweet, fresh, and angelic; I think of them as scents of paradise, as I imagine paradise would smell. The use of the flower essence has been pioneered by the Flower Essence Society, which uses it to restore a person's connection to the spiritual realm. In this sense, Angelica functions like archangel Gabriel, as a messenger of God and a mediator between worlds. In my experience, it aligns people with their guardian angel—in fact, alighting the angel above their crown chakra. As the angel or higher self then communicates, the divinely inspired energy enters the crown and pours through the aura. Angelica flower essence allows people who felt cut-off from spiritual guidance or grace to reconnect, as well as those shocked out of the body into the astral realm to come back in. Thus, it makes a fine support for shamanic or other soul retrieval. We can see that Angelica really functions as a channel, helping us both to connect out into the higher realms and to return after losing our earthly connection. Angelica is said to cause disgust for spirituous liquors. This may be because, once we are in tune with our spiritual purpose, we no longer find it necessary to partake of spirits to create that link.

As we look around, we find that other plants share similar signatures; while Angelica births, the secondary flower stands out of wrappings or leaf sheaths. Onion, another birth-enhancing herb, births its flowers out of an amniotic sheath-like wrapping. Onion and Elder share the feature of hollow stems, indicating the clearing of bodily tubes, as well as the flower umbels, and all are journeying plants.

Black and Blue Cohosh are gynecological remedies with sets of three leaves. There are many other plants with a purple hue, such as Gravelroot, indicating that they clear toxicity from the body. The way the leaves wrap around the stem make for a great joint signature, similar to Teasel, and Angelica is well-known for warming cold joints, having been used much in chronic rheumatism and gout. As the flower heads grow upward, they feature the famous snake signature, and, sure enough, Gerard writes that "it cureth the bitings of mad dogs and all other venomous beasts."

RESOURCES

HERBS

Flower Power Herbs and Roots

Excellent herb store with a wide selection of quality dried herbs and tinctures

406 East 9th Street

New York, NY 10009, United States

(212) 982-6664

www.flowerpower.net

Herbalist & Alchemists

High quality organic or wildcrafted herbal tinctures

51 South Wandling Avenue

Washington, NJ 07882

(908) 689-9020

www.herbalist-alchemist.com

Herb Pharm

High quality organic or wildcrafted herbal tinctures.

Available at health food stores throughout the United States

www.herb-pharm.com

Zack Woods Herb Farm

Highest quality dried and potted herbs

278 Mead Road

Hyde Park, VT 05655

(802) 888-7278, United States

www.zackwoodsherbs.com

FLOWER ESSENCES

Green Tara Flower Essences

Lily Circle

Provides lily and some other essences
mentioned throughout this book

Available through Flower Power herb store

www.lilycircle.com

Flower Essence Society

P.O. Box 459

Nevada City, CA 95959, United States

(530) 265-9163

www.flowersociety.org

Healing Herbs

High quality range of the flower essences
developed by Dr. Bach

Available through the Flower Essence Society
in the United States

P.O. Box 65

Hereford, HR2 0UW, United Kingdom

(44) 1873-890218

www.healingherbs.co.uk

SEEDS AND PLANTS

Horizon Herbs

Very wide range of high quality organic
medicinal herbs and plants from
around the planet

P.O. Box 69

Williams, OR 97544-0069

(541) 846-6704

www.horizonherbs.com

Ruehlemann's

More than 1,200 medicinal and fragrant
plants and seeds

Ruehlemann's Kraeuter & Duftpflanzen

Auf dem Berg 2

27367 Horstedt

Germany

(49) 4288-928558

www.kraeuter-und-duftpflanzen.de

REFERENCES

Almanach du Facteur 2010, édition Corrèze (Official Calender of the Postman for the Corrèze, France, 2010). *Le langage des fleurs* (inside of back cover).

Arvigo, Rosita, and Balick, Michael. *Rainforest Remedies: One Hundred Healing Herbs from Belize.* 2nd rev. ed. Twin Lakes, WI: Lotus Press, 1998.

Bensky, Dan, Steven Clavey, Eric Stoger, with Andrew Gamble, eds. *Chinese Herbal Medicine: Materia Medica.* Seattle, WA: Eastland Press, 2004.

Bisio, Tom. *A Tooth from the Tiger's Mouth: How to Treat Your Injuries with Powerful Healing Secrets of the Great Chinese Warriors.* New York: Fireside, 2004.

Blamey, M., Fitter, R., Fitter, A. *The Wild Flowers of Britain and Northern Europe.* London: Collins, 1974.

Blum, Jeanne Elisabeth. *Woman Heal Thyself: An Ancient Healing System for Contemporary Women.* Boston: Tuttle, 1995.

Burgess, Isla. *Weeds Heal; A Working Herbal.* New Zealand: Viriditas Publishing, 1998, reprinted 2002.

Coles, William. *Adam in Eden: or, Natures Paradise.* London: Streater, 1657.

Culpeper, Nicolas. *The English Physician, enlarged* (commonly called "Culpeper's Herbal"). First published in London, 1653. London: The Folio Society, 2007.

Cunningham, Scott. *Cunningham's Encyclopedia of Magical Herbs.* 2nd ed. Woodbury, MN: Llewellyn, 2005.

Davis, Patricia. *Aromatherapy A–Z: The Most Comprehensive Guide to Aromatherapy Ever Published.* London: Random House, 2004.

Delaveau et al. *Geheimnisse und Heilkraefte der Pflanzen.* 2nd rev. ed. Stuttgard: Das Beste, 1980,

Della Porta, Giambattista. *Natural Magick.* Online at http://homepages.tscnet.com/omard1/jportah.html; accessed Feb. 2011.

Densmore, Frances. *How Indians Use Wild Plants For Food, Medicine And Crafts.* (Formerly "Uses of Plants by the Chippewa Indians"). New York: Dover, 1974.

Dioscurides. *Materia Medica.* English trans. by T.A. Osbaldeston and R.P.A. Wood. Online at http://www.ibidispress.scriptmania.com/box_widget.html; accessed Feb. 2011. German trans. by Julius Berendes. Online at http://www.pharmawiki.ch/materiamedica/images/Dioskurides.pdf; accessed Feb. 2011.

Foster, Steven and James A. Duke. *A Field Guide to Medicinal Plants and Herbs: of Eastern and Central North America.* New York: Peterson Field Guides, Houghton Mifflin, 1990.

Frawley, David, and Vasant Lad. *The Yoga of Herbs: An Ayurvedic Guide to Herbal Medicine.* Santa Fe, NM: Lotus Press, 1986.

Fruehauf, Heiner. *Five Organ Networks.* Online compendium on Traditional Chinese Medicine at http://www.itmonline.org/5organs/5organs.htm; accessed Feb. 2011.

Fuchs, Leonhart. *Leonhart Fuchs: The New Herbal of 1543.* Köln: Taschen, 2001.

Gerard, John. *The Herbal or General History of Plants.* 1633 ed., rev. by Thomas Johnson. New York: Dover, 1975.

Gilchrist, Cherry. *Alchemy: The Great Work. A History and Evaluation of the Western Hermetic Tradition.* Wellingborough, Northamptonshire, UK: Aquarian, 1984.

Glas, Norbert. *Reading the Face: Understanding a Person's Character Through Physiognomy: A Spiritual-Scientific Study.* vols. 1 & 2. London: Temple Lodge, 2008.

———. *Die Hände offenbaren den Menschen* ("The hands reveal humankind"). Stuttgart: Mellinger Verlag, 1994

Goethe, Johann Wolfgang. *Italian Journey, vol. 6 (Italienische Reise).* Edition Suhrkamp (in *Italian Journey: 1786–1788.* New York: Penguin, 1962).

Gould, Jennifer. *Identifying the Benefits of Vinca major and Vinca minor in a Modern Herbal Practice.With a Historical Review of the Herbs and Analysis of current Use by Herbal Practitioners.* Dissertation at the Scottish School of Herbal Medicine, 2008.

Graeme, Tobyn. *Culpeper's Medicine: A Practice of Western Holistic Medicine.* Rockport, MA: Element, 1997.

Graf, Eva and Eugene. *Herbs.* (Unknown private publisher). 1978.

Grieve, M. *A Modern Herbal: The Medicinal, Culinary, Cosmetic and Economic Properteis, Culitvation and Folk-Lore of Herbs, Grasses, Fungi, Shrubs & Trees with Their Modern Scientific Uses* (2 vols.). New York, NY: Dover, 1982.

Grohmann, Gerbert. *The Plant: A Guide to Understanding Its Nature,* vols. 1 & 2. Kimberton, PA: Biodynamic Farming and Gardening Association, 1989.

Gyatso, Lobsang. *Lorig Nyerkho Kun Tu [blo rigs nyer mkho kun btus].* Dharamsala, India: Institute of Buddhist Dialectics, 1998 (Mahayana Buddhist monastic text on cognitional theory).

Harding, Sarah (ed., trans.). *Machik's Complete Explanation: Clarifying the Meaning of Chöd.* Ithaca, NY: Snow Lion, 2003.

Harris, Ben Charles. *The Compleat Herbal: Being a Description of the Origins, the Lore, the Characteristics, the Types, and the Prescribed Uses of Medicinal Herbs, Including an Alphabetical Guide to All Common Medicinal Plants,* 2nd ed. New York: Bell, 1985.

Hoffmann, Julia. "The Traditional Midwives of the Matibi Area." Unpublished doctoral thesis. Kiel, Germany, 1990.

Jacobi, Jolande. *Paracelsus: Arzt und Gottsucher an der Zeitenwende.* 2nd rev. ed. Olten, Germany: Walter, 1991.

Kaminski, Patricia. *Flowers that Heal: How to use Flower Essences.* Dublin: Gill & MacMillan, 1998

———. and Richard Katz. *Flower Essence Repertory: A Comprehensive Guide to North American and English Flower Essences for Emotional and Spiritual Well-Being,* rev. ed. Nevada City, CA: Flower Essence Society, 1996.

———. *Range of Light Essences.* Product brochure for the Range of Light Kit. Nevada City, CA: The Flower Essence Society, 2009.

Kaptchuk, Ted J. *The Web that has no Weaver: Understanding Chinese Medicine,* 2nd ed. New York: McGraw-Hill, 2000 (No direct reference in this book, but it will help the reader understand some things stated here about Chinese medicine).

Kushi, Michio. *Your Face Never Lies; What Your Face Reveals about You and Your Health: An Introduction to Oriental Diagnosis.* New York: Avery/Penguin, 1983.

Lebling, Robert. *The Treasure of Tarthuth.* Online at http://www.aramcoexpats.com/articles/lifestyles/travel-and-leisure/art-and-entertainment/2584.aspx; accessed Feb. 2011.

Lepage, Dominique. *Miscéllanées Végétales: Un Autre Regard sur les Plantes.* Tulle, France: Le Jardin du Centaure, 2007.

———. *Promenades Mythologiques: Une promenade dans les légendes et les mythes de notre flore sauvage et cultivée.* Tulle, France: Le Jardin du Centaure, 2005.

McIntyre, Anne. *Flower Power: Flower Remedies for Healing Body and Soul Through Herbalism, Homeopathy, Aromatherapy, and Flower Essences.* New York: Henry Holt, 1996.

Merchant, Carolyn. *The Death of Nature: Women, Ecology and the Scientific Revolution.* New York: Harper & Row, 1983.

Mooney, James. *History, Myth, and Sacred Formulas of the Cherokees.* NC: Bright Mountain Books, 1992.

Murphy, Robin. *Homeopathic Remedy Guide: 1,200 Homeopathic and Herbal Remedies.* Blacksburg, VI: H.A.N.A. Press, 2nd ed., 2000.

Pelikan ,Wilhelm. *Heilpflanzenkunde I.* 1958. Dornach, Switzerland:

Philosophisch-Anthroposophischer Verlag am Goetheanum, 4th ed. 1980.

——. *Heilpflanzenkunde II*. 1962. Dornach, Switzerland: Philosophisch-Anthroposophischer Verlag am Goetheanum, 3rd rev. ed., 1982.

——. *Heilpflanzenkunde III*. 1978. Dornach, Switzerland: Philosophisch-Anthroposophischer Verlag am Goetheanum, 2nd ed., 1984.

——. *Sieben Metalle*. Dornach, Switzerland: Philosophisch-anthroposophischer Verlag am Goetheanum, 3rd ed, 1968.

Pogačnik, Marko. *Sacred Geography: Geomancy: Co-Creating the Earth Cosmos*. Great Barrington, MA: Lindisfarne Books, 2007.

Reid, Daniel. *A Handbook of Chinese Healing Herbs*. Boston: Shambhala, 1995.

Rivière, Patrick. *Paracelse, Médecin-Alchimiste, "Philosophe par le Feu"*. Paris: De Vecci, 2000.

Scheffler, Mechthild. *Selbsthilfe durch Bach-Blüten-Therapie: Blumen, die durch die Seele heilen*. München, Germany: Wilhelm Heyne, 1992.

Sheldrake, Rupert. *A New Science of Life*, 3rd ed. Crows Nest, NSW: Allen & Unwin, 2009.

Stavish, Mark. *The Path of Alchemy. Energetic Healing and the World of Natural Magic*. Woodbury, MN: Llewellyn, 2006.

Steiner, Rudolf. *Goethe's World View*. Spring Valley, NY: Mercury Press, 2007.

——. *Intuitive Thinking as a Spiritual Path: A Philosophy of Freedom*. Great Barrington, MA: Anthroposophic Press, 1995 (*Die Philosophie der Freiheit. Grundzüge einer modernen Weltanschauung*. Frankfurt am Main: Fischer Verlag, 1985).

——. *Fruits of Anthroposophy*. London: Rudolf Steiner Press, 1986.

Storl, Wolf. *Healing Lyme Disease Naturally. History, Analysis, and Treatments*. Berkeley, CA: North Atlantic, 2010.

Svoboda, Robert. *Prakruti: Your Ayurvedic Constitution*, 2nd ed. Bellingham, WA: Sadhana, 1998, 1989.

Thun, Maria and Thun, Matthias. *Biodynamic Sowing and Planting Calendar* (annual biodynamic gardening calender for Europe), Edinburgh: Floris Books, annual.

——. *Hinweise aus der Konstellationsforschung*. ("References from the constellation research)", Biedenkopf, Lahn, Germany: Aussaattage M. Thun Verlag, 8th ed., 1994.

——. *North American Biodynamic Sowing and Planting Calendar* (annual biodynamic gardening calender for North America), Edinburgh: Floris Books, annual.

Trisgemistus, Hermes. *Emerald Tablet*. Several translations in Wikipedia online, accessed 2010.

White, Ian. *Australian Bush Flower Essences*. New York: Bantam, 1996.

Wood, Matthew. *The Magical Staff: The Vitalist Tradition in Western Medicine*. Berkeley, CA: North Atlantic, 1992.

——. *Seven Herbs: Plants as Teachers*. Berkeley, CA: North Atlantic, 1986.

——. *The Book of Herbal Wisdom: Using Plants as Medicines*. Berkeley, CA: North Atlantic, 1997.

——. *The Practice of Traditional Western Herbalism: Basic Doctrine, Energetics, and Classification*. Berkeley, CA: North Atlantic, 2004.

——. *The Earthwise Herbal: A Complete Guide to Old World Medicinal Plants*. Berkeley, CA: North Atlantic, 2008.

——. *The Earthwise Herbal: A Complete Guide to New World Medicinal Plants*. Berkeley, CA: North Atlantic, 2009.

——. *Herbal Diagnosis: Traditional Western Herbalism* (unpublished). Minnetrista, MN: Sunnyfield Herb Farm, 2000.

——. *An Intuitive Study of Rabbit Tobacco [Gnaphalium obtusifolium]*. Paper written for the Scottish School of Herbal Medicine. 2005.

Wright, Craig. *Agapanthus africanus: An Herbal Monograph*. Written for the Scottish School of Herbalism, 2007.

——. *Investigating the Medicinal Actions of Plants II: Goethean Science Plant Study*. Lecture for the School of Medicinal Plant Studies. London, 2009.

GENERAL INDEX

PLANT INDEX